P9-DNN-941

BOOK 5

HOUGHTON MIFFLIN COMPANY BOSTON

Atlanta Dallas Geneva, Illinois Palo Alto Princeton Toronto

Program Authors

William K. Durr, John J. Pikulski, Rita M. Bean, J. David Cooper, Nicholas A. Glaser, M. Jean Greenlaw, Hugh Schoephoerster, Mary Lou Alsin, Kathryn Au, Rosalinda B. Barrera, Joseph E. Brzeinski, Ruth P. Bunyan, Jacqueline C. Comas, Frank X. Estrada, Robert L. Hillerich, Timothy G. Johnson, Pamela A. Mason, Joseph S. Renzulli

Senior Consultants

Jacqueline L. Chaparro, Alan N. Crawford, Alfredo Schifini, Sheila Valencia

Program Reviewers

Donna Bessant, Mara Bommarito, Yetive Bradley, Patricia M. Callan, Clara J. Hanline, Fannie Humphery, Barbara H. Jeffus, Beverly Jimenez, Sue Cramton Johnson, Michael P. Klentschy, Petra Montante, Nancy Rhodes, Julie Ryan, Lily Sarmiento, Ellis Vance, Judy Williams, Leslie M. Woldt, Janet Gong Yin

Acknowledgments

For each of the selections listed below, grateful acknowledgment is made for permission to adapt and/or reprint original or copyrighted material, as follows:

"The Adventures of Eustace," from *The Voyage of the* Dawn Treader by C.S. Lewis. Reprinted by permission of the Estate of C.S. Lewis and Collins Publishers.

"Best Friends," from *Felita* by Nicholasa Mohr. Text copyright © 1979 by Nicholasa Mohr. Reprinted by permission of the publisher, Dial Books for Young Readers.

"Boarding House," from *A Local Habitation and a Name* by Ted Kooser. Copyright © 1974 by Ted Kooser. Reprinted by permission of Solo Press.

"The Boy Who Drew People Upside Down," by Jean Friedman. Copyright © 1980. Originally appeared in *Cricket* magazine. Extensive efforts to locate the rights holder were unsuccessful. If the rights holder sees this notice, she should contact the School Division Permissions Department, Houghton Mifflin Company, One Beacon Street, Boston, MA 02108.

Continued on page 491.

Copyright © 1989 by Houghton Mifflin Company.
All rights reserved.
No part of this work may be reproduced or transmitted in any form or by any means, electronic or mechanical, including photocopying and recording, or by any information storage or retrieval system without the prior written permission of the copyright owner unless such copying is expressly permitted by federal copyright law. With the exception of non-profit transcription in Braille, Houghton Mifflin is not authorized to grant permission for further uses of copyrighted selections reprinted in this text without the permission of their owners. Permission must be obtained from the individual copyright owners as identified herein. Address requests for permission to make copies of Houghton Mifflin material to Permissions, Houghton Mifflin Company, One Beacon Street, Boston, MA 02108.

Printed in the U.S.A.

ISBN: 0-395-47702-6

J-VH-965432

Contents

1. Perseverance

2. Creating and Accepting Change

3. A Display of Courage

4. Understanding Self and Others

5. Facing Challenges of Nature

6. Appearances Can Be Deceiving

INSTRUCTIO
H.M.S.

1

Perseverance

an excerpt from

The Midnight Fox

by Betsy Byars

The Stormy Rescue

Ten-year-old Tom, a quiet, unathletic, and somewhat timid city boy, was spending the summer on the farm with Aunt Millie and Uncle Fred while his parents were in Europe. His aunt and uncle's sons, Bubba and Fred Jr., had long since married and left the farm, and their daughter Hazeline was planning her wedding. Bored and lonely, Tom found that time hung heavy — until the day he saw the black fox. Fascinated, he stalked the beautiful wild creature for two months, asking little more of life than the chance to watch her hunting, tending her young, free and at home in the woods. When the fox began to steal Aunt Millie's chickens, Uncle Fred went out hunting for the thief and found her den. Grief-stricken, Tom couldn't bear to think of what would happen to the fox.

As Uncle Fred began to dig, I closed my eyes and pressed my hands against my eyelids, and I saw a large golden sunburst, and in this sunburst the black fox came running toward me.

I opened my eyes and watched Uncle Fred. He dug as he did everything else — powerfully, slowly, and without stopping. His shovel hit a rock and he moved the shovel until he could bring the rock out with the dirt. At my feet the gravelly pile of earth was growing.

I turned away and looked across the creek, and I saw for the fifteenth and last time the black fox. She moved anxiously toward the bushes and there was a tension to her steps, as if she were ready to spring or make some other quick, forceful movement. She barked. She had lost the dog again, and this bark was a high clear call for Uncle Fred and me to follow her.

There was a grunt of satisfaction from Uncle Fred and I turned to see him lift out, on the shovel, covered with sand and gravel, the baby fox.

He turned it onto the sack and the baby fox lay without moving.

"He's dead," I said.

Uncle Fred shook his head. "He's not dead. He's just play-acting. His ma taught him to do that."

We both looked down at the little fox without speaking. I knew that if I lived to be a hundred, I would never see anything that would make me feel any worse than the sight of that little fox pretending to be dead when his heart was beating so hard it looked like it was going to burst out of his chest.

I looked over my shoulder and the black fox was gone. I knew she was still watching us, but I could not see her. Uncle Fred was probing the den with his shovel. I said, "I don't think there are any more. She just had one."

He dug again, piled more earth on the pile, then said, "You're right. Usually a fox has five or six cubs."

"I think something happened to the others."

He bent, folded the ends of the sack, and lifted the baby fox. I took the shovel, he the gun, and we started home, the baby fox swinging between us. The dog joined us as we crossed the creek and began to leap excitedly at the sack until Uncle Fred had to hold it shoulder-high to keep it from him.

We walked back to the house without speaking. Uncle Fred went directly to some old rabbit hutches beside the garage. Bubba had once raised rabbits here, but now the cages were empty. Uncle Fred opened one, shook the baby fox out of the sack, and then closed the wire door.

The baby fox moved to the back of the hutch and looked at us. His fur was soft and woolly, but his eyes were sharp. Nervously he went to one corner.

Aunt Millie came out and looked. "Just like a baby lamb," she said. "It's a sweet little thing, isn't it?"

"That's not the way you were talking yesterday," Uncle Fred said.

"Well, I'm not going to have anything after my chickens," she said. "Not *anything!* I'd be after you with the broom if you bothered my chickens." They laughed. Her spirits seemed greatly improved now that the fox was doomed, and she called, "Hazeline, come on out here and look at this cute little baby fox."

"No."

Uncle Fred went into the shed, returned, and snapped a lock over the cage latch.

"You think somebody's going to steal your fox?" Aunt Millie laughed.

"I wouldn't put it past a fox to open up an unlocked cage to get her baby."

Aunt Millie shook her head in amazement, then said, "Well, you men have got to get washed up for supper."

We went into the house and I said to Uncle Fred, "What are you going to do with the baby fox?"

"That's my bait. Every hunter alive's got some way to get a fox. They got some special trap or something. Mr. Baynes down at the store makes up a special mixture that he says foxes can't resist. My way is to set up a trap, using the baby fox for bait. I'll sit out on the back porch tonight and watch for her."

"Oh."

"It never fails. That is one bait a fox can't resist."

"Are you getting sick?" Aunt Millie asked at supper that night.

"I guess I'm a little tired."

"Well, I should think so! Helping with the pump out in the broiling sun all morning and then tracking that fox all afternoon. It's a wonder you don't have heat stroke. You eat something though, hear? You have to keep up your strength."

"I'm just not hungry."

"It's the heat. But, listen, you drink your tea. You *will* have heat stroke sure enough if you let your body get dried out."

I finished my tea and went up to my room. I did not even look out the window, because I knew I could see the rabbit hutch by the garage and I never again wanted to see that baby fox cowering against the wall.

Hazeline came out of her room and looked in at me on the bed. "You feeling better?"

I nodded. "You know that fox I was telling you about? The black one?"

"Sure."

"Well, your dad has her baby out in the rabbit hutch and he's going to shoot her."

"I know it. I heard. But, listen, don't let it upset you, hear?"

"Hazeline, I don't want anything to happen to that fox."

"Tommy, listen, all wild animals die in some violent way. It's their life. Wild animals just don't die of old age. They get killed by an enemy or by the weather or they have an accident or they get rabies or some other disease or they get shot. That's the way nature is."

"I know that," I said quickly, because I did not want to hear any more.

"You just forget the fox. Tomorrow maybe we can go to the picture show in Clinton or something."

"All right."

I got up and went down the steps and walked to the tree in front of the rabbit hutch. I could not explain why I did this. I didn't want to see the baby fox again, and yet here I was.

He did not see me. He was busy biting the wires of his cage with great fury and determination. I could hear the clicking of his sharp tiny teeth against the wire, but he was making no progress. Then he stopped. He still had not seen me, but he had heard or smelled something and he raised his head and let out a short cry. He waited, then after a moment he began biting the wires again.

I remained by the tree watching him, listening for the quavering cry that he uttered from time to time.

"Don't get your fingers in the cage," Uncle Fred warned behind me. "He may not be able to cut wire yet, but he sure could hurt a finger."

"All right."

"In a bit, when it starts getting dark, you can sit up here with me and watch for the fox."

As I went into the kitchen where Aunt Millie was standing in front of the electric fan, I heard the cry of the baby fox again, and I thought I would be hearing that sound forever. One time Petie Burkis fell down and broke his leg on the school playground and he said, "Oh!" in this real terrible, painful way, and I never could forget it. Later I tried to make him say it again that same way, and one whole afternoon Petie did nothing but say the word *Oh* over and over — a thousand times maybe, and in all those thousand tries, he never sounded that same way again. I still remember it though, exactly, like I will always remember the way that baby fox sounded when he cried.

It seemed to get dark quickly that night. Uncle Fred was already out on the back porch. He had brought out a chair and was sitting with his gun beside him, pointing to the floor. I never saw anyone sit any quieter. You wouldn't have noticed him at all he was so still.

I stood behind him inside the screen door. Through the screen I could see the tiny fox lift his black nose and cry again. Now, for the first time, there was an answer — the bark of his mother.

I looked toward the garden, because that's where the sound had come from, but Uncle Fred did not even turn his

head. In a frenzy now that he had heard his mother, the baby fox moved about the cage, pulling at the wire and crying again and again.

Just then there was the sound of thunder from the west, a long rolling sound, and Aunt Millie came to the door beside me and said, "Bless me, is that thunder?" She looked out at the sky. "Was that thunder, Fred?"

"Could be," he said without moving.

"Look!" Aunt Millie said. "I swear I see black clouds. You see, Tom?"

"Yes'm."

"And feel that breeze. Honestly, when you think you have reached absolutely the end of your endurance, then the breeze comes. I could not have drawn one more breath of hot air, and now we are going to have a storm."

We stood in the doorway, feeling the breeze, forgetting for a moment the baby fox.

Then I saw Uncle Fred's gun rise ever so slightly in the direction of the fence behind the garage. I could not see any sign of the fox, but I knew that she must be there. Uncle Fred would not be wrong.

The breeze quickened, and abruptly the dishpan which Aunt Millie had left on the porch railing clattered to the floor. For the first time Uncle Fred turned his head and looked in annoyance at the pan and then at Aunt Millie.

"Did it scare your fox off?" she asked.

He nodded, then shifted in the chair and said, "She'll be back."

In just this short time the sky to the west had gotten black as ink. Low on the horizon forks of lightning streaked the sky.

"Now, Fred, don't you sit out here while it's thundering and lightning. I mean it. No fox is worth getting struck by lightning for."

He nodded and she turned to me and said, "You come on and help me shut the windows. Some of those upstairs are stuck wide open. Just hit them with the heel of your hand on the side till you can get them down."

I started up the stairs and she said again, "Fred, come on in when it starts storming. That fox'll be back tomorrow night too."

I went upstairs and started hitting the sides of the windows. I had just gotten one window to jerk down about two inches when I heard the gunshot. I had never heard any worse sound in my life. It was a very final sound, like the most enormous period in the world. Bam. Period. The end.

I ran out of my room and down the steps so fast I could not even tell you how many times my feet touched the stairs, none maybe. I went out the back door, opening it so fast I hit the back of Uncle Fred's chair. I looked toward the rabbit hutch, said, "Where?" then looked at the back fence. Then I looked down at Uncle Fred, who was doing something with his gun.

"Missed," he said.

Suddenly I felt weak. My legs were like two pieces of rope, like that trick that Hindu magicians do when they make rope come straight up out of a basket and then say a magic word and make the rope collapse. My legs felt like they were going to collapse at any second. I managed to force these two pieces of rope to carry me up the stairs and into the room.

I closed two windows, and the third one, in sympathy perhaps, just banged down all by itself. Then I sank to the bed.

I had no intention of going to sleep when I lay down on the bed; I did not think I would ever be able to sleep again, but that is what I did. I fell right asleep and did not even move until four hours later when I awoke. It was one o'clock in the morning.

The storm was in full force, or perhaps it was a second storm, but the house was quiet. I got up and went out into the hall. I could not hear anything but the sound of the rain and Hazeline's transistor radio, which was sputtering with static beside her on the pillow.

I went down the stairs, one by one. I did not make a sound. I stepped on the part of the steps near the wall because Petie Burkis had told me that was how burglars got up stairs unheard. I was just stepping into the hall when without warning the hall light went on. Aunt Millie was standing there in her bathrobe squinting at me.

"What's wrong?" she asked.

"Nothing. I just didn't know what time it was."

"Well" — she looked closely at her watch — "it's just past one o'clock."

"I went to sleep in my clothes."

"Well, you get on your pajamas and get back to bed. This is the first good sleeping night we've had, and you mustn't let it go to waste."

"Sure."

"Well, go on back up the steps." She watched me go up two steps and then she said, "Goodness, we've gotten on so well all summer, I'd hate for anything to happen now right before your parents get home."

"Aunt Millie, did Uncle Fred get the fox?"

"No."

"Is he still out on the porch?"

"In this rain? No, he is fast asleep in his bed like you ought to be."

She waited until I was up the stairs and then she turned out the light. I went into my room and she called, "Are you getting in bed?"

I lay down. "Yes."

"And go to sleep."

I lay in bed for a long time, still in my clothes, and then I got up very carefully. I walked over to the window and looked out at the tree Bubba and Fred Jr. used to just run up and down all the time like monkeys. I could imagine them climbing up, laughing and brown, racing, going out on all sorts of perilous limbs just to be first at the window. I opened the window, pushed out the screen, reached out into the rain, and felt for the smooth spot Aunt Millie had told me was worn into the bark of the tree.

I took off my shoes and knelt on the window sill. There was an enormous flash of lightning that turned the whole world white for a moment, and then I climbed out onto the nearest branch and circled the trunk round with my arms.

I thought that I could never get one step farther. I thought that I could never move even one muscle or I would fall. I thought that in the morning when Aunt Millie came up to see why I wasn't at breakfast she would find me here, pressed into the tree, still frozen with fear.

The rain was hard and slanting directly into my face. Finally I got up just enough courage to turn my face out of the rain. Then the lightning flashed again and I saw the ground about a million miles below. I held the tree so tightly the bark was cutting into my cheek.

I don't know how long I stayed that way. If I had tried to look at my watch, just that little movement would have thrown me off balance. After a while, though, I began to sort of slip down the tree. I never let go of the main trunk for a second. I just moved my arms downward in very small movements. Then, slowly, when I was practically kneeling on the first limb, I let my foot reach down for the next one.

If there were smooth spots on those branches, my feet never found them. They only touched one rough limb after another as, slowly, I kept inching down the tree, feeling my way, never looking down at the ground until, finally, my foot reached out for another limb and felt the cold wet grass. It shocked me for a moment and then I jumped down, landing on my hands and knees.

I got up and ran to the rabbit hutch. The baby fox was huddled in one corner of the pen where there was some shelter from the rain. The lightning flashed and I saw him watching me.

"I'm going to get you out," I said.

He crouched back farther in the hutch. In the next flash of lightning I looked on the ground for a rock and I saw at my feet a small dead frog. I knew that the black fox in all this rain had brought that frog here to her baby. She was right now watching me somewhere.

There were bricks stacked in a neat pile under the hutch and I took one and began to bang it against the lock. I was prepared to do this all night if necessary, but the lock was an old one and it opened right away.

The noise had scared the baby fox and he was now making a whimpering sound. I unhooked the broken lock, opened the cage, and stepped back against the tree.

The baby fox did not move for a moment. I could barely see him, a small dark ball in the back of the cage. He waited, alert and suspicious, and then, after a moment he moved in a crouch to the door of the cage. He cried sharply. From the bushes there was an answering bark.

He crouched lower. The lightning flashed again and in that second he jumped and ran in the direction of the bushes. He barked as he ran. There was an immediate answer, and then only the sound of the rain. I waited against the tree, thinking about them, and then I heard the black fox bark one more time as she ran through the orchard with her baby.

And I thought, Someday I will be in a famous museum, walking along on the marble floors, looking at paintings. There will be one called "Blue Flowers" and I will look at that for a while, and the next one will be "Woman on the Beach" and I will look at that for a while, and then I will glance at the name of the next painting and it will be "Fox with Baby at Midnight," and I will look up and my heart will stop beating

because there it will be, just the way it was this night, the black fox and her baby running beneath the wet ghostly apple trees toward a patch of light in the distance. And I thought, leaning against that tree in the rain, if there is a picture like that, I hope sometime I will get to see it.

Suddenly the rain began to slacken and I walked around the house. I had never been so wet in my life and now that it was over I was cold too. And I was tired. I looked up at the tree and there didn't seem to be any point in climbing back up when in just a few hours everyone would know what I had done anyway. I went up on the porch and rang the doorbell.

In all my life I have never felt so dumb and foolish as I did barefooted, soaking wet on that slick porch at two o'clock in the morning, waiting for someone to come and answer the door.

It was Aunt Millie in her cotton robe who turned on the porch light and peered out through the side windows at me.

I must have been an awful sight, like the poor little match girl, for she flung open the door at once and drew me in.

"What are you doing out there? What are you doing?"

"Who is it?" Uncle Fred asked as he came into the hall. He was pulling his pants up over his pajamas.

"It's Tom," Aunt Millie said.

"I meant who's at the door."

"Tom," she said again.

"Tom?"

"Yes, he was just standing out there on the porch."

They both turned and looked at me, waiting for an explanation, and I cleared my throat and said, "Uncle Fred and Aunt Millie, I am awfully sorry but I have let the baby fox out of the rabbit hutch." I sounded very stiff and formal, and I thought the voice was a terrible thing to have to depend on, because I really did want them to know that I was sorry, and I didn't sound it the least bit. I knew how much Uncle Fred had looked forward to the hunt and how important getting rid of the fox was to Aunt Millie, and I hated for them to be disappointed now.

There was a moment of silence. Then Aunt Millie said, "Why, that's perfectly all right, isn't it, Fred? Don't you think

another thing about that. You just come on to bed. You're going to get pneumonia standing there in that puddle." She started for the linen closet. "I'll get you some towels."

Uncle Fred and I were left in the hall alone and I looked up at him and he looked like an enormous blue-eyed Indian.

"I'm sorry," I said again.

He looked at me and I knew he was seeing through all the very casual questions I had been asking all summer about foxes, and seeing through the long days I had spent in the woods. He was remembering the sorry way I had tried to keep him from finding the fox's den and the way I had looked when we did find it. I think all those pieces just snapped into place right then in Uncle Fred's mind and I knew that if there was one person in the world who understood me it was this man who had seemed such a stranger.

He cleared his throat. "I never liked to see wild things in a pen myself," he said.

Aunt Millie came down the hall and threw a towel over my head and started rubbing. "Now get upstairs. I am not going to have you lying in bed with pneumonia when your mother arrives."

We went upstairs, she rubbing my head the whole way, me stumbling over the steps, and Hazeline calling from her room, "Who was that at the door?"

"Tom," Aunt Millie said.

"Who?"

"Me," I said.

"Oh."

We went into my room. "There," Aunt Millie exclaimed at the sight of my open window, "I knew it! I knew you'd be out there on that tree at the first opportunity." She shut the window with a bang. "There is no explaining a boy."

She turned down my bed, went out, and came back with a glass of milk.

"I'm sorry about your turkey and hen," I said.

"Oh, that! I bet you think I'm awful, carrying on the way I did."

"No."

"It was more the heat than anything else, like Fred said. Just don't think about it any more. That fox and her baby are miles away from here now, and they'll never come back to bother my birds. That's one thing about a fox. He learns."

She turned out the light, said, "It is starting to rain again. I declare we are going to be flooded out," and then went downstairs.

The next week I spent in the woods, assuring myself that the black fox had gone. I sat on the rock over the ravine, I lay by the creek, I went back to the den again and again to look at the ruins, I sat by the field where the mice ran. I never once saw or heard the black fox and I knew I never would again.

Author

Betsy Byars began her career by writing magazine articles. As her children grew, she became interested in writing books for young readers and now has more than twenty to her credit. She won the Newbery Medal for her book *The Summer of the Swans* and the Dorothy Canfield Fisher Award for *The Eighteenth Emergency. The Midnight Fox,* from which this excerpt was taken, received the Lewis Carroll Shelf Award. Of this book Mrs. Byars says, "This is my favorite book because it is very personal. A great deal of my own children and their activities went into it, and a great deal of myself."

An excerpt from

Phoebe and the General

by Judith Berry Griffin

Thank You, Phoebe Fraunces

In 1776, during the American Revolution, Phoebe Fraunces was sent to General George Washington's headquarters in Mortier House in New York City. Her father, Sam Fraunces, was a free black man and owner of the Queen's Head Tavern in New York City. A trusted Patriot, he had heard of a plot to kill General Washington. Phoebe's job was to help with the household chores while acting as a spy. She was to watch particularly anyone whose name began with T, *the only clue Sam Fraunces had to the identity of the person who was planning to assassinate Washington. Every day Phoebe met her father along the waterfront to tell him anything that she had learned.*

Phoebe soon settled into her job. The work wasn't as hard as she thought it would be. Mrs. Washington had brought her own quilts and feather beds. It was Phoebe's job to air and turn these every morning, as well as to see to the buying of food and the serving of meals. She had to keep the silver cleaned and shining and the furniture dusted and polished. She did not have any special jobs to do for General Washington, except to see that his meals were served on time. He was very particular about having dinner served promptly at four o'clock, and Phoebe sometimes had a hard time getting everything finished by then.

General Washington never said very much. He was tall, with a quiet voice. He looked like the kind of man who could win a war. Mrs. Washington was to have a fresh egg each day, and Pompey, who was a lot of company to Phoebe even though he was only eight years old, helped by visiting the hen house early every morning. When dinner was over, he and Phoebe often stood on the kitchen steps and fed the hens leftover scraps of bread from the table.

Phoebe was a good housekeeper. But she did not forget why she was there. Day after day she watched, and waited, and listened. General Washington came and went. The house was full of people all the time — officers of the Army, friends, members of the bodyguard. Phoebe slipped among them silent as a shadow, as her father had taught her. Whenever she saw anyone talking softly, she stopped to poke the fire, fill their glasses, light new candles. But still she saw nothing, heard nothing.

Each day at noon she took a basket and went down to the waterfront to do the day's marketing. When she was finished, she would make her way to the edge of the harbor and stand looking out over the ocean. No one took any notice of her, in her clean white apron and cap, a shawl thrown across her shoulders. Nor did anyone particularly notice the man who always came to stand beside her, his curly hair powdered and pulled back, his brown face plump and smiling.

The two of them would stand together for a few moments, seeming to talk of nothing important. Sometimes Phoebe would throw out a few crumbs to the gulls, which would gather noisily at their feet. After a time they would move off in different directions — Phoebe back to Mortier House, Sam Fraunces back to the Queen's Head.

Phoebe never had anything to report. She was particularly careful to watch every member of the general's bodyguard who came to the house. None was called by a name starting with T. They all seemed to be truly fond of the general and laughed and joked with him. Two members of the bodyguard did stand out from the others. One was especially nice. Mr.

Hickey was his name. He smiled at Phoebe while she was serving and often came into the kitchen to joke with her and Mary while Mary was preparing the meals.

Phoebe was the youngest servant in the house except for Pompey. When the others were talking, she often felt left out. She was glad to have someone to talk to. Hickey seemed much younger than the other men — not much older, in fact, than Phoebe herself. And he seemed glad to talk to her, too. Like Phoebe, he seemed not to have many friends. Phoebe often saw him sitting by himself at the edge of the woods.

Mr. Green was another member of General Washington's bodyguard who kept to himself, but he was not like Hickey.

He never spoke to Phoebe at all, even when he saw her in the yard. Phoebe would always say, "Evening, sir," but he never so much as looked at her. From what she could tell, he didn't say much to anyone, even at dinnertime when everyone did a lot of talking. Though his name didn't begin with T, Phoebe made up her mind to watch him very carefully. There was something about him she didn't like.

One day, when Hickey came to the kitchen, he had a small cloth bag with him. He handed it to Phoebe. "Here," he said. "It's some seed for your precious chickens."

Phoebe was surprised. She didn't know anyone had noticed that she fed them. She opened the bag. "But it's good seed, sir!" she protested. "It's too good to feed the chickens!"

Hickey laughed. "It's only the king's true men who'll be missing it," he said. "Let's see if your chickens will get fatter from British grain than from American bread crumbs!"

Phoebe smiled. She didn't ask him how he had got the seed. But he began to bring it home to her often. Sometimes he would bring it himself. Other times she would find a bag lying on the table when she came into the kitchen. Sometimes there would be a bright ribbon tied around it. Then Hickey would say, "The ribbon's for you, pretty Phoebe. Compliments of King George III!" Sometimes there would be a stick of candy inside — always, he said, stolen from those loyal to the King of England.

Soon she was looking forward to his visits every day. And as the days went by and Phoebe still could find no one who seemed to be plotting to take General Washington's life, she thought about asking Mr. Hickey for help. Her father had told her to trust no one. Still . . . perhaps she could trust him. She would wait and see.

Weeks went by. The beautiful house, once so strange to her, was now like a good friend. Phoebe enjoyed using the fine china plates and crystal glasses. She enjoyed serving Mary's deliciously prepared meals to General Washington and his important guests, while Pompey followed solemnly behind with the salt cellar and pepper mill.

She knew she was there to save General Washington's life. But as the days went by and she still heard nothing, she began to wonder if perhaps her father was mistaken. No one seemed to be plotting anything, and it was now the beginning of June. Phoebe had been at Mortier House almost two months.

Then one day, when she went to the market, her father wasn't there. Phoebe stood by the water a long time, waiting and wondering. Should she go to the Queen's Head? Or back to Mortier House? As she was trying to decide, she saw her father hurrying toward her. He looked very worried. For the first time he seemed not to care that people might notice them. He held her by the shoulders and looked into her face.

"Phoebe," he said urgently, "I have heard that General Washington will be leaving Mortier House in a very few days. The person known as T will act before that time. You must find out who it is!"

Phoebe's mind was whirling as she hurried back toward the house. She was frightened, but she was also determined. She *would* save General Washington! She had long ago figured that he would likely be shot. During dinner he always sat in a chair by the window. He would make an easy target for anyone waiting outside.

If only she could get him to change his place, away from that window! His good friend General Gates would be a dinner guest at the house this evening. Everyone else was part of the family or a member of the bodyguard. Over and over she said their names. No one's name began with T.

As she reached the kitchen door, she saw Hickey sitting on the steps. "Why are you so solemn, pretty Phoebe?" he asked.

"Oh, Mr. Hickey, sir," said Phoebe breathlessly. "I'm so worried. . . ." She paused. She did need help! Should she tell him? Maybe he knew something, had seen something that had escaped her notice. After all, he was a member of the bodyguard — it was his job to protect General Washington. Her father's words came back to her. "Trust no one," he had said. "No one." She sighed. She'd have to keep trying alone.

"Well," said Hickey after a moment. "I've something to bring a smile back to that pretty face. Fresh June peas for the general's dinner — first of the season! His favorite and mine — and enough for us both! Some friends of the king will be mighty hungry tonight!" He handed her a large sack, filled to the brim with pea pods. Phoebe smiled in spite of herself.

"Grown men — soldiers of the American Army — stealing peas!" she said.

Hickey pretended to be hurt. "All right," he said, snatching the sack from her and holding it over his head. "I'll just throw them out to your chickens — "

"No, no, Mr. Hickey." Phoebe laughed. "Here — I'll fix them myself."

Hickey handed her the sack. "I'll be here to fill my plate at dinnertime," he promised.

All afternoon, as she went about her chores, Phoebe worried. *How* could she get the general's chair away from that window? She would have to stand in front of it, blocking the view from outside. But then, would someone shoot her?

By the time dinnertime arrived she was almost sick with fear. She was in the kitchen with Pompey getting ready to serve the plates when a voice behind her made her jump. It was Hickey.

"I've come for my peas," he said softly.

"Oh! Mr. Hickey, sir!" she said. "You gave me such a start! I was — " She stopped and looked at him, even more startled. He looked ill? frightened? She couldn't tell which.

"Which is my plate, and which is General Washington's?" he said. "It wouldn't do for him to have more than me." He spoke quickly, without smiling this time.

"I never heard of such carryings on over a pile of peas!" Phoebe said. "This is the general's plate, and this is yours!" She turned away to fill Pompey's salt cellar and turned back just in time to see Hickey's hand move quickly away from

General Washington's plate and slide into his pocket. Something winked for a second in the light — something shiny, like glass.

"What are you doing to General Washington's plate?" she said. "I told you yours is here!" She picked up the plate. Was it her imagination, or was there something grainy, like sugar, on the peas? Phoebe looked more closely, but as she looked, whatever it was seemed to have disappeared. An instant later she wasn't sure — had she seen anything at all? She thought of the window again and forgot about the peas. She had to serve General Washington.

Leaving Hickey standing in the kitchen, Phoebe nervously entered the dining room, Pompey following with the salt. As she walked toward the general, Phoebe looked at every face around the table. Some of the guests were talking, some merely smiling. None seemed nervous or frightened.

And then she noticed the empty chair. Who was missing? But even as she asked herself the question, she knew. It was Mr. Green. Was he outside the house, with a gun, waiting? General Washington was sitting by the window, as she had feared. He sat back easily in his chair, listening to something General Gates was saying. The window was open! As she went past, Phoebe looked outside anxiously. There was not a sound, not a shadow, not a movement. The green grass was smooth and unruffled. Even the leaves in the trees beyond were still.

"Well, Phoebe!" General Washington exclaimed as she stopped beside his chair. "June peas! How did you get them so early in the season?"

"It wasn't me, sir," replied Phoebe, looking past him out the window. "It was your Mr. Hickey brought them in, fresh today. He says they're your favorite."

"And mine as well!" said General Gates. "Where is Mr. Thomas Hickey? I want to thank him!"

Phoebe started to put the plate down in front of General Washington. Then, in a flash, it came to her who she was looking for. Mr. Green was not hiding outside the window to shoot at the general. The person who was trying to kill him was here — in the kitchen! Phoebe stood like a stone, the plate still in her hands. She saw Hickey again — Thomas Hickey — laughing and teasing, bringing her candy and ribbons and seed for her chickens. And then bringing June peas for the general and sprinkling them with poison! T was for Thomas, member of General Washington's bodyguard!

Still holding the plate, she whirled around. Pompey was waiting behind her. "Run!" she screamed. "Run! Get my father!"

Everyone stopped talking. Pompey looked at her in amazement. "Y-your father?" he stammered.

"Sam Fraunces! At the Queen's Head! Go!" And she stamped her foot. Pompey had never heard Phoebe sound like that before. He dropped the salt cellar and ran through the kitchen door.

Everyone in the dining room sat frozen. All eyes were on Phoebe. "General Washington!" she cried. "Mr. Hickey has put poison in your dinner! I saw him!" There was a gasp from the table.

"What jest is this?" roared General Gates, getting up from his place and reaching for the plate. But before he could take it from her, Phoebe ran to the open window and threw the whole plate out into the yard.

Now the dining room was in an uproar. Chairs overturned; wine spilled as the men jumped to their feet in confusion. Some ran toward the window where Phoebe was standing, as if they feared she might try to escape. Others started for the kitchen. Some ran to surround General Washington. No one knew what to do.

It was General Gates who first noticed the chickens in the yard and shouted, pointing out the window, "Look!"

Three of Phoebe's chickens had come to peck at the peas she had thrown outside. Two had already fallen dead. The third was still moving its wings, but as they watched, it, too, grew still. The poison, meant for General Washington, had killed the chickens instead.

"Get Hickey!" bellowed General Gates, and members of the bodyguard rushed to obey. Minutes later Thomas Hickey was dragged in from the yard, his face white with terror. He had not been able to escape. Minutes after that, Sam Fraunces burst into the room. Phoebe was still standing by the window, shaking. He ran to her and held her tightly. Phoebe clung to him, burying her face in his shoulder.

"Well done, Daughter," Samuel Fraunces said quietly. "Well done."

After the excitement had died down and Hickey had been taken away, General Washington came to speak to Phoebe and her father. "It's nice to know people whom I can trust," he said simply. "Thank you."

General Washington went on to lead the American Army to victory, and the United States was born. So freedom did

come to some Americans, but not all. In 1783, when the war was won, General Washington chose to give his victory party at Fraunces' Queen's Head Tavern; there he said good-bye to the leaders of his army. And when he became the first President of the United States, he invited Sam Fraunces to become his official steward. Fraunces held that job until 1796.

Thomas Hickey was tried and convicted of trying to kill George Washington. Seven days later he was hanged. As was usual in those days, everyone turned out to watch. No one knows whether Phoebe was there. No one knows what happened to Phoebe after that. But we do know that she was a good spy.

Thank you, Phoebe Fraunces.

Author

Born and raised in Chicago, Judith Berry Griffin also earned her college degrees there. She has been a teacher and an elementary school principal as well as a writer. Her third book for children, *Phoebe and the General,* a part of which you have just read, was selected as a Notable Children's Trade Book in the Field of Social Studies.

74th Street

by Myra Cohn Livingston

Hey, this little kid gets roller skates.
She puts them on.
She stands up and almost
flops over backwards.
She sticks out a foot like
she's going somewhere and
falls down and
smacks her hand. She
grabs hold of a step to get up and
sticks out the other foot and
slides about six inches and
falls and
skins her knee.

And then, you know what?

She brushes off the dirt and the
blood and puts some
spit on it and then
sticks out the other foot

again.

From Myra Cohn Livingston, *The Malibu and Other Poems* (Atheneum, 1972).

GRAMP

from the book *Luke's Garden and Gramp*
by Joan Tate

Simon had lived with his parents and Gramp in an old house with a yard that included a garden and Gramp's workshop shed. There Gramp had taught Simon to use tools, and together they had built a guinea pig hutch. When the row of houses where they lived was torn down, the tenants were moved to a high-rise building where there was no room for Gramp's tool bench.

That summer when Simon was ten was a time full of new things. Gradually, the apartment became home. Gramp and Mum put everything right and soon Simon was quite used to the differences, even liking his room in the sky, and going up and down in an elevator, or even sometimes running the whole way down the stairs, hundreds of steps, to arrive breathless and panting at the bottom, dizzy with it all.

The school took some getting used to, but it had a good playing field. Simon sometimes went there after school, too, because there was no space to play around the apartments, or at least nowhere to play without getting chased away every five minutes. But the school was several streets away, and he only went there for scrimmage. Best of all, he had found a place for his guinea pigs.

Gramp had fixed it up. The shed down in the yard was very small, one of a row all alike, a very large closet with a door-sized door, that was all. There was just room for Dad's motorbike, some odds and ends, and a shelf at the end for cans of paint and that kind of thing. Gramp cleared the shelf, stacked the paint cans all at one side, cut the legs off the hutch, and put the guinea pigs there.

"Now don't forget to feed them," he said. "It's a bit dark, but not too bad. It's up to you to see they get fed and cleaned."

Simon had a small plastic bucket up in the apartment and Mum put all the leftover green leaves and stale bread in it. Every day after school, Simon took the key from the hook inside the kitchen cabinet and went down to feed the guinea pigs. They were getting big now and needed quite a lot of food. Sometimes he wandered all over the building sites down the road, looking for dandelions and groundsel and other wild greenstuff for them. Sometimes the greengrocer gave him leftover cabbage leaves, or a carrot or two. So the guinea pigs did well. And Simon was pleased.

But it was not the same with Gramp. At first it was all right, as there was a lot to do to help Mum put the apartment to rights. But then the apartment was finished and it was easy to clean and look after too, much easier than the house. Mum got a part-time job, mornings only, and Gramp was alone a lot. He sat in his room or in the living room, not even watching television, but just sitting there, staring out the window, or staring at nothing, not even smoking his pipe.

Sometimes he sat on his bed, staring at his feet, and Simon went in to talk to him, to tell him about his guinea pigs.

"They're big now, Gramp," he said. "Why don't you come down and look?"

Gramp looked up at him.

"That's good, boy," he said. "That's good."

"Come down and look," said Simon again.

Gramp shook his head.

"Too far down there," he said.

"But there's the elevator. It'd only take five minutes."

But Gramp shook his head.

"What's the matter with you, Gramp?"

"Nothing's the matter," he said. "Nothing, that's it."

"You mean you've nothing to do?"

"That's it," said Gramp, looking at his hands. "Nothing."

"Why don't you put a bench up here?" said Simon.

Gramp looked around.

"In here?" he said. "In this room? There's not room."

"You could have a small one," said Simon. "Just so that you could fasten the vise on, anyhow."

"The mess, boy," Gramp said. "The mess. She wouldn't stand for it. You can't do that sort of thing indoors, in an apartment like this."

"We could keep it clean," persisted Simon.

"You don't know what you're talking about," said Gramp curtly, and then he just turned his head away, refusing to talk anymore, not looking at Simon.

"Gramp!"

But it was no good. Gramp had been talking in a way he had never talked before. Then he gradually got more and more silent and would not speak to any of them sometimes, for days on end. Even Dad could not get a word out of him if he was feeling in that mood. Gramp began to sit in a chair at his window, all day long, sitting there with a small hammer in his hands, turning it over and over, rubbing it with his hands, polishing the wood over and over again and resting the head against his thumb, the hammer which he never used anymore. Simon could not bear seeing him sitting there, mumbling to himself, but he did not know what to do.

Mum just said that he was getting old and she told Simon not to bother him.

"He's always been old," protested Simon. "And he never minded me bothering him before."

"Older, then," said Mum. "You get like that when you're old."

"Like what?"

"Like Grandpa."

"But he wasn't like that before."

"Before what?"

"Before we came here."

"What d'you mean, before we came here?" said Mum. "He's better off here than where we were before. The room's lighter and cleaner and not so damp. It's warmer too."

Simon fell silent. She didn't understand. Then he looked at his mother, standing by the table in the kitchen, mixing something in a big bowl. He watched her turning the mixture over and beating at it with a spoon, then slicing through it with a knife. She moved quickly and took things out of the kitchen drawer, shut the drawer, darted across the kitchen, fetched a baking tin, switched the oven on, came back.

"What are you standing there staring at?" she said. "Go on down and out into the fresh air."

"Gramp would be all right if he had a bench. Like you," said Simon, holding his breath, knowing his mother would be cross.

"Oh, you and Grandpa and that bench!" she said. "Where can you find a workbench in a place like this?"

"We could try."

Simon did not know why he went on about it, because he knew his mother was right. But he kept thinking of their old shed, of him and Gramp talking and working, sometimes saying nothing, and now it had all gone. He had no one to talk to and Gramp didn't like it, either. His mother leaned across the table and knocked a small bowl off the edge by mistake. It fell to the tiled floor and broke.

"Oh, drat!" she said. "Now look what you've gone and made me do. That was your fault, standing there carrying on about Grandpa and his bench and all that. Getting in my way and making me drop things. Get along now. If it's that important to you, why don't you go out and find him a bench yourself? Go on, go and find him one for yourself!"

"All right!" shouted Simon. "All right! All right! I will! I'll find him one. No one cares about him any longer. No one. Only me. You've all got things to do and you don't care about him anymore."

"Now you know that's not true," said Mum. "You know it. Just you say you're sorry now, or I'll tell Dad what you said."

"No!" said Simon. "No, I won't. I won't!"

And he turned and dashed out of the kitchen straight through the hall, wrenched open the door, and slammed it hard behind him. He felt hot and angry and he couldn't wait for the elevator. He began stamping down the stairs, crashing his feet on each step, until they were both sore.

"I'll find him one somewhere," he said to himself. "I will. I'll find him one. I'll get one somewhere, so he can use his tools again and we can talk again." He stumped down the road, not quite sure where he was going to start looking, his hot face slowly cooling. Where did you look? Where did you find things like that? Where did people do their odd jobs when they lived in apartments? Perhaps they didn't have odd jobs to do. Perhaps Gramp *was* too old. Perhaps they would put him in a home next. Simon felt cold at the thought. His friend

Ken's granddad had gone to a home and had hated it, Ken said. Simon didn't know what a home was, but he knew he didn't want Gramp to go to one, knew he would hate it too. Who would teach him to use the tools then? Not Dad, because he wasn't interested, and no one in the whole world used tools as well as Gramp did.

The other blocks of apartments on the opposite side of the road were going up fast. The one opposite Simon's was complete on the outside and the crane had gone from the top of it. There were painters and decorators inside it now. The next two blocks were about halfway up, and the next two just beginning to grow out of the ground. Simon saw them every day from his window, and on his way to school, and each day they were a little higher. Soon they would all be full of people.

He stopped and looked through the gap in the fencing. The site was dry and dusty and the doors of all the builders' sheds were open in the sunlight. There were workers standing about everywhere, as it was payday and they were just getting off work.

The sheds?

They were fine sheds, wooden and sturdy, much larger than the shed they had had at home. In fact, some of them were almost as large as a small house. Surely one of them would have enough room inside for a bench for Gramp? Surely he wouldn't be in the way there? And he might even be useful, mending and making things for the men and the engineers.

Simon moved inside the fence. He knew you weren't supposed to go in, but no one seemed to notice him. He waited until the workers had gone away and then he moved over toward one of the huts.

It was big and roomy and had a kind of desk inside it. There were charts and papers all over the walls, and papers everywhere. There were chairs against the desk, just like an

office. There wasn't much room for anything else. He turned around and began to walk toward the next one.

"Hi, you!" a voice cried out. "What are you up to over there?"

Simon turned around. A man was standing in the doorway of a smaller hut near the gateway.

"Get on out of there!" the man shouted. "You've no business here. Beat it!"

Simon walked slowly over toward him, trying to think what he would say. If he ran away now, he'd never find anywhere for Gramp. What should he say? Have you got a workbench to spare? The man would laugh.

"I was just looking," he said, as he came nearer the man.

"Well, just you go off and do your looking somewhere else. You're trespassing, you know. I could put the police onto you."

"I suppose it wouldn't be possible for my grandpa to have a bench anywhere here?" he said, boldly looking straight at the man.

"A *what*, did you say?"

"A bench, a workbench, where he could have his tools. Where he could come every day and do a bit of work at the bench."

"What? Here? On a building site?"

The man looked puzzled now. Now that he was closer to him, Simon could see that the man was rather like Dad, a little older perhaps but not much.

"My grandpa," he went on. "We've come to live in the apartments there." He pointed back the way he had come. "And Gramp hasn't got a shed for his tools and a bench. And he's . . . he's . . ."

For some reason he couldn't go on. He couldn't understand why tears had come into his eyes, and he hurriedly wiped them away with his sleeve. Perhaps it was because the man in front of him wasn't looking angry anymore, and that he looked rather like Dad. All he could think of was Gramp sitting there in a chair, rubbing his hands up and down the handle of a small hammer. The one he used for tacks and little brass pin-nails.

"I'm looking for a place for him — somewhere near. Where he can put his bench. A new bench. He's got all his tools and nowhere to use them."

"Well," said the man, scratching his head, "I've heard some pretty funny things here, but you're the first to come and ask for a place for a bench."

"It wouldn't take up much space," said Simon. "And he wouldn't be a lot of trouble. He's awfully tidy. He just wants somewhere to come every day for a while. He would be useful, too. He's very good with the tools. He's teaching me. Or he was."

The man just shook his head.

"I know just what you mean, son," he said. "But I can't help you. This is a building site and it's as much as my job's worth[1] to let your granddad come on the site even, much less use a bench. You can see for yourself that these huts are all used. The men use them. The engineers have that one, this one is an office, and the others are all full of supplies. We can't have old gents coming along here to do their carpentry, now, can we?"

"I suppose not."

Simon sounded so miserable that the man put his hand on his shoulder and shook him gently.

"I know what you mean," he said. "The old man doesn't like the apartments, I suppose. They never do, the old ones. I know. But I can't do anything about it. I've got my own worries. And anyhow all these sheds will be gone soon. Now, you scat along now and get back to your mum."

He gave Simon a push toward the gap in the fencing.

Simon went home. There was nothing else he could do. When he got there, he closed his eyes and waited for the row that was going to fall on his head.[2] But his mother said nothing but "Tell Grandpa his tea's ready, will you?"

Gramp was sitting in his room, the hammer in his hand.

"Tea's ready, Gramp," he said.

The old man didn't even turn his head.

That night Simon dreamed he had found a bench for Gramp, down at the end of the road, in one of the factories there. The dream was so clear that when he woke he could hardly believe that it wasn't true.

Simon tried the factory the next morning. He felt he knew just where Gramp could go, and just what they would say, it had all been so real the night before. He walked straight down the road to the far end and then turned in at the factory gate. For the first time, he hesitated, suddenly not so hopeful.

---

[1]it could cost me my job

[2]the punishment that he expected

The factory looked large and not what Gramp would like at all. But he would have to try. He couldn't go back without even trying.

The gatehouse had two men in it, one of them in a peaked cap. Simon went up to the open window.

"Well, my young feller, me lad, what can I do for you this fine morning? Looking for a job, are you?"

It was the man in the peaked cap speaking, and Simon saw him wink across the room.

Simon drew a deep breath. It was not easy to explain. He thought he would try the other way around this time.

"I've come to live in the new apartments," he said.

"Oh, yes, and how do you like that, eh?"

"Oh, it's all right, but it's not that."

"What's not that?"

"It's not that I've come about. It's my grandfather."

"Oh, indeed. And what can I do for your grandfather, may I ask?"

"At our old place, where we used to live on the other side of town, we had a bit of garden and a shed. It was Gramp's shed, really. He used it all the time and had his bench and tools in it. He made all sorts of things and mended things for Mum."

"Here, come and listen to this, Jim. Here's someone with some rigmarole about his granddad."

The other man came over to the open window too, and they both leaned out and looked down at Simon.

"Well, go on then. Does your granddad want a job, or something?"

"Oh, no," said Simon. "Nothing like that. He just wants somewhere where he could put his bench and tools."

"Is that all?" said the second man. "So you came along here, did you? Smart young chap you are, aren't you?"

Simon's hopes began to rise. Perhaps they would find a small space somewhere. Perhaps they understood. Perhaps they even had an old bench that Gramp could use just like that. He went on.

"He wouldn't be a nuisance. He would just come every day for a while to use the bench. He wouldn't be in the way. It's just that he hasn't anything to do when he hasn't got a bench, you see! You can't have workbenches in those apartments."

"You can't indeed," said the man in the peaked cap. "You're dead right there."

"There isn't room, you see."

"Yes, indeed I see," said the peaked cap man again. "And so you came along here to see if we had a bench to spare for your poor old granddad eh? Is that it?"

"Yes, please."

Both men suddenly burst out into loud raucous laughter, loud laughs which rained down over Simon's ears like hailstones.

"Oh, my, I've not heard such a good one for a right long time," gasped one of the men. "Old people's home, that's what we'd be in no time at all. Lor' help us, just imagine, every old person for miles traipsing in through the gate for their little bit of workshop!"

Both the men stopped laughing and the man in the peaked cap frowned.

"Now, look here, my lad," he said. "Just you get cracking and get off these premises. If you think this is a place to dump your old granddad, then you're dead wrong, see? This is a factory, and a couple of thousand men work here for their living, see? Just think what'd happen if every granddad for miles around came around here asking for a bench. Now, off you go, and grow up a bit. Go on, scram!"

Simon had already turned around to go. He felt hot and uncomfortable and he hated the two men. They'd made a fool of him. Perhaps he was childish and silly. Perhaps he was a fool after all. Perhaps it was hopeless and Mum was right. Perhaps Mum knew all the time and when she said, "What can *I* do about it?" she knew that she couldn't do anything. Perhaps she knew that Gramp was miserable, but she hadn't asked to move to the apartment, had she? It hadn't been her idea. She'd been sent there.

He walked slowly back toward the apartments. He did not want to go in. He didn't want Gramp and Mum and Dad to see that he hadn't been able to do anything either. He didn't want them to laugh at him, too. He went to the yard shed to look at his guinea pigs. But then he remembered that he hadn't got the key. He thought about going into town to the park, but then he couldn't be bothered. It was too far to walk and he hadn't any money on him for the fare. He wandered about and then finally pushed his way through the big glass doors into the hall of the building. Neither of the elevators was down, so he stood there waiting. There was no one there at all.

Just as he heard the elevator coming down, a man came in through the main doors and headed for the stairs that led down to the basement, where there was a notice saying

KEEP OUT

Simon knew who the man was. It was Mr. Gideon, who lived on the ground floor around the other side, and Mr. Gideon was the caretaker. He sometimes kept some greenstuff for Simon's guinea pigs.

"'Lo, Simon," he said.

"'Lo," said Simon.

"Well, that's a long face to pull on this fine morning. Anything wrong with those guinea pigs of yours?"

"No," said Simon.

"If you wait there a minute, I've got some greens for them," said Mr. Gideon. "Hang on a moment and I'll be back."

He started off down the basement steps. Then he stopped and came back again.

"Like to have a look around?" he said.

"What? Me?" said Simon, in surprise, because he knew Mr. Gideon didn't allow anyone down there, especially boys.

"Yes. Come on, then," said Mr. Gideon. "I'll show you."

Simon followed him down the stone steps. At the bottom there was a heavy metal door which Mr. Gideon opened with a key, and suddenly they were in a different world altogether. This was where the heating of the whole building came from and Mr. Gideon was in charge of it all.

There were pipes everywhere, and great tanks and boilers and things that looked like clocks with handles below them. It was all quite clean and Simon was surprised, for the only other boiler house he had ever seen had been the one at his old school, a dirty place, full of dust. Mr. Gideon kept this place clean and spent a lot of time down here in the winter, adjusting the heating and the flow of oil. He almost lived down here, as it was his job, and he had been caretaker for the block ever since it had been built.

Mr. Gideon took Simon around and showed him how the heating system worked. Of course it was not all turned on now, as it was summer, but the smaller boiler for water heating was working. Pipes snaked all around, some of them as thick as drainpipes, others smaller, disappearing up through the ceiling to the apartments above. Mr. Gideon had three boiler houses to look after, but this one was the biggest.

"Looks like a factory, doesn't it?" he said as Simon bent his head all the way back to look up at the pipes high up on the ceiling.

Alongside one of the storage tanks was a long rack of wrenches, all hanging in a row, each one slightly bigger than the last one, twelve of them altogether. Simon counted them. Mr. Gideon took one down, turned a large nut on one of the pipes, and then put the wrench back.

Simon stared.

Mr. Gideon took a large broom down from a double hook on the wall and began sweeping around the bases of the boilers.

Simon stared.

When he had finished sweeping, Mr. Gideon put the broom back in its place, took a rag out of his overall pocket, and wiped all the clock faces and the handles below them. They shone brightly already, but he wiped each one carefully all the same.

Simon stared.

Simon was so quiet that Mr. Gideon noticed.

"What's up with you today? Lost your tongue, or something?"

But Simon was still staring. Right in the far corner of the boiler room, up against the wall, quite empty and unused, there was an ordinary wooden workbench.

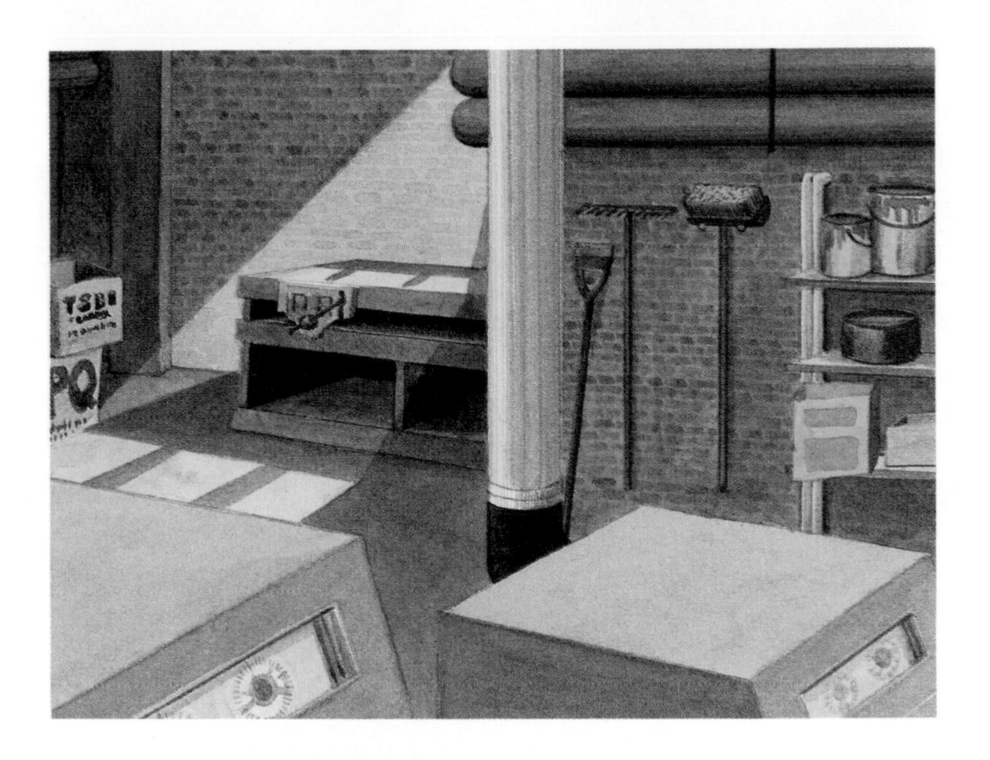

"What are you staring at?"

Simon slowly lifted one hand and pointed at the bench.

"That bench. Is it yours?"

"Oh, that," said Mr. Gideon. "That's been here all the time. Only use it now and again. It's for repairs, smaller ones. But since everything is new here, I've had nothing much to repair so far."

"Do you know my granddad?" said Simon.

"Didn't even know you'd got one. Here, do you mean? Here in the apartments?"

"Yes, I told you. He helped me make my hutch."

"Oh yes, I remember now. But I didn't know he was here. Does he live with your mum and dad, then?"

"Yes," said Simon.

"Well, of course, I wouldn't know which he was, would I? I can't tell one granddad from another, can I? And they're mostly younger here."

"He doesn't like it and he doesn't go out much now, either. He's lost his workbench and has nothing to do."

"That's bad."

"I've been out today and yesterday," said Simon, "looking for a place for him to have a bench, you see? He used to have one in the garden shed, you see? And now he's got his tools up in the storeroom and nowhere to put them. He couldn't . . . he couldn't . . . ?"

Mr. Gideon turned around and looked at the bench on the other side of the boiler room.

"So that's what it's all about, is it? Thought you were in a bit of a state about something," he said. "Well, no one uses it. Except me, and I haven't got any tools down here as yet. It's an idea. I don't see why not. Bring him down one day and we'll see what we can do. He'd have to fit in with my times, mind you, because I lock up when I go out of here. Got to keep you young mischiefs out of the place, haven't I?"

"You mean he could? Can I go and get him down now?"

"If you like. No time like the present. I've got about another half hour down here. After that, I'll have gone."

Simon ran as he had never run before. He ran up the basement steps and around to the elevators. As usual, both were up somewhere. He couldn't wait. He began running up the stairs, but soon found he was puffing and panting like a grampus and his legs felt weak and feeble. He slowed down and struggled on up the stairs, his chest heaving and his face scarlet. But he got there in the end and in his excitement could hardly get his key into the lock.

No one was home except Gramp.

Simon rushed into Gramp's room, trying to calm down a little.

"You been running up them stairs, or something," said Gramp, looking up as Simon appeared so suddenly.

Simon nodded.

"What's all the hurry today then?"

"I . . . I . . . I . . ."

"Come on, then, out with it. What's the excitement?"

"I've found a bench for you."

"What did you say?"

"I've found a bench and a place for your tools. I think."

"What d'you mean, a bench? And what d'you mean, you think?"

"Well, you may not like it."

"A bench?"

"Yes."

"A workbench."

"Yes."

"Where?"

"Come with me. I'll show you."

"Are you pulling my leg?"

"Gramp!"

"Oh, all right, then. What, now?"

"Yes."

"Where?"

"Only downstairs."

"Downstairs?"

"Yes."

"Well, I suppose I'd better come and see what tricks you've been up to, or I'll have you making a mess of things again."

It took a long time, a very long time, to get Gramp down to the basement, and Simon was afraid Mr. Gideon would have gone. Gramp had got out of the habit of going anywhere. But they did get there. Mr. Gideon was still there. They talked. They looked at the workbench. They talked again.

"I could make a rack to go on the wall there," said Gramp.

"Yes," said Simon.

"Perhaps I could do a job or two for you, Mr. Gideon?" said Gramp.

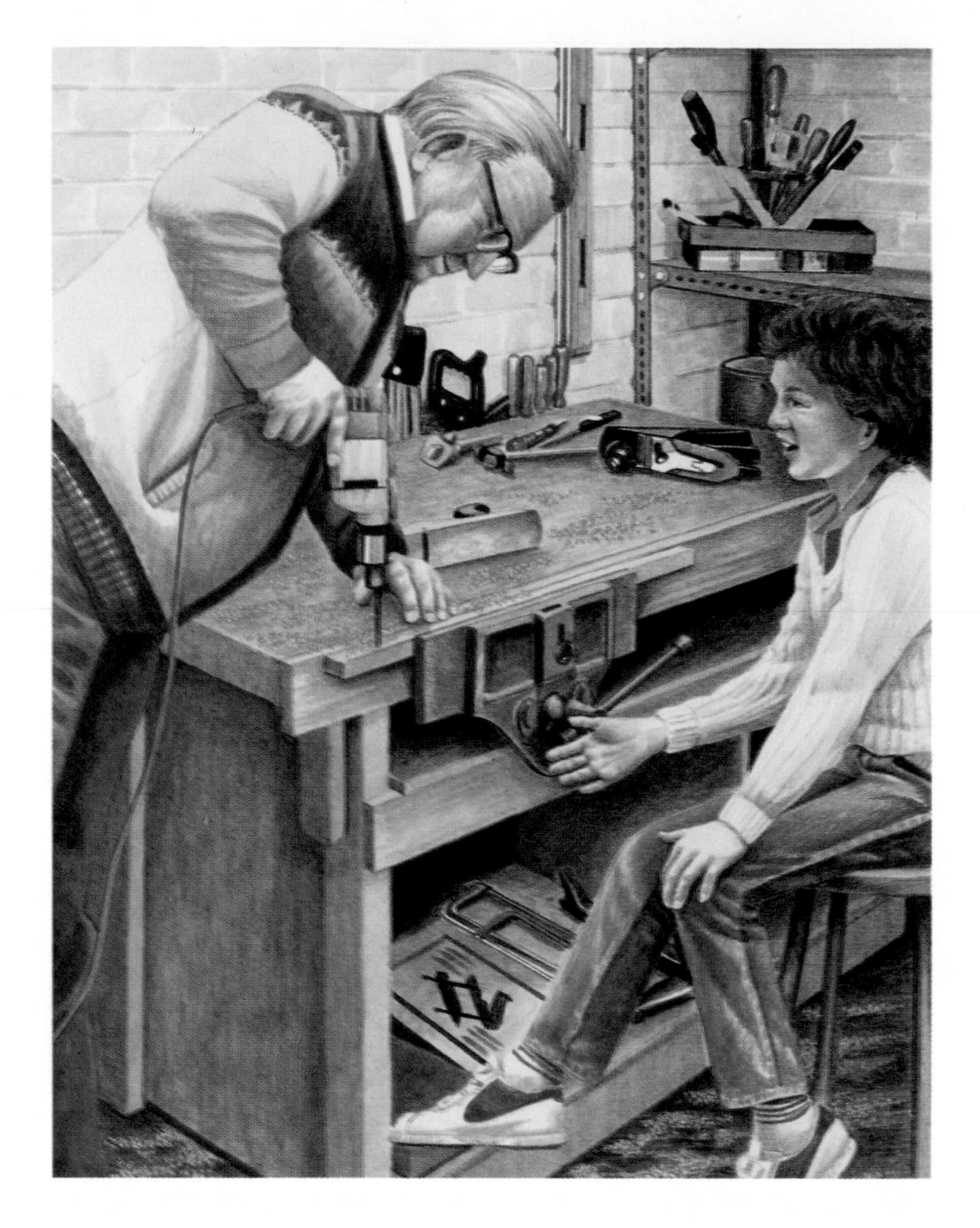

"Perhaps you could," said Mr. Gideon. "There's odd things that want doing all the time."

"I could get my tools down from the roof storeroom, couldn't I?" said Gramp.

"I could help you sharpen them," said Simon.

"You'll not touch a single one until I say so," said Gramp.

They looked at each other. They grinned. That was more like Gramp.

So it was arranged.

It took a long time. Gramp's tools had to be got out and that meant waiting for Dad to get back. Then Gramp had to make a rack for them, and that took a lot of mornings down there in the basement. Gramp had got slow. Then he had to clean and sharpen all his tools and put them in the new rack. Then it was ready.

Each day, Gramp seemed a little younger, a little quicker. Each day he moved a little more quickly. Each day he went down to the basement in the same building and each day he got his tools down and made something, mended something, or put something in order.

Each day, he told them what he had done.

"I found Gramp a shed in the end, didn't I, Mum?" said Simon, one night, long afterward, at tea.

"You certainly did," she said.

"You certainly did," said Dad. "Some shed, too."

"You certainly did," said Gramp. "Biggest blooming shed in the whole wide world, I'd say."

His old blue eyes were bright.

Author

Joan Tate, who was educated in England and in Sweden, is a British translator and the author of more than a hundred books for children and young adults. She says, "I write all the time and read when I'm not writing." The author and her family live in England, where *Gramp* was first published as a separate book. In the United States it appeared as *Luke's Garden and Gramp* and was chosen a Notable Children's Trade Book in the Field of Social Studies.

Ride the Red Cycle

from the book by
Harriette Gillem Robinet

"Jerome's got something to say, Mama, and you gotta listen!"

Jerome felt a warm blush rise up from his neck as Tilly, his fifteen-year-old sister, spoke for him. He wished she wouldn't do that. It made him feel he wasn't real.

Once he had liked the word *special*, special classes, special bus. Then he decided it meant "not like other boys."

The trouble was that people were always helping him. His speech was slow and slurred, and someone was always finishing what he wanted to say. When he played baseball, he would kneel to bat the ball and someone would run the bases for him. When he tried to roll his wheelchair at school, one of the kids would insist on pushing it. Everything happened to him, but he never got a chance to make things happen himself. Like a chick breaking out of an egg, he wanted to break free.

Sitting at the breakfast table on that sunny spring morning, he felt a little dizzy; his heart beat faster, the room looked fuzzy to him. It was now or never, he thought. Would they laugh at him? It didn't matter, this was something he had to do. He had to make a break, and this was how he was going to do it. There was a dream that haunted him, and he had to do something about that dream. He wished he spoke more clearly, but since he couldn't, he asked very slowly.

"I wann tricycle to rrr-ride!"

"How's Jerome gonna ride, when he can't walk yet, Papa?" Liza asked innocently. Jerome picked up his fork and struck her on the arm; when she screamed, he made a face at her.

"Jerome, you stop that!" Mama said. She looked thin and nervous, her fingers tapped on the table.

Round-faced Liza was only five, but already she could ride Tilly's big two-wheeler. She didn't mean to hurt anyone when she reminded the family that eleven-year-old Jerome, who was in the fifth grade, couldn't even walk.

As a baby, he had walked at nine months. By his first birthday he was running around strong. But when he was two years old, a virus infection had gone to his brain and left damage that affected his whole body. When he got better, he had to learn to support his head, turn over, and crawl all over again. And his legs remained crippled.

Nervous and angry, Mama began clearing the breakfast table even though no one was finished. Papa, Liza, Tilly, and plump little three-year-old Gordon grabbed at toast as Mama whisked plates away.

"That ungrateful boy," Mama grumbled, "never says thank you, but always demandin' somethin'. It's take him here, take him there. Clinics, doctors, physical therapy, speech therapy. Seems that's all I do, take Jerome Johnson somewheres. Now he want a tricycle at eleven years old. Lordy, what's comin' next?"

Papa, a short stocky man with dark brown skin, cleared his throat. "What *they* say, Mary?"

Jerome felt angry tears springing into his eyes. He felt so angry he hit Gordon under the table and Gordon started to cry. Jerome's throat ached from wanting to cry, too, but he couldn't blink or someone would notice.

He didn't mind what Mama said, she was always grumbling. Besides, Mama was fussing because she was scared that her big son couldn't ride a tricycle. He knew how his mother felt because he was scared himself. But how would he ever find out if he never tried? No, he wasn't angry with Mama, but Papa wanted to know what *they* had to say.

All his life *they* — all the people in his life that other boys never had to worry about — got to say things about him.

They were the physical therapists who exercised his legs, the speech therapists, the bone doctors, the nerve doctors, the eye doctors, and the social workers who got money for Mama to pay for his braces and his special shoes and his eyeglasses and his wheelchair. *They* were all the people he had to be grateful to. He was tired of being grateful. He hated to say thank you, it got stuck in his throat.

They made all the decisions in his life; but just once he wanted to do something all by himself! This time he didn't care what *they* said. He had thought for a long time, and he had chosen carefully for himself. A teenager with cerebral palsy told him that a two-wheeler was out of the question; it took balance to ride a two-wheeler. But three wheels . . .

Of course he was pleased with the wheelchair. He got around the neighborhood with it, except for curbs. Until he was six, his folks had to carry him everywhere.

The wheelchair was all right, but Jerome had a wonderful dream. In it he was speeding fast, with the wind in his face, eyes squinted tight, leaning forward like the leather-jacket guys on motorcycles. That was his dream, and in his dream hundreds of thousands watched as he raced along a track. Cheers and clapping sounded like thunder in the sky. He was reckless and calm and cool, and millions knew his name. And as he stepped off his cycle, he walked with a casual swagger. Jerome Johnson, cycle rider!

All right, he couldn't race a motorcycle, but he had seen a gray-haired man on a three-wheel cycle once, the kind of cycle he wanted. Summer vacation started in a few weeks, and with real wheels he would be able to go everywhere. He didn't care what *they* said. Oh! for a set of wheels!

Mama answered Papa softly.

"John, physical therapist say it be good leg motion, good for his legs. But Dr. Ryan say that left leg real stiff."

Then in a louder voice aimed at Jerome, she said, "'Sides, that boy's gotta learn to be grateful for what he got!"

"Ha!" Papa jumped at the mention of Dr. Ryan. "Dr. Ryan didn't think he could learn to crawl neither, but he did. I think the boy oughta have a tricycle!"

"Hey now, Papa!" Tilly said triumphantly. "Jerome and me'll be ready to go shopping when you come home." Saturdays Papa worked half-day at the post office.

Mama finished clearing the breakfast table and went to tell the news to Mrs. Mullarkey, the next-door neighbor. Liza, her round face grinning, and little brother Gordon ran out to play. Tilly, tall and thin, dug her hands into her skirt pockets and followed. She sighed. It looked like Jerome was off again. But she knew that no matter what he did, she'd always back him up.

Jerome sat alone in his wheelchair. He wore a green shirt and short brown pants that he hated because his leg braces showed. He was so excited that his eyeglasses steamed up on the inside. He took them off and cleaned them with a tissue. When he put them back on, the room changed from a lazy blur to the sharply outlined kitchen. The round table and chairs showed a hint of white paint on their scrubbed wooden surfaces. Dishes were stacked neatly on clean open shelves across from him.

He had worn eyeglasses since the virus. He thought they made him look smart, like a professor; other people said he looked like an angry owl. These particular glasses were a victory for him. When he broke his last frames, he had demanded thick black rims.

"I won't wear any pale eyeglasses," he had said.

But the eyeglass man said, "We don't have black rims for a child that age . . ."

While the man was talking, Tilly found some in the eyeglass catalogue. It took an extra two weeks for them to come, but at last he got the thick black frames for his big, sparkling black eyes.

He had to admit Tilly sometimes knew how he felt. She was the one who made sure the kids called him his full name. He hated being called Jerry; it sounded like a girl's name or a baby's name to him. With Tilly's help he was called Jerome. He thought Jerome Johnson had a noble sound!

And he liked his extra-strong brown arms and broad shoulders too. His arms had grown strong from supporting him when his legs wouldn't. But he hated his skinny legs and the braces he wore attached to high-top shoes. None of that would matter, though, when he got his three-wheel cycle.

Whirling in his chair, he saw a limp balloon on the kitchen sideboard. It was one Gordon had been playing with. He reached over, grabbed it and tried to pop it with his broad clumsy hands. Straining violently, half-afraid but wanting to hear the loud bang, he grunted, "Brrr-reak balloonnn."

It was too hard. His hands were too stiff to pop the silly old balloon. Something else he couldn't do.

Outside, Gordon overheard Jerome say "break balloon" just as Papa was coming home from work. Breathless, Gordon met his father.

"Papa, papa," Gordon called. "Jerome's gonna make the moon — he gonna ride his cycle to the moon, Papa?"

Papa smiled wearily and hugged Gordon. He didn't know where that little boy got his wild ideas! Inside, Tilly and Jerome were ready to go shopping, and they were soon on their way.

In the bicycle shop window, Jerome saw what he wanted. The seat was higher than those on small two-wheelers, the wheels were really big, and the color was orange-fire red. It was redder than any fire engine would dare to be.

"Papa, Uh wannn-n tha' un," he called out.

Oh! He could feel the wind whizzing through his soft black hair as he sped along the highways. Highways? Well, along the sidewalk anyway.

Tilly pushed his wheelchair straight up to the big three-wheel cycle while Papa went to get a salesman. There was no price tag on the cycle, and he was afraid to hope. His heart beat faster and he felt breathless for the second time that day. He was so close. This was the cycle he wanted. Would it cost too much?

He was thrilled and happy and afraid too. Maybe Mama was right and he was being foolish. Just then Jerome saw Tilly's foot. He turned his wheelchair quickly and ran over it. He didn't mean to exactly, but he was anxious and getting angry. Papa hadn't come back yet.

Tilly yelled out and looked at him sharply. Why was her brother so mean? Here she was backing him up and he was mean to her again. Why did she ever bother with Jerome? The hurt brought tears to her eyes, but Jerome didn't say he was sorry.

Papa came back and lifted his son onto the seat of the big red cycle. It must be all right; he'll buy it for me, Jerome thought. He gripped the handles and noticed red and white streamers on the plastic handle grips — how they would fly in the wind as he rode! But he felt shaky, up so high on the seat, and as he held on and looked around, Papa noticed.

"Never you mind, son, I'll build up the pedals and make the seat broader," Papa told him. Then to the salesman he said, "We'll take this 'un."

Papa paid at the cash register, and soon Jerome was riding home with his dream cycle tied down in the trunk of the car.

At the house, Mama and Mrs. Mullarkey were standing in the sunshine talking. Jerome was glad Mama hadn't gone to the bicycle shop. She would have made a fuss over the price and would have made him thank Papa, thank the salesman. He didn't thank anybody.

"Lord-a-mighty! What's that?" Mama said, shocked at the big, bright-red, shiny cycle.

"Boy's gonna kill himself on that, Mary!" Mrs. Mullarkey whispered.

Jerome slid out of the car onto the sidewalk. He crawled past Tilly who reached to help him; he crawled past Papa who unfolded his wheelchair for him. He kneeled up straight and, looking at Mama and Mrs. Mullarkey, he said slowly, "Here muhhh cycle. Papa gonna fit it for to rrr-ride!"

Then he lumbered across the grass, up the steps, and into the house. He would show them, maybe, he thought. Everyone watched him in silence.

Suddenly Mama called after him. "Hope yuh told yuh Papa thank you!"

Papa frowned at Mama and said, "Boy don't havta be beholdin' to no one."

Tilly thought, he could've said he was sorry, though, when he ran over my foot.

It took Papa almost a week of evenings after work to finish outfitting the cycle. He attached wooden blocks to the pedals and put leather straps on the blocks to hold his son's shoes. Without the straps Jerome couldn't keep his feet on the pedals.

Since his son kept sliding off the seat, Papa made a new one. From a secondhand chair he got a plastic seat and back, all in one piece. He drilled holes and screwed the new seat onto the cycle, then put a seat belt around it.

On the first of June, Jerome sat on his cycle outdoors for the first time, but he didn't try riding until Papa came home. Everyone was excited. Kids and their mothers from the other row houses on the block gathered on his front doorsteps. For the millionth time Mama told them how much trouble he had been because he wasn't grateful for just being alive.

"Lordy, I never thought my boy'd be livin' today, the way he was. He lay there two weeks, didn't know nobody. All but dead before he come to." Mama was always harping on how sick he had been with the virus.

One mother told Mama he was a brave boy, but Mama shook her head. "Stubborn and foolish," she said.

Neighborhood kids were riding their bicycles in circles and then standing astride them. Liza, a proud grin across her face, rode up and down the block calling people to come see her brother's new cycle.

Jerome thought Mama looked a little proud of him in spite of what she said. She stood on the steps with her thin arms crossed tightly. He was glad people were calling it a cycle and not a tricycle. It was big enough not to look like the tricycles little Gordon's friends rode.

When Papa came home, he pulled his son's handlebars slowly and showed him how to push from his knees to pedal. Jerome leaned forward panting, his tongue showing, but his legs wouldn't move. His legs wouldn't move!

After a while the neighbors and kids grew tired of watching him and they agreed it would be a long time before he learned to ride, if ever. As they began drifting away, he felt disappointment drape over him. He didn't really expect to ride the first day, but somehow he had hoped . . .

The kids went their ways, calling noisily to each other and racing off on bicycles, but Papa and Tilly stayed, giving him pushes.

"Papa, yook, eh catch," Jerome whispered to his father. At each rotation of the wheel, the brace on his left leg caught in the front wheel. Papa shifted his foot further.

"I'll put a shield on the sides to keep them braces from catchin'," he told his son.

The shields did keep the braces from catching in the wheel, but they didn't make Jerome's legs turn the wheels of the cycle. He spent every afternoon after school sitting and trying to rock his cycle, but he never moved. Sometimes kids came along and pulled or pushed him.

He had been able to get around by himself in the wheelchair, but now he often got stranded on his cycle. The kids would go in and leave him around the corner or down the street and he couldn't follow them. When dinner time came, Mama or Tilly had to go looking for him. Mama now added *contrary* to *ungrateful* when she fussed at him.

And then something exciting happened. One day he was turning the handlebars, weaving back and forth, as some boys ran behind pushing him. One sharp turn and the red cycle fell over. Mama fussed about the bump on his forehead and his scraped knee, but he felt happy and victorious.

"Yook, Papa," he called later when Papa came in from work. "Uh gohh Band-Aid. Uh busted muh knee."

He had calluses on his knees and hands from crawling, but he never had a good hurt knee before. Now he had joined all those other kids who got to wear Band-Aids on their knees. Somehow it made him feel he was really learning to ride. Other kids fell off bicycles when they were learning to ride, and he had fallen too. That night he thought and thought and came up with a plan.

"Eh, Tilly," he called the next day. "Take muh up by alley where slants to da strrrr-eet."

"Trucks come in the alley by the factory, Jerome. You gotta stay on the sidewalk," Tilly told him.

"Buttt Tilly, yuh be wid muh," he begged. "I cann-nn rrr-ride dere."

So Tilly pulled him along the block, not telling anyone where they were going. When they reached the alley, she sat in the uncut grass and chickweed watching for cars and reading a book. She enjoyed the peace and quiet. No one was around, so Jerome could grunt and sway all he needed, trying to pedal.

Three weeks passed and school was out. Every morning Tilly and Jerome went on their secret trip for a couple of hours. When Mama asked them where they went all morning, Jerome said, "Uh beennn near." Mama accepted the fact that he stayed close.

Soon Jerome could shake the cycle enough on the slope so that his right leg got down fast enough for the left leg to reach the top of its pedal. Then he could grunt the stiff left leg down. He pedaled, but not always. He never could be sure. The dream of success was becoming a nightmare. He felt foolish and silly, not being able to depend on his rotten old legs.

"Tilly donnn' tellll," he begged. Every day they went to the alley. Tilly pulled the cycle out of the way when trucks came up to the factory, then she put her brother back on the slope and sat yawning, chin in hands, watching him struggle with the red cycle. What was simple for a three-year-old was hard for her eleven-year-old brother!

Sometimes she wished he were somebody else's brother; sometimes she almost hated him, he was so stubborn and

mean. Her head got all confused when Jerome was mean, and she often felt she didn't love him at all, but she stuck by him all the time.

By July he could ride down the slant, but he fought and struggled to ride up. Soon his legs moved one after the other, and he was riding. Some days Jerome nearly burst with triumph and Tilly wanted to tell Mama and Papa right away. But other days there was only failure. On those days his legs wouldn't push as he wished; in fact, they wouldn't move at all. He had nightmares about his legs not working when he tried to show Mama. In his dreams, Mama and Papa were watching and his legs wouldn't budge. His legs must learn to move one after the other all the time. He knew it wouldn't be easy and he was fighting hard. Gradually he became more sure of being able to pedal; his legs worked more often than they didn't.

In August smothering heat arrived, but Jerome forced his legs to move in spite of the sweat pouring off him. Besides Tilly, no one else knew how hard he was trying.

At home Mama was afraid to hope; it broke her heart to watch him sit still out front on that red cycle. Papa was afraid not to hope.

By then the kids on the block had decided that Jerome would never ride. He had been fun the way he was; if only he would be satisfied with himself. What was so important about riding that cycle?

The summer before, he had played baseball with the other kids and Tommy usually ran bases for him. But this summer he tripped Tommy and made his nose bleed. Then David ran his bases one day and Jerome threw a stone at him and David needed an ice pack. Now all Jerome did was sit alone on the big red cycle. The kids thought he was mean and they stopped playing with him. Why did he want that big cycle anyway?

But Jerome had his dream and he had chosen it carefully. It was something he could do, it was possible, and he would do it. It was one thing he would get to do all by himself. Tilly, it was true, brought him to the slanted drive, but *he* was the one fighting his legs to ride. He'd show Tommy and David and all the kids — he'd even show Tilly, because there was something secret he was practicing late at night all by himself.

By the end of August he could hardly wait to show off. As he became sure of himself, the perfect occasion came up. The neighbors planned a block party for Labor Day weekend.

That Saturday morning police closed the street at both ends, and teen-agers decorated trees with yellow crepe-paper banners. Neighbors held brightly colored balloons, and marching music filled the air. Everyone was dressed in cool, colorful clothes for the hot summer day.

In the morning there was a pet parade, then games with water-filled balloons. Artists of all ages drew pictures on the sidewalk with colored chalk. In the afternoon there was a program of local talent.

David played drums, Liza sang a funny song, and another girl arranged a mushroom dance with five little girls. Jerome knew that Tilly had put his name next on the program.

For the mushroom dance the little girls held umbrellas covered with brown paper. Everyone liked the silly twirling dance, and when they finished, Mrs. Mullarkey called out, "And next on our program is Jerome Johnson who will, who will . . . Jerome Johnson, folks!"

Everyone clapped politely. Then there was an eerie quiet. Adults and kids looked at one another to see if anyone knew what was going to happen. What was he going to do?

Tilly pulled her brother out into the street at the end of the block, and left him sitting on the shiny orange red cycle. Her heart was pounding and she lowered her head and stuck her hands in her jean pockets as she strolled away from him. He was on his own.

Mama folded her arms to calm herself; Papa sat down on

the curb because his knees grew weak. Liza hugged Gordon and waited. Gordon wondered if his brother would go to the moon now.

Jerome, frowning and gritting his teeth, struggled for what seemed like hours to get his legs moving. After two long minutes, slowly but firmly, he began pedaling — gripping the handles and leaning forward as though he were speeding along. There was no wind whipping in his face, but that didn't matter. He was riding his cycle himself; he was riding. That was all he could think.

The neighbors murmured and nodded to each other. Mrs. Mullarkey forgot she was holding the loudspeaker and blew her nose. The noise made everyone giggle nervously.

His progress down the street was slow, deliberate, and strangely rhythmic. People could hardly wait to applaud and, as he neared the end, clapping burst forth and the kids cheered, but he remained calm and cool.

"O.K.," he muttered to himself, "wid Tilly's help Uh learnnnn tuh ride. But nnnnnn-now Uh really show um."

He stopped in the middle of the street, opened the seat belt, and bowed with a flourish to the people on his right. When he bowed, he made sure he slipped his right foot out of the pedal strap. He bowed and waved to the people clapping on his left and slipped his left foot out of the pedal strap just as he had planned. His hands trembled.

Tilly wondered why he had stopped in the middle. She started toward him, but he stopped her with an icy scowl. Papa stood up, but Jerome frowned at him too.

Mama muttered, "Lordy, ain't enough he can ride, that silly boy gonna crawl off in the middle of the street."

The neighbors got quiet again.

Carefully Jerome slid his right leg around and off the cycle. He stood crouched on both feet, his knees and hips bent under his weight. He was grateful for the braces that kept his feet flat on the ground. At night when he had practiced this with his braces off, he stood on his toes.

He heard himself saying, "Uh wannn-na tank evv-body help muh, 'pecially muh sister Tilly, and muh Papa, and muh Mama." He nodded at Mama — he had said thank you and it didn't stick in his throat this time. There was a mild sprinkling of applause.

Then, while eighty people held their breath, he let go of the cycle. His arms wavered at his sides, balancing him. His head was high, his chin jutted forward. In spite of his eyeglasses everybody and everything was blurred.

He slid his stiff left leg forward, feet and knees twisted in; then he stepped jerkily off on his right foot. He dragged his left leg, stepped with his right. Deliberate, slow, arms waving in the air, one leg after the other, Jerome Johnson walked. It was stiff and clumsy walking, with twisted legs, but these were his first steps, practiced late at night.

Before he reached his wheelchair, he fell to the street. No one moved toward him. Clapping and cheering could be heard for five blocks. It was almost like thunder in the sky. His dream had come true.

He didn't try to get to his feet again, he crawled to his wheelchair. He'd work on walking with his physical therapist now that it wasn't a secret anymore. Now that he'd shown them how much he could do all by himself.

Mama was thanking the Lord, Papa cried and didn't care who saw him. Liza and Gordon were staring with mouths hanging open. For Gordon, his brother's going to the moon had seemed a simple thing; his brother's walking was far more wonderful.

Tilly rolled on the grass, laughing and crying and hugging herself for joy. Her tough, stubborn little brother had learned to ride a cycle and had taught himself to walk.

Jerome saw Tommy and David among the neighbors. Maybe he'd play some baseball with them. After all, he could walk now. Maybe next summer he would be running — even running his own bases.

Maybe he'd even . . .

Jerome was dreaming again.

Author

Harriette Gillem Robinet, who has a son with cerebral palsy, has met many children with similar disabilities. For them she wanted to write a book that would reflect some of their frustrations, dreams, and victories. Dr. Robinet, who has a doctor's degree from Catholic University, has been a biology teacher and a research scientist.

The Crow and the Pitcher

A fable by Aesop, retold by Joseph Jacobs

A Crow, half-dead with thirst, came upon a Pitcher which had once been full of water; but when the Crow put its beak into the mouth of the Pitcher he found that only very little water was left in it, and that he could not reach far enough down to get at it. He tried, and he tried, but at last had to give up in despair. Then a thought came to him, and he took a pebble and dropped it into the Pitcher. Then he took another pebble and dropped it into the Pitcher. Then he took another pebble and dropped that into the Pitcher. Then he took another pebble and dropped that into the Pitcher. At last, at last, he saw the water mount up near him; and after casting in a few more pebbles he was able to quench his thirst and save his life.

Where there is a will there is a way.

Houghton Mifflin Literature

In each of the selections you have read from *Perseverance,* the characters were persistent in overcoming some obstacle or problem.

Now you will read the book *From the Mixed-up Files of Mrs. Basil E. Frankweiler* by E. L. Konigsburg. It is about eleven-year-old Claudia and her brother Jamie, who run off to New York City from their home in Connecticut. Their perseverance in planning the trek and in finding a place to hide involves them in a peculiar art mystery.

2

Creating and Accepting Change

FORD
8L 1437

The Cat
and the
Golden Egg
from a book by
Lloyd Alexander

Quickset, a silver-gray cat, lived with Dame Agnes, a poor widow. Not only was he a cheerful companion, but clever at helping the old woman make ends meet. If the chimney smoked, he tied a bundle of twigs to his tail, climbed up the flue, and cleaned it with all the skill of the town sweep. He sharpened the old woman's knives and scissors, and mended her pots and pans neatly as any tinker. Did Dame Agnes knit, he held the skein of yarn; did she spin, he turned the spinning wheel.

Now, one morning Dame Agnes woke up with a bone-cracking rheumatism. Her joints creaked, her back ached, and her knees were so stiff she could no way get out of bed.

"My poor Quickset," she moaned, "today you and I must both go hungry."

At first, Quickset thought Dame Agnes meant it was the rheumatism that kept her from cooking breakfast, so he answered:

"Go hungry? No, indeed. You stay comfortable; I'll make us a little broiled sausage and soft boiled egg, and brew a pot of tea for you. Then I'll sit on your lap to warm you, and soon you'll be good as new."

Before Dame Agnes could say another word, he hurried to the pantry. But, opening the cupboard, he saw only bare shelves: not so much as a crust of bread or crumb of cheese; not even a dry bone or bacon rind.

"Mice!" he cried. "Eaten every scrap! They're out of hand, I've been too easy on them. I'll settle accounts with those fellows later. But now, mistress, I had best go to Master Grubble's market and buy what we need."

Dame Agnes thereupon burst into tears. "Oh, Quickset, it isn't mice, it's money. I have no more. Not a penny left for food or fuel."

"Why, mistress, you should have said something about that before now," replied Quickset. "I never would have let you come to such a state. No matter, I'll think of a way to fill your purse again. Meantime, I'll have Master Grubble give us our groceries on credit."

"Grubble? Give credit?" Dame Agnes exclaimed. "You know the only thing he gives is short weight at high prices. Alas for the days when the town had a dozen tradesmen and more: a baker, a butcher, a greengrocer, and all the others. But they're gone, thanks to Master Grubble. One by one, he's gobbled them up. Schemed and swindled them out of their businesses! And now he's got the whole town under his thumb, for it's deal with Grubble or deal with no one."

"In that case," replied Quickset, "deal with him I will. Or, to put it better, he'll deal with me."

The old woman shook her head. "You'll still need money. And you shall have it, though I must do something I hoped I'd never have to do.

"Go to the linen chest," Dame Agnes went on. "At the bottom, under the good pillowslips, there's an old wool stocking. Fetch it out and bring it to me."

Puzzled, Quickset did as she asked. He found the stocking with a piece of string tied around the toe and carried it to

Dame Agnes, who undid the knot, reached in and drew out one small gold coin.

"Mistress, that's more than enough," said Quickset. "Why did you fret so? With this, we can buy all we want."

Instead of being cheered by the gold piece in her hand, Dame Agnes only sighed:

"This is the last of the small savings my dear husband left to me. I've kept it all these years, and promised myself never to spend it."

"Be glad you did keep it," said Quickset, "for now's the time you need it most."

"I didn't put this by for myself," Dame Agnes replied. "It was for you. I meant to leave it to you in my will. It was to be your legacy, a little something until you found another home. But I see I shall have to spend it. Once gone, it's gone, and that's the end of everything."

At this, Dame Agnes began sobbing again. But Quickset reassured her:

"No need for tears. I'll see to this matter. Only let me have that gold piece a little while. I'll strike such a bargain with Master Grubble that we'll fill our pantry with meat and drink a-plenty. Indeed, he'll beg me to keep the money and won't ask a penny, that I promise."

"Master Grubble, I fear, will be more than a match even for you," Dame Agnes replied. Nevertheless, she did as Quickset urged, put the coin in a leather purse, and hung it around his neck.

Quickset hurried through town to the market, where he found Master Grubble sitting on a high stool behind the counter. For all that his shelves were loaded with victuals of every kind, with meats, and vegetables, and fruits, Grubble looked as though he had never sampled his own wares. There was more fat on his bacon than on himself. He was lean-shanked and sharp-eyed, his nose narrow as a knife blade. His mouth was pursed and puckered as if he had been sipping vinegar, and his cheeks as mottled as moldy cheese. At sight of Quickset, the storekeeper never so much as climbed down from his stool to wait on his customer, but only made a sour face; and, in a voice equally sour, demanded:

"And what do you want? Half a pound of mouse tails? A sack of catnip? Out! No loitering! I don't cater to the cat trade."

Despite this curdled welcome, Quickset bowed and politely explained that Dame Agnes was ailing and he had come shopping in her stead.

"Sick she must be," snorted Master Grubble, "to send a cat marketing, without even a shopping basket. How do you mean to carry off what you buy? Push it along the street with your nose?"

"Why, sir," Quickset answered, "I thought you might send your shop boy around with the parcels. I'm sure you'll do it gladly when you see the handsome order to be filled. Dame Agnes needs a joint of beef, a shoulder of mutton, five pounds of your best sausage, a dozen of the largest eggs — "

"Not so fast," broke in the storekeeper. "Joints and shoulders, is it? Sausage and eggs? Is that what you want? Then I'll tell you what I want: cash on the counter, paid in full. Or you, my fine cat, won't have so much as a wart from one of my pickles."

"You'll be paid," Quickset replied, "and very well paid. But now I see your prices, I'm not sure I brought enough money with me."

"So that's your game!" cried Grubble. "Well, go and get enough. I'll do business with you then, and not before."

"It's a weary walk home and back again," said Quickset. "Allow me a minute or two and I'll have money to spare. And, Master Grubble, if you'd be so kind as to lend me an egg."

Apples
Apples

"Egg?" retorted Grubble. "What's that to do with paying my bill?"

"You'll see," Quickset answered. "I guarantee you'll get all that's owing to you."

Grubble at first refused and again ordered Quickset from the shop. Only when the cat promised to pay double the price of the groceries, as well as an extra fee for the use of the egg, did the storekeeper grudgingly agree.

Taking the egg from Master Grubble, Quickset placed it on the floor, then carefully settled himself on top of it.

"Fool!" cried Grubble. "What are you doing? Get off my egg! This cat's gone mad, and thinks he's a chicken!"

Quickset said nothing, but laid back his ears and waved his tail, warning Grubble to keep silent. After another moment, Quickset got up and brought the egg to the counter:

"There, Master Grubble, that should be enough."

"What?" shouted the storekeeper. "Idiot cat! You mean to pay me with my own egg?"

"With better than that, as you'll see," answered Quickset. While Grubble fumed, Quickset neatly cracked the shell and poured the contents into a bowl. At this, Grubble ranted all the more:

"Alley rabbit! Smash my egg, will you? I'll rub your nose in it!"

Suddenly Master Grubble's voice choked in his gullet. His eyes popped as he stared into the bowl. There, with the broken egg, lay a gold piece.

Instantly, he snatched it out. "What's this?"

"What does it look like?" returned Quickset.

Grubble squinted at the coin, flung it onto the counter and listened to it ring. He bit it, peered closer, turned it round and round in his fingers, and finally blurted:

"Gold!"

Grubble, in his fit of temper, had never seen Quickset slip the coin from the purse and deftly drop it into the bowl. Awestruck, he gaped at the cat, then lowered his voice to a whisper:

"How did you do that?"

Quickset merely shook his head and shrugged his tail. At last, as the excited storekeeper pressed him for an answer, he winked one eye and calmly replied:

"Now, now, Master Grubble, a cat has trade secrets just as a storekeeper. I don't ask yours, you don't ask mine. If I told you how simple it is, you'd know as much as I do. And if others found out — "

"Tell me!" cried Grubble. "I won't breathe a word to a living soul. My dear cat, listen to me," he hurried on. "You'll have all the victuals you want. For a month! A year! Forever! Here, this very moment, I'll have my boy take a cartload to your mistress. Only teach me to sit on eggs as you did."

"Easily done," said Quickset. "But what about that gold piece?"

"Take it!" cried Grubble, handing the coin to Quickset. "Take it, by all means."

Quickset pretended to think over the bargain, then answered:

"Agreed. But you must do exactly as I tell you."

Grubble nodded and his eyes glittered. "One gold piece from one egg. But what if I used two eggs? Or three, or four, or five?"

"As many as you like," said Quickset. "A basketful, if it suits you."

Without another moment's delay, Grubble called his boy from the storeroom and told him to deliver all that Quickset

ordered to the house of Dame Agnes. Then, whimpering with pleasure, he filled his biggest basket with every egg in the store. His nose twitched, his hands trembled, and his usually sallow face turned an eager pink.

"Now," said Quickset, "so you won't be disturbed, take your basket to the top shelf and sit on it there. One thing more, the most important. Until those eggs hatch, don't say a single word. If you have anything to tell me, whatever the reason, you must only cluck like a chicken. Nothing else, mind you. Cackle all you like; speak but once, and the spell is broken."

"What about my customers? Who's to wait on them?" asked Grubble, unwilling to lose business even in exchange for a fortune.

"Never fear," said Quickset. "I'll mind the store."

"What a fine cat you are," purred Grubble. "Noble animal. Intelligent creature."

With that, gleefully chuckling and licking his lips, he clambered to the top shelf, hauling his heavy burden along with him. There he squatted gingerly over the basket, so cramped that he was obliged to draw his knees under his chin and fold his arms as tightly as he could; until indeed he looked much like a skinny, long-beaked chicken hunched on a nest.

Below, Quickset no sooner had taken his place on the stool than Mistress Libbet, the carpenter's wife, stepped through the door.

"Why, Quickset, what are you doing here?" said she. "Have you gone into trade? And can that be Master Grubble on the shelf? I swear he looks as if he's sitting on a basket of eggs."

"Pay him no mind," whispered Quickset. "He fancies himself a hen. An odd notion, but harmless. However, since Master Grubble is busy nesting, I'm tending shop for him. So, Mistress Libbet, how may I serve you?"

"There's so much our little ones need." Mistress Libbet sighed unhappily. "And nothing we can afford to feed them. I was hoping Master Grubble had some scraps or trimmings."

"He has much better," said Quickset, pulling down one of the juiciest hams and slicing away at it with Grubble's carving knife. "Here's a fine bargain today: only a penny a pound."

Hearing this, Master Grubble was about to protest, but caught himself in the nick of time. Instead, he began furiously clucking and squawking:

"Cut-cut-cut! Aw-cut!"

"What's that you say?" Quickset glanced up at the agitated storekeeper and cupped an ear with his paw. "Cut more? Yes,

yes, I understand. The price is still too high? Very well, if you insist: two pounds for a penny."

Too grateful to question such generosity on the part of Grubble, Mistress Libbet flung a penny onto the counter and seized her ham without waiting for Quickset to wrap it. As she hurried from the store, the tailor's wife and the stonecutter's daughter came in; and, a moment later, Dame Gerton, the laundrywoman.

"Welcome, ladies," called Quickset. "Welcome, one and all. Here's fine prime meats, fine fresh vegetables on sale today. At these prices, they won't last long. So, hurry! Step up!"

As the delighted customers pressed eagerly toward the counter, Master Grubble's face changed from sallow to crimson, from crimson to purple. Cackling frantically, he waggled his head and flapped his elbows against his ribs.

"Cut-aw-cut!" he bawled. "Cut-cut-aw! Cuck-cuck! Cock-a-doodle-do!"

Once more, Quickset made a great show of listening carefully:

"Did I hear you a-right, Master Grubble? Give all? Free? What a generous soul you are!"

With that, Quickset began hurling meats, cheese, vegetables, and loaves of sugar into the customers' outstretched baskets. Grubble's face now turned from purple to bilious green. He crowed, clucked, brayed, and bleated until he sounded like a barnyard gone mad.

"Give more?" cried Quickset. "I'm doing my best!"

"Cut-aw!" shouted Grubble and away went a chain of sausages. "Ak-ak-cut-aak!" And away went another joint of beef. At last, he could stand no more:

"Stop! Stop!" he roared. "Wretched cat! You'll drive me out of business!"

Beside himself with fury, Master Grubble forgot his cramped quarters and sprang to his feet. His head struck the

ceiling and he tumbled back into the basket of eggs. As he struggled to free himself from the flood of shattered yolks, the shelf cracked beneath him and he went plummeting headlong into a barrel of flour.

"Robber!" stormed Grubble, crawling out and shaking a fist at Quickset. "Swindler! You promised I'd hatch gold from eggs!"

"What's that?" put in the tailor's wife. "Gold from eggs? Master Grubble, you're as foolish as you're greedy."

"But a fine cackler," added the laundrywoman, flapping her arms. "Let's hear it again, your cut-cut-awk!"

"I warned you not to speak a word," Quickset told the storekeeper, who was egg-soaked at one end and floured at the other. "But you did. And so you broke the spell. Why, look at you, Master Grubble. You nearly turned yourself into a dipped pork chop. Have a care. Someone might fry you."

With that, Quickset went home to breakfast.

As for Master Grubble, when word spread that he had been so roundly tricked, and so easily, he became such a laughing-stock that he left town and was never seen again. At the urging of the townsfolk, Dame Agnes and Quickset took charge of the market, and ran it well and fairly. All agreed that Quickset was the cleverest cat in the world. And, since Quickset had the same opinion, it was surely true.

Author

Lloyd Alexander was born in Philadelphia and wanted to be a writer from the age of fifteen. He read widely as a child, including the stories of King Arthur and books of Celtic mythology. "After a good many years of writing for adults," he says, "my happiest surprise came when I began writing for children." His first fantasy for children, *Time Cat*, led to his attempt to create an entire fantasy world, which he did in the five *Prydain Chronicles*, a highly acclaimed fantasy series. His books have won major awards for children's literature, including the Newbery Medal, the National Book Award, and the American Book Award. *The Town Cats and Other Tales,* from which "The Cat and the Golden Egg" was taken, was an American Library Association Notable Book and reflects the author's love of cats.

Catalogue

by Rosalie Moore

Cats sleep **fat** and walk thin.
Cats, when they sleep, **slump;**
When they wake, pull in—
And where the **plump's** been
There's skin.
Cats walk thin.

Cats wait in a **lump,**
Jump in a *streak.*
Cats, when they jump, are sleek
As a grape slipping its skin—
They have technique.
Oh, cats don't creak;
They *sneak.*

Cats sleep **fat.**
They spread out comfort underneath them
Like a good mat,
As if they picked the place
And then **sat.**
You walk around one
As if he were the City Hall
After that.

If male,
A cat is apt to sing on a major scale;
This concert is for everybody—this
Is wholesale.
For a baton, he wields a tail.

(He is also found,
When happy, to resound
With an enclosed and private sound.)

A cat condenses.
He pulls in his tail to go under bridges,
And himself to go under fences.
Cats fit
In any size box or kit;
And if a large pumpkin grew under one,
He could arch over it.

When everyone else is just ready to go out,
The cat is just ready to come in.
He's not where he's been.
Cats sleep **fat** and walk thin.

Teaching Snoopy to Dance:

Bill Meléndez and the Art of Animation

by Valerie Tripp

Pictures That Move

Have you ever watched the scene in a Charlie Brown television special where Lucy holds a football for Charlie Brown to kick? Lucy holds the football on the ground with one finger. Charlie Brown gets ready to run. A flicker of doubt crosses his face; but he lifts up his elbows, leans forward, and runs. His feet move so fast they are a blur. His arms pump up and down. He gets to the football, and *WHOOSH!* Lucy grabs it away. "ARRGH!" Charlie Brown flies up into the air. *WHOMP!* He hits the ground so hard the dust rises.

Without a word spoken, the scene tells a story that is both funny and sad. Lucy has done it again. She has fooled poor Charlie Brown.

Charlie Brown is not the only one who was fooled. You were too. Charlie Brown and Lucy are not people. They are drawings. They are made up of lines, circles, and colors on flat pieces of paper. They can't move. Yet, as

Left: Animator Bill Meléndez works on a drawing of Snoopy. Right: Lucy and Charlie Brown are two of the many characters Bill Meléndez has animated.

you watched that scene, you saw Lucy and Charlie Brown move. You saw expressions on their faces. You saw them make movements as smooth and as natural as your own hand when it turns the pages of this book. Who fooled you? The animator who drew those pictures that seemed to move. In this case, the animator's name is Bill Meléndez.

Forty-Five Years in Animation

Charlie Brown and his friends are only a few of the cartoon characters Bill Meléndez has animated during his forty-five years in the business.

Bill Meléndez started out at Walt Disney Studios as an assistant animator on Mickey Mouse and Donald Duck cartoons. He also worked on the films *Bambi, Dumbo,* and *Fantasia.*

"I never planned to be an animator," Bill explains, "but when I finished school, Disney Studios was the only place that had jobs. The Mickey Mouse cartoons were so successful, they needed lots of animators. They were hiring anybody who could draw a straight line! Now I had never really studied art, but in school I was always doodling. I was drawing, drawing, drawing, just for the fun of it, all the time. So, when I was hired by Disney I thought, 'What a fun job!' It was fascinating to me. I learned animation by watching what the people around me were doing."

After Mickey Mouse, Bill worked on Bugs Bunny, Mr. Magoo, Porky Pig, and Daffy Duck cartoons. He has won hundreds of awards for his work on thousands of projects from television commercials to animated films. Bill says, "The most rewarding thing is that after forty-five years, I still love it. I still look forward to going to work."

What Animation Is

Today, Bill spends his time not only drawing animated characters, but also talking to people about animation. He has taught animation at college and has led workshops at children's museums. At the workshops, Bill explains what animation is and how it works.

"Animation is a simple, forthright talent," says Bill Meléndez. "It is the ability to create the illusion of movement. You do it by illustrating the movement in a series of still drawings."

To illustrate a movement, you must study it carefully. Many

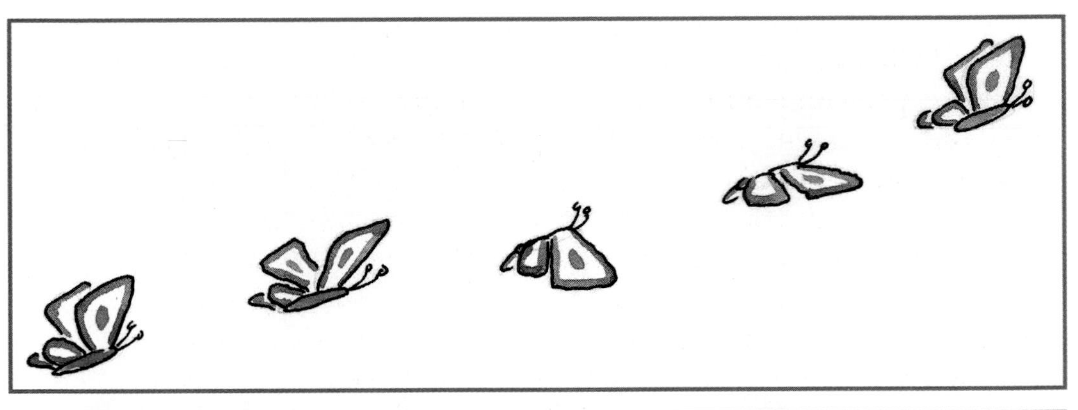

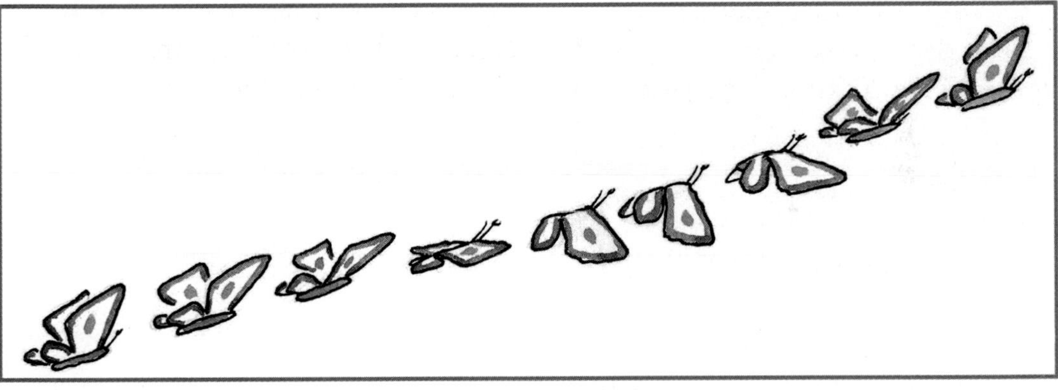

A flap of a butterfly's wings, divided into five parts (top) and nine parts (bottom). Notice that the drawings in the series of nine change more slowly. What do you think would happen if you divided the action into fifty parts?

animators keep a mirror next to their drawing boards so they can check how they make simple movements. How does a hand look when it is waving? How does a mouth look when it is laughing?

You cannot illustrate a movement in one drawing. You must divide the movement into parts. Then you must draw each part separately to show the beginning, middle, and end. The picture at the top of the page shows how you could illustrate the flapping of a butterfly's wings.

Once you have "stopped" the movement in a series of still drawings, you make it "go" again by moving the drawings. If you moved the series of nine drawings shown above, it would look as if the wings flapped. The more drawings you made, the smoother the action would look. That's what animation is.

Bill Meléndez, an editor, and a layout person check characters' movements at a Moviola.

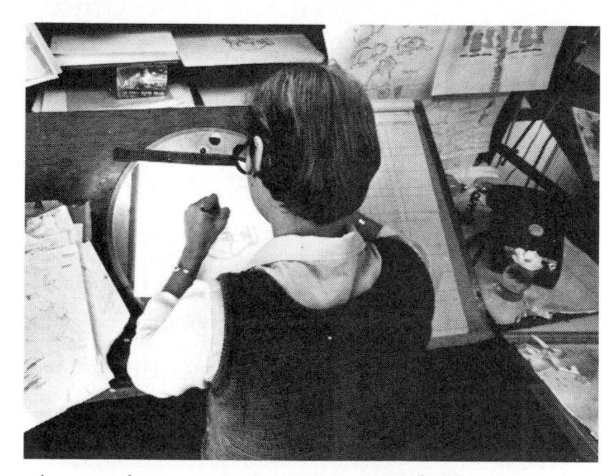

An assistant animator carefully tracing one drawing at a time to make the characters "move."

An animation checker working on inked cels before they are painted. She wears a glove to prevent smudges.

Animated Cartoons

Now, what is an animated cartoon? It is a series of still drawings, each slightly different from the one before. The drawings are photographed one at a time, and the film is projected like a movie.

Look at the two pieces of film shown on the left. When you run either piece of film through a projector, it looks as if the figures or objects are moving. This is because the pictures are rolling by so smoothly that you don't notice the separate frames. You can't tell that you are really seeing twenty-four frames a second.

The only difference between the two pieces of film is that in the animated film the pictures in the frames are of a drawing, not real people. That's an important difference. With a drawing, anything is possible. Bugs Bunny can be shot out of a cannon, squashed flat by a steamroller, or bounced like a ball. No matter what happens, Bugs Bunny always comes up laughing,

On the left is a piece of an animated cartoon film. The film is a series of still drawings in small boxes called frames. Next to it is a strip of regular film. It, too, is a series of still pictures in frames. However, these pictures are of a real scene.

chewing a carrot, asking, "What's up, Doc?"

The next time you see Bugs Bunny chewing that carrot, remember that you are really seeing 1440 drawings every minute. In a half-hour television show, you are seeing 43,200 drawings, each one only slightly different from the next. Animating sounds like dull work, doesn't it? Bill Meléndez doesn't think it is. "Animators don't think of it as drawing one drawing after another after another. We think of it as illustrating *action,*" Bill says.

Illustrating even a simple action can take dozens of drawings. Hundreds are thrown away because they are not quite right. Bill says, "You can tell if you are making a good drawing as you go along. Experience tells you if it is convincing."

For an animated action to look real, it should take as long as the same action would take live. The characters should move in the same way live actors would move, as in the example shown below.

Bill Meléndez says the most important thing he tells animators is, "You must keep the overall action in mind, not think of it as drawing one, two, three, four, five little drawings, or you will make it mechanical. You'll make the movement without the emotion. The joy of it is that with a light and fun touch, you can create the feeling that these are real people."

People lean forward when they walk. To look convincing, animated characters should lean forward when they walk, too.

An animator can use flourishes, or extra touches, to make actions convincing. Some of these are shadows (top, left); dust clouds (top, right); speed lines (bottom, left); and water splashes (bottom, right).

Sparking an Idea for a Peanuts Special

Bill Meléndez has made Charlie Brown, Lucy, and Snoopy seem real to millions of television viewers. The Charlie Brown characters started out in a comic strip called "Peanuts," created by Charles Schulz. When Bill animated some of the Peanuts characters for television commercials, his work showed Charles Schulz that the characters could move. The Peanuts gang entered a whole new world. Bill has animated more than thirty Charlie Brown specials over the last twenty-five years, including "It's the Great Pumpkin, Charlie Brown" and "A Charlie Brown Christmas."

How does a Charlie Brown television special come to be?

It begins with an idea thought up by Charles Schulz. Bill Meléndez calls Charles Schulz "Sparky." It seems like a good name for someone who sparks so many wonderful stories and characters.

"Sparky comes up with a story situation, or premise. We get together and talk about it. I scribble down notes and sketches as we talk," explains Bill. "Then I roar back to my studio and put the story together like a comic strip. I draw a few key pictures and write captions under them. That's called a story board. I bring the story board to Sparky, and he suggests changes. Then I roar back to my studio and make the changes we decided on. If we're on the right track, if we have a good premise, our work usually goes very fast. In just a few days, Sparky's idea is developed into a whole story."

From Story to Script

Scriptwriters turn the story into a script that shows actors what they are supposed to say.

"As soon as the script is ready, we gather actors to record the narration, musicians to record the music, and technicians to record the sound effects." The recording of the voices, music, and sounds is called the sound track. Doing the sound track is fun for Bill Meléndez because he gets into the act. He is Snoopy's voice. "I do Snoopy's growls, grunts, and howls," he explains. "*AAOOOOOO!* Recognize that howl?"

First the Sound Track

The sound track has to be recorded first, because the animator draws pictures to match the sounds. If Charlie Brown says "G-O-O-D G-R-I-E-F!" the animator has to know when he says it in the story; for how long he says it; and if he is happy, sad, or mad. The animator has to draw the face and body expressions to match what the characters say and do. Snoopy has to dance for as long as the music lasts. Charlie Brown's mouth has to be in the correct position for every syllable he speaks.

To help the animator, the sound track is put on movie film, which is divided into blank frames. A machine called a sound reader counts how many blank frames go by while one syllable is heard. If twenty frames go by while Charlie Brown says "Good," then the animator has to fill those twenty frames with pictures of Charlie Brown looking like he's saying "Good."

Next the Drawings — Thousands of Them

When the animator knows what action must be pictured in each frame, he draws key drawings called extremes. Extremes show how the scene moves from the start of an action to the end. They do not show every drawing needed to illustrate an action. Assistant animators called inbetweeners draw the illustrations that go in between the extremes.

There are ways to cut the number of different drawings from 43,200 for a half-hour show to twenty or thirty thousand. Drawings are usually shown for at least two frames; otherwise, the action looks jerky. Sometimes a character will stand still, so the

The first and last drawings are the same. This series could be repeated over and over to show the woman hopping on the pogo stick as long as needed.

same drawings can be shown for several frames. Those drawings are called holds. Often, actions are repeated. Look at the drawings on page 109 showing a person hopping on a pogo stick.

Finishing Touches

When the drawings are finished, they are traced by people called inkers onto clear sheets called cels. The inker traces each line carefully. People called opaquers then color in the outlines.

The colored cels are placed over backgrounds. Backgrounds are drawn separately from figures so that figures can be moved separately. Sometimes the background will be still while the characters move. Other times, the background will move and the characters will be still.

When the colored cels and the backgrounds are ready, they are photographed. An editor matches the film to the sound track, and the animated cartoon is then complete.

"Nothing Is Impossible"

It takes time and talented people to make an animated film. One half-hour show takes four to six months from start to finish. There are sometimes as many as sixty people working in Bill Meléndez's studio. He wouldn't have it any other way. "I tried working alone at home — it just made me nervous! At the studio there's a team of us, a whole bunch of people laughing over this and that, giving each other feedback. It makes work fun and easier."

Wouldn't it be *easier* to make a live movie? "The best animation does what can't be done in live action," Bill Meléndez says. "Nothing is impossible in animation. That's the magic of it!"

Author

Valerie Tripp has traveled to every state except Alaska, meeting and talking with people in all parts of the country. A writer for ten years, she especially enjoys writing for children. The best part of writing about Bill Meléndez, she says, was learning that, like herself, he has found work that he loves to do. Valerie Tripp has received degrees from Yale and Harvard.

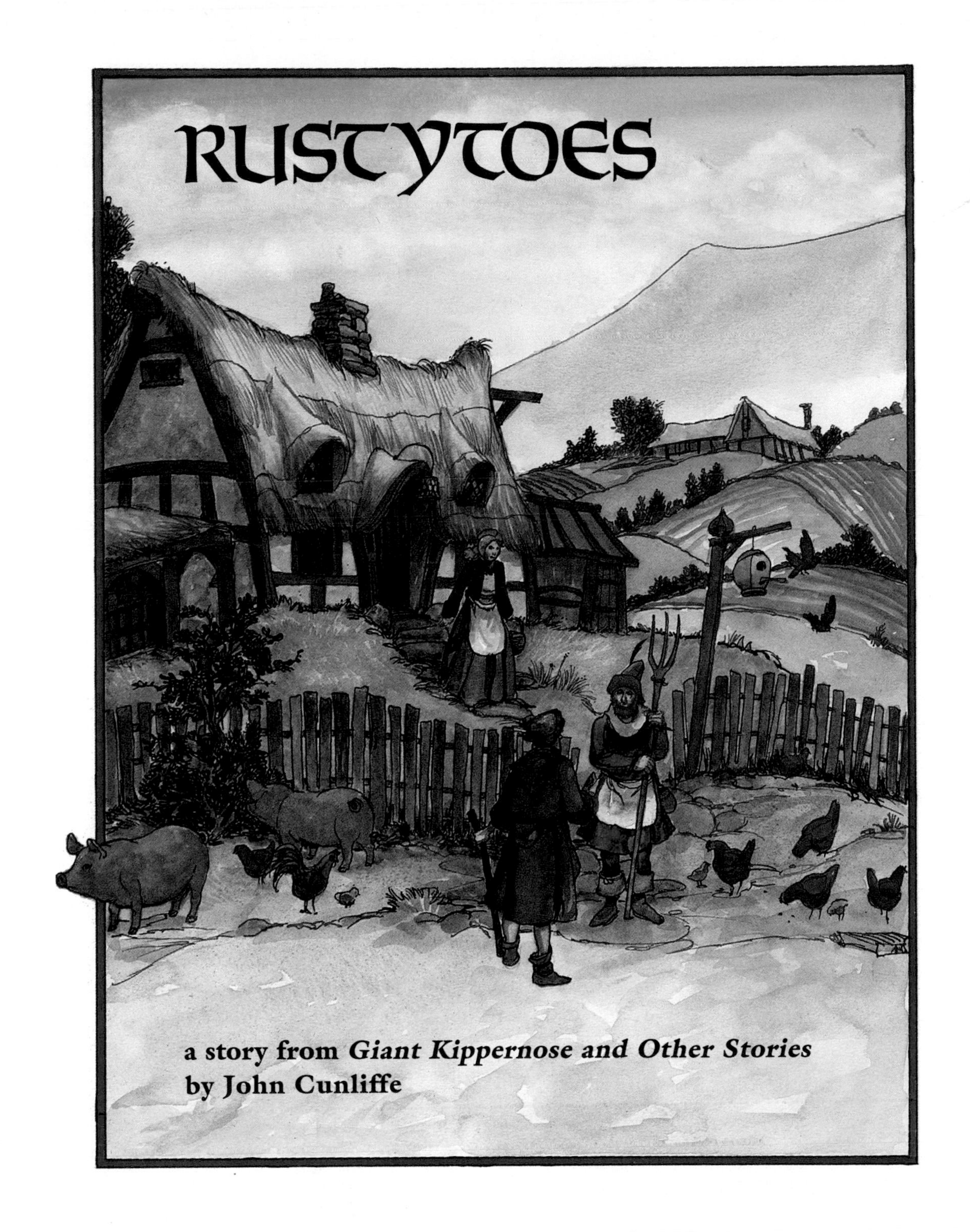
RUSTYTOES
a story from Giant Kippernose and Other Stories
by John Cunliffe

There was a farmer who lived in a good country of rich and easy land, and it was bad luck to his neighbours when he died, for he was the best farmer, and his was the best farm, in all those parts.

'Who will buy the farm, now Grimble's gone?' they said. 'For there's none will be able to make it thrive as he did.'

None of his neighbours had the money to buy it, so it went to a stranger. They were all keen-eyed to see what kind of a man the new owner would be, but not a soul saw him arrive. He came at the dead of night, with his great cart rumbling along the lane, disturbing people in their sleep. But the word soon went round:

'The new man's come to Grimble's Farm. No one saw his coming. They say he came by night. There's a strange thing.'

There was a shaking of heads, and worried faces everywhere, but for some days no one had a sight of him. There was smoke from the chimneys, and a sound of hammering at Grimble's farm. There were strange roars and rumblings, but no sign of man or beast in the lanes or fields. But when the postman knocked on Farmer Rice's door on Friday morning, he said,

'Good morning, Farmer Rice. And how do you like your new neighbour?'

'I cannot tell you that, Billy, for I've never seen him yet,' said Farmer Rice, crossly. 'I don't even know his name. What kind of a neighbour is that? He'll come round soon enough when he wants to borrow a thresher.'

'As to his name,' said Billy, 'I can tell you that. I've just taken him a letter. He's called Garlick Rustytoes!'

'Garlick Rustytoes?' said Farmer Rice. 'What sort of a name is that? Not an honest one. Certainly not a name of our valley. Perhaps he's from the mountains, or beyond?'

'I cannot say,' said Billy, 'but his name isn't the worst thing about him.'

'Well, tell us what *is* the worst of him,' said Mrs. Rice. 'If this outlandish fellow's to live along by us we'd better know his worst; his best will be no hurt to find out for ourselves. Now sit you down, Billy, and tell us what you know.'

'Outlandish is right,' said Billy. 'Aye, that's the word. *Outlandish*. Right well outlandish! Well . . . I'm walking into the stack-yard with this letter for him, when I hears this awful loud snorting and gurgling coming out of the barn. Something like an elephant snoring, it was. Then I creeps nearer, and I nearly falls over myself for simple fright. Sticking out of the barn, there's this pair of feet.'

'There's nothing frightening about a pair of feet, Billy,' said Farmer Rice.

'There was about *this* pair of feet,' said Billy. 'I've not told you their size. You see, they were the size of your kitchen table! And they were on the end of legs as thick as a tree! And I'm standing there, trying to believe the truth of what I can see, when the toes begin to wriggle. I didn't wait to see more. I threw the letter on the ground, and ran for it."

'But, Billy, be sensible,' said Farmer Rice, patiently. 'Our kitchen table is four feet long. You couldn't have seen feet that size.'

'I could, and I did. Not ten minutes ago,' said Billy, indignantly.

'But if those feet were that size . . .' said Mrs. Rice.

'How big would the man be on the other end of them?' demanded Farmer Rice. 'Are you trying to tell us . . .'

'I'm only telling you what I saw,' Billy grumbled.

'But a man with feet so big would be anything up to twenty feet tall!' cried Mrs. Rice.

'Are you trying to tell us we have a *giant* for our new neighbour?' asked Farmer Rice.

'Make what you can of it,' said Billy, 'but I swear I'm telling you the truth of what I saw.'

'We cannot have giants living about here,' said Farmer Rice. 'This is a peaceful valley. Oh, it's different in those mountainous places. All sorts of things go on there, but it's five hundred years or more since giants were known in these parts. We're too settled and comfortable now for such goings on: and on the next farm, too. No, Billy, you must have been dreaming. You must have been.'

'My granny used to say . . .' began Mrs. Rice.

'She was another dreamer,' retorted Farmer Rice.

'You'll see for yourself soon enough,' said Billy. 'I must get on with my letters, or I'll never be finished today.' And off he went.

What Farmer Rice didn't see, was a huge hairy arm coming over the hedge, and a great hand picking up his best cow and whisking it away. Three more cows disappeared in the same way before dinner time. Poor bewildered creatures, they found themselves in a new home, with a fearsome master. Garlick Rustytoes had stolen them. When it came to milking-time, there was a great to-do. The cow-man came running, shouting,

'Master, master, four of our beasts are gone.'

'Gone? Gone? What do you mean, man, they cannot be gone. We have the best hedges and fences in the valley. There's no way my beasts could be gone,' shouted Farmer Rice.

'But they are, master, come and see!"

So they went together, all round the farm. There was no gap in hedge or fence. No gate was open. They counted the cows again, and yet again. They even brought Mrs. Rice to count them. There was no mistaking it — four were missing, and the best milkers, too.

'Whoever could have taken them, knew what he was about,' moaned Farmer Rice.

'But all your gates are locked,' said Mrs. Rice. 'There's no

way they could have been taken, unless . . . unless . . .' She looked in the direction of Rustytoes' Farm.

'Unless, *what,* woman. What do you mean to say?' cried Farmer Rice.

'Well, if that postman were right. I mean if this Rustytoes *is* a giant . . .' said Mrs. Rice.

'Oh, I'll not believe such tales,' Farmer Rice snapped, and stamped out of the house.

At all the farms bordering on to Rustytoes' land, strange things began to happen.

Ten sheep disappeared at Apple Tree Farm. A horse and three pigs vanished from Hill Top Farm. A hut full of hens was whisked away at night at Mill Farm, so swiftly and smoothly that not a single hen wakened on its roost to give a warning. Farmer Rice even lost a barn and all the hay and oats in it, from an outlying field. There was only a pale square of grass to show where it had been!

'Now what did I tell you?' said Mrs. Rice. 'There's only one sort of person could do a thing like that, and that's . . .'

'Now I'll not have you frightening people with talk of giants,' grumbled Farmer Rice. 'There are lots of ways these things could happen. Have you never heard of gypsies and rogues and vagabonds? They did a lot of mischief in the old days. Who knows they may have come back again.'

'Gypsies, indeed,' snorted Mrs. Rice, but she said no more, seeing the mood her husband was in. She attacked her pastry with the rolling pin, as if to say, 'There's for your gypsies!'

But things got worse. Heavy footsteps shook the country roads by night, and things began to disappear from more distant farms, up and down the valley. A plow and a cart disappeared as far away as Windmill Farm. Mysterious shadows fell across bedroom windows in the moonlight, and people trembled in their beds. Though the dogs barked, no one dared to go out to see what was stirring. The whole valley was afraid, and no one knew what to do. Until the postman called again at Rice's Farm, and Farmer Rice had an idea.

'Pass the word round, Billy,' he said, 'to every farm you visit. Tell every farmer who has had anything stolen to meet on Crompton village green at ten o'clock on Wednesday morning. Then we'll *all* visit Rustytoes. We'll have to get to the bottom of this, and I can think of no other way.'

'That I will,' said Billy. 'It's the best idea I've heard yet.' And off he went to carry his message about the valley.

Billy did his work well. At ten o'clock on Wednesday morning, there was a large and angry crowd of farmers on Crompton Green. There was someone from almost every farm for ten miles around. Each person carried a pitchfork or a stout stick.

'Friends,' shouted Farmer Rice. 'You all know why we're here, don't you?'

'Aye, we do,' murmured the farmers.

'Every man here has had stock and machinery stolen in the last two weeks,' went on Farmer Rice, 'and no ordinary thief could carry off cows in broad daylight, with no sight or sound of their going. Besides, we're honest folks in this valley. There's been no thieving here for hundreds of years. But we have a new neighbour — this Garlick Rustytoes; and I cannot help noticing that his fields are suddenly full of cattle and sheep, when he's not once been to market since he came here. Indeed, nobody has so much as seen his face. So, men, I suggest we all pay a call on our new neighbour, and ask him a few questions!'

'But, Farmer Rice,' called Jim Dobson, 'some say this Rustytoes is nothing less than a giant!'

'There's no need to upset people with wild talk of giants,' said Farmer Rice. 'Nobody's set eyes on the fellow yet, so how can anyone say?'

Luckily for Farmer Rice, Billy was away with his letters, for his story of Rustytoes' enormous feet could have scared even these angry farmers away.

'To Rustytoes' Farm, then!' shouted Farmer Rice. 'Come on, let's rouse him!' And he led the way, with the buzzing mob of farmers following, their staves and pitchforks jaunting at the ready.

There seemed to be no one about at Rustytoes' Farm, but as they approached the house the farmers grew more and more excited as they spied their stolen property. Cries went up on

all sides: 'There's my sheep! There's my Daisy and her two calves! Bless me, there's my barn, and all the hay still in it! So that's where my thresher went to!' And so on, all the way up to Rustytoes' door. By then they were so angry that they hammered on the door fit to break it down.

'Come out, you thief!' they shouted. 'We've come for our property! It's no good hiding; we've got eyes to see. Come on, hand it all over!'

Some looked in the windows, but couldn't see anyone. Then, a thunderous voice boomed out of the sky at them, 'What, little midgets, do you dare to come and trouble Rustytoes?'

They all looked upwards. A great grinning face loomed above them. Rustytoes was leaning on the farmhouse roof as though it were a low gate, and leering over at them.

'I'll take what I want, and none can stop me, so take yourselves off before I squash you!' he roared. Then he came stamping round the house to show his full height. Not one of them stayed to argue. You cannot argue with an angry giant, for that is what he truly was, twenty or thirty feet high. They all scampered off as fast as they could go, with Rustytoes' laughter bellowing after them.

They didn't stop until they reached Crompton Green again. Then they all flopped on to the grass to get their breath back.

'What are we going to do?' moaned Farmer Rice. 'Billy was right, and Rustytoes *is* a giant. I was right, and he *has* stolen our things, and means to go on stealing. But we cannot send a giant to prison, and we cannot fight him. What can we do?'

'He'll take what he wants, until we're all too poor to go on farming,' said Jim Dobson gloomily. 'He'll take our land next, and we'll have to go and live in the mountains.'

'Oh, it cannot be as bad as that, surely,' said Farmer Rice, but he couldn't convince even himself. They all fell into a gloomy silence, and drifted off home one by one.

Things did get worse: much worse. Rustytoes took what he wanted, and the farmers of the valley grew poorer and poorer. Rustytoes was so big and strong that no one could stop him.

Soon Rustytoes began to make the other farmers do all his work, too. He had his bed in the big barn, and he lay there all day eating sweets. He lay on the straw, laughing at the little people as they hurried about to do his work. Rustytoes grew rich and fat and lazy, but he was as strong as ever, and everyone feared him.

'Can you not think of a way of overcoming this Rustytoes?' Mrs. Rice demanded of her husband.

'I cannot,' said Farmer Rice. 'He's just too big and strong to be defied.'

'Then what will become of us,' moaned Mrs. Rice.

'I cannot tell, my dear, but it's a black outlook,' said Farmer Rice, and went gloomily off to bed.

But something did overcome Garlick Rustytoes. Something quite simple. Something natural.

One morning, the neighbourhood woke to a strange sound. A roaring, moaning, bellowing sound, that came and went with the wind, and sighed amongst the trees. There it was again, louder.

'What in the world is that?' exclaimed Mrs. Rice, at breakfast.

'Bless me, I don't know,' said Farmer Rice. They went outside to listen.

A yowling and howling echoed across the fields.

'What a dreadful noise,' said Farmer Rice. 'It will turn the milk sour.'

'It's coming from Rustytoes' Farm,' said Mrs. Rice.

'It's some new trick of his,' said Farmer Rice.

'No, it sounds like someone in pain,' said Mrs. Rice. 'Come on, we must go and see. It sounds so pitiful.'

So they crept up to Rustytoes' farm, and fearfully approached the big barn, whence all the noise seemed to be coming. Great roars and yells, low moans growing to a sound like thunder, thumpings and gaspings, sighing and weeping, issued from the open door. Rustytoes' feet, sticking out, threshed about. Trembling, Farmer Rice and his wife looked in. There was poor Rustytoes, lying on the straw with the side of his face all swollen.

'Oh, help me, please help me,' he moaned, seeing them.

'Why, you great fellow, what's befallen you?" asked the astonished Mrs. Rice, who had never seen him before.

'*Toothache.* I've got toothache,' moaned Rustytoes. 'Oooooooh, and it does hurt.'

'A giant toothache, too,' said Mrs. Rice. 'The pain's as big as he is, and it must be dreadful. It's laid him low, great as he is. Poor fellow, he has an abscess on that tooth the size of a cow, and nothing hurts more.'

'But he's bad, and he's a giant, and it serves him right,' whispered Farmer Rice.

'Bad he may be, but we must help him. You cannot let anyone suffer so, and not help,' protested Mrs. Rice. To Rustytoes she said, 'Now lie still, and I'll make you a poultice, and I'll gather some herbs that will ease your pain. Then we'll bring the dentist from the village, and see if he can get that tooth out of you.'

'You're a kind woman, Mrs. Rice,' said Rustytoes, groaning between his words. 'Oooh! Owch! If only you'll help me, I'll promise to be good and kind to you and all the farmers. Oooh! I cannot bear the pain. I've been awake all night with it. It's too much for me. I'll die if you don't take this pain away! I'll

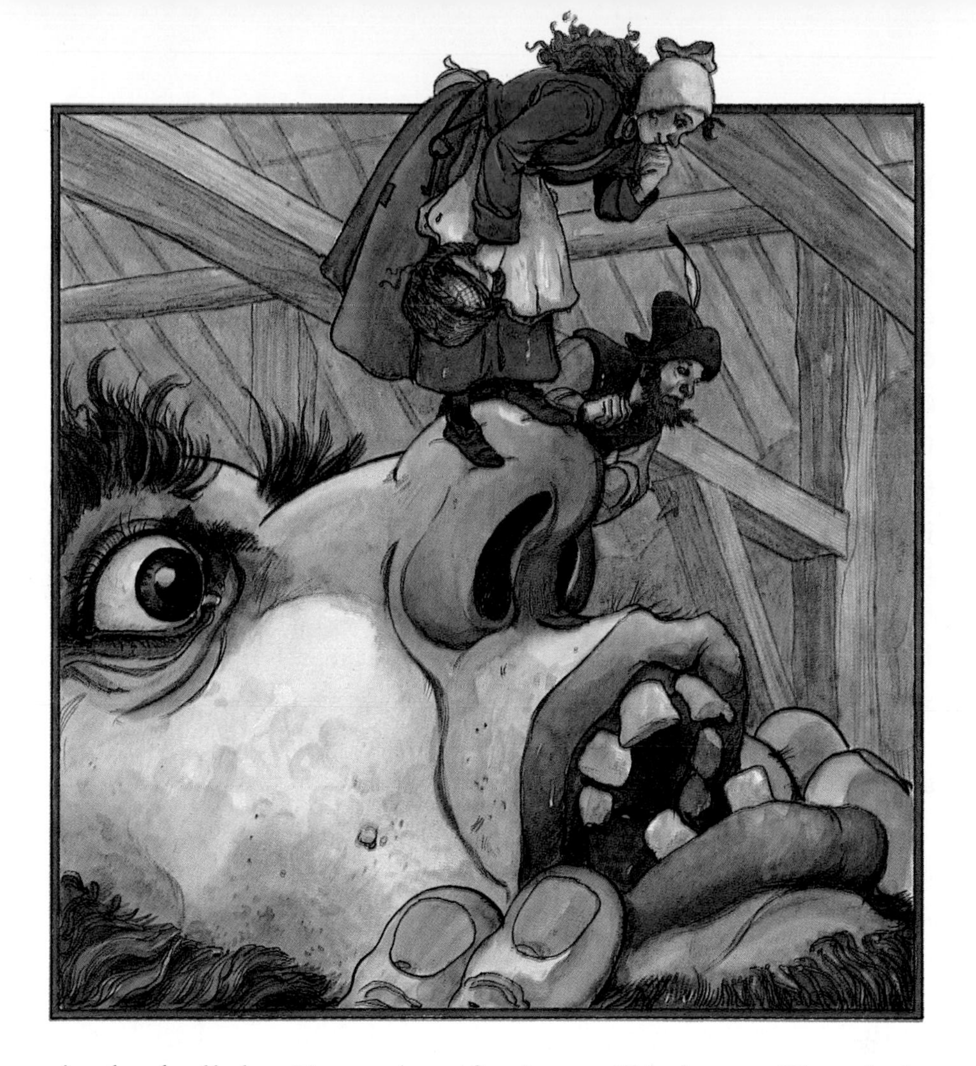

give back all that I've stolen, if only you'll help me. *Please* help me, good people.'

'Do you *promise*?' said Farmer Rice. 'Do you promise to give back all that you have stolen? Everything?'

'Yes. Yes. Everything.'

'Do you promise to be good to all your neighbours, and never steal or frighten anyone again?'

'Yes. I promise. All you say,' moaned Rustytoes. 'Anything to be rid of this pain.'

'Then we'll do all we can to make you better,' declared Farmer Rice.

'Oh, stop your talking, and let's see to the poor fellow,' said Mrs. Rice, and she got quickly to work.

There never was such a busy scene. More people arrived, and Mrs. Rice set them to work. They gathered herbs, and made a giant poultice with two bedsheets. Farmer Rice excitedly told all the farmers about Rustytoes' promises. The dentist was sent for, and he climbed bravely into Rustytoes' mouth, to examine the bad tooth. He came out looking dazed, saying the tooth was the size of a loaf, and that it would have to come out. A big rope-sling was made, to pull the tooth. Ten horses were brought and harnessed to a long rope fastened to the sling. All the while, Rustytoes moaned on, though Mrs. Rice's herbs had soothed his pains. At last, all was ready. The sling was round the tooth, and the horses ready to pull.

'Take the strain!' called Farmer Rice. The ropes tightened, as the horses tensed their muscles.

'Pull!' shouted Farmer Rice, and all the people urged their horses on.

'Heave! Come on, my beauty! Pull, my girl! Come on, now!' So they coaxed them on, and the horses pulled with all their strength. The ropes creaked and cracked with the great strain. All eyes were on the tooth. It didn't move. More horses were brought — fifteen, then twenty. They all pulled again, and the great tooth moved slightly. Then the men took the ropes, and pulled with the horses.

'All together!' called Farmer Rice. 'One. Two. Three, and pull.' Horses and men pulled and pulled with all their strength. There was a loud crack. The tooth shot out, releasing the rope, so that the horses galloped off down the lane, and everyone fell over in a heap. Amid all the noise and muddle, there was Rustytoes, sitting up and smiling all over his face.

'It's gone!' he exclaimed. 'It's gone. Oh, what a wonderful feeling.' They all looked at him. 'What good people you are,'

he said. 'I've been as bad as I could be to you, and yet you all come to help me, when I'm in pain.'

'But you made us some promises,' Farmer Rice reminded him.

'And I'll keep them,' said Rustytoes, happily. 'Better than that, I'll be the best neighbour you ever had, from this day on. I'll help you with your work, and protect you from your enemies. Whatever you want doing, I'm your giant; at your service, good friends.'

Rustytoes kept his word. He gave everything back. He worked hard to help anyone who asked him. He moved barns, and uprooted trees. He dug new roads, and dammed a river. He helped to build houses and farms. No one ever dared to attack the people of the valley, with a giant to defend them, so there was peace as never before. The people of the valley became happy and prosperous, and they grew very fond of their giant. Everyone knew him as Dear Old Man Rustytoes, and they all loved and trusted him. Even so, Farmer Rice kept an eye on him.

'You can never be sure, with giants,' he said.

'Never fear,' said Mrs. Rice. 'Old Man Rustytoes has a great many more teeth in his head, and he might need another one pulling, one of these days.'

Author

John Cunliffe, who loves telling stories, has been a librarian and an elementary school teacher in England, where he was born. He says, "Children are the most avid, attentive, and enthusiastic audience anywhere in the world."

An excerpt from

Tuck Everlasting

by Natalie Babbitt

What would it be like to live forever? For many people, the promise of eternal life may seem like a wonderful, impossible dream. For the Tuck family, eternal life is a terrible burden that they must bear forever. The Tucks have unknowingly drunk from the spring of eternal life and will forever remain the same. When ten-year-old Winnie Foster stumbles on the Tucks' sad secret, the family kidnaps her, intending to keep her with them until they can teach her the horrible truth about their secret and convince her not to tell anyone about the spring. After supper on Winnie's first day with the Tucks, Pa Tuck takes her for a rowboat ride. Pa Tuck's words during this ride teach Winnie an important lesson about life, death, and change.

It was a good supper, flapjacks, bacon, bread, and applesauce, but they ate sitting about in the parlor instead of around a table. Winnie had never had a meal that way before and she watched them carefully at first, to see what rules there might be that she did not know about. But there seemed to be no rules. Jesse sat on the floor and used the seat of a chair for a table, but the others held their plates in their laps. There were no napkins. It was all right, then, to lick the maple syrup from your fingers. Winnie was never allowed to do such a thing at home, but she had always thought it would be the easiest way. And suddenly the meal seemed luxurious.

After a few minutes, however, it was clear to Winnie that there was at least one rule: As long as there was food to eat, there was no conversation. All four Tucks kept their eyes and their attention on the business at hand. And in the silence, given time to think, Winnie felt her elation, and her thoughtless pleasure, wobble and collapse.

It had been different when they were out-of-doors, where the world belonged to everyone and no one. Here, everything was theirs alone, everything was done their way. Eating, she realized now, was a very personal thing, not something to do with strangers. *Chewing* was a personal thing. Yet here she was, chewing with strangers in a strange place. She shivered a little, and frowned, looking round at them. That story they had told her — why, they were crazy, she thought harshly, and they were criminals. They had kidnapped her, right out of the middle of her very own wood, and now she would be expected to sleep — *all night* — in this dirty, peculiar house. She had never slept in any bed but her own in her life. All these thoughts flowed at once from the dark part of her mind. She put down her fork and said, unsteadily, "I want to go home."

The Tucks stopped eating, and looked at her, surprised. Mae said soothingly, "Why, of course you do, child. That's only natural. I'll take you home. I promised I would, soon's we've explained a bit as to why you got to promise you'll never tell about the spring. That's the only reason we brung you here. We got to make you see why."

Then Miles said, cheerfully and with sudden sympathy, "There's a pretty good old rowboat. I'll take you out for a row after supper."

"No, *I* will," said Jesse. "Let *me*. I found her first, didn't I, Winnie Foster? Listen, I'll show you where the frogs are, and . . ."

"Hush," Tuck interrupted. "Everyone hush. *I'll* take Winnie rowing on the pond. There's a good deal to be said and I think we better hurry up and say it. I got a feeling there ain't a whole lot of time."

Jesse laughed at this, and ran a hand roughly through his curls. "That's funny, Pa. Seems to me like time's the only thing we got a lot of."

But Mae frowned. "You worried, Tuck? What's got you? No one saw us on the way up. Well, now, wait a bit — yes, they did, come to think of it. There was a man on the road, just outside Treegap. But he didn't say nothing."

"He knows me, though," said Winnie. She had forgotten, too, about the man in the yellow suit, and now, thinking of him, she felt a surge of relief. "He'll tell my father he saw me."

"He knows you?" said Mae, her frown deepening. "But you didn't call out to him, child. Why not?"

"I was too scared to do *anything*," said Winnie honestly.

Tuck shook his head. "I never thought we'd come to the place where we'd be scaring children," he said. "I guess there's no way to make it up to you, Winnie, but I'm sure most awful sorry it had to happen like that. Who was this man you saw?"

"I don't know his name," said Winnie. "But he's a pretty nice man, I guess." In fact, he seemed supremely nice to her now, a kind of savior. And then she added, "He came to our house last night, but he didn't go inside."

"Well, that don't sound too serious, Pa," said Miles. "Just some stranger passing by."

"Just the same, we got to get you home again, Winnie," said Tuck, standing up decisively. "We got to get you home just as fast as we can. I got a feeling this whole thing is going to come apart like wet bread. But first we got to talk, and the pond's the best place. The pond's got answers. Come along, child. Let's go out on the water."

The sky was a ragged blaze of red and pink and orange, and its double trembled on the surface of the pond like color spilled from a paintbox. The sun was dropping fast now, a soft red sliding egg yolk, and already to the east there was a darkening to purple. Winnie, newly brave with her thoughts of being rescued, climbed boldly into the rowboat. The hard heels of her buttoned boots made a hollow banging sound against its wet boards, loud in the warm and breathless quiet. Across the pond a bullfrog spoke a deep note of warning. Tuck climbed in, too, pushing off, and, settling the oars into their locks, dipped them into the silty bottom in one strong pull. The rowboat slipped from the bank then, silently, and glided out, tall water grasses whispering away from its sides, releasing it.

Here and there the still surface of the water dimpled, and bright rings spread noiselessly and vanished. "Feeding time," said Tuck softly. And Winnie, looking down, saw hosts of tiny insects skittering and skating on the surface. "Best time of all for fishing," he said, "when they come up to feed."

He dragged on the oars. The rowboat slowed and began to drift gently toward the farthest end of the pond. It was so quiet that Winnie almost jumped when the bullfrog spoke again. And then, from the tall pines and birches that ringed the pond, a wood thrush caroled. The silver notes were pure and clear and lovely.

"Know what that is, all around us, Winnie?" said Tuck, his voice low. "Life. Moving, growing, changing, never the same two minutes together. This water, you look out at it every morning, and it *looks* the same, but it ain't. All night long it's been moving, coming in through the stream back there to the west, slipping out through the stream down east here, always quiet, always new, moving on. You can't hardly see the current, can you? And sometimes the wind makes it look like it's going the other way. But it's always there, the water's always moving on, and someday, after a long while, it comes to the ocean."

They drifted in silence for a time. The bullfrog spoke again, and from behind them, far back in some reedy, secret place, another bullfrog answered. In the fading light, the trees along the banks were slowly losing their dimensions, flattening into silhouettes clipped from black paper and pasted to the paling sky. The voice of a different frog, hoarser and not so deep, croaked from the nearest bank.

"Know what happens then?" said Tuck. "To the water? The sun sucks some of it up right out of the ocean and carries it back in clouds, and then it rains, and the rain falls into the stream, and the stream keeps moving on, taking it all back again. It's a wheel, Winnie. Everything's a wheel, turning and turning, never stopping. The frogs is part of it, and the bugs, and the fish, and the wood thrush, too. And people. But never the same ones. Always coming in new, always growing and changing, and always moving on. That's the way it's supposed to be. That's the way it *is*."

The rowboat had drifted at last to the end of the pond, but now its bow bumped into the rotting branches of a fallen tree that thrust thick fingers into the water. And though the current pulled at it, dragging its stern sidewise, the boat was wedged and could not follow. The water slipped past it, out between clumps of reeds and brambles, and gurgled down a narrow bed, over stones and pebbles, foaming a little, moving swiftly now after its slow trip between the pond's wide banks.

And, farther down, Winnie could see that it hurried into a curve, around a leaning willow, and disappeared.

"It goes on," Tuck repeated, "to the ocean. But this rowboat now, it's stuck. If we didn't move it out ourself, it would stay here forever, trying to get loose, but stuck. That's what us Tucks are, Winnie. Stuck so's we can't move on. We ain't part of the wheel no more. Dropped off, Winnie. Left behind. And everywhere around us, things is moving and growing and changing. You, for instance. A child now, but someday a woman. And after that, moving on to make room for the new children."

Winnie blinked, and all at once her mind was drowned with understanding of what he was saying. For she — yes, even she — would go out of the world willy-nilly someday. Just go out, like the flame of a candle, and no use protesting. It was a certainty. She would try very hard not to think of it, but sometimes, as now, it would be forced upon her. She raged against it, helpless and insulted, and blurted at last, "I don't want to die."

"No," said Tuck calmly. "Not now. Your time's not now. But dying's part of the wheel, right there next to being born. You can't pick out the pieces you like and leave the rest. Being part of the whole thing, that's the blessing. But it's passing us by, us Tucks. Living's heavy work, but off to one side, the way *we* are, it's useless, too. It don't make sense. If I knowed how to climb back on the wheel, I'd do it in a minute. You can't have living without dying. So you can't call it living, what we got. We just *are,* we just *be,* like rocks beside the road."

Tuck's voice was rough now, and Winnie, amazed, sat rigid. No one had ever talked to her of things like this before. "I want to grow again," he said fiercely, "and change. And if that means I got to move on at the end of it, then I want that, too. Listen, Winnie, it's something you don't find out how you feel until afterwards. If people knowed about the spring down there in Treegap, they'd all come running like pigs to slops. They'd trample each other, trying to get some of that water.

"That'd be bad enough, but afterwards — can you imagine? All the little ones little forever, all the old ones old forever. Can you picture what that means? *Forever?* The wheel would keep on going round, the water rolling by to the ocean, but the people would've turned into nothing but rocks by the side of the road. 'Cause they wouldn't know till after, and then it'd be too late."

He peered at her, and Winnie saw that his face was pinched with the effort of explaining. "Do you see, now, child? Do you understand? Oh, Lord, I just got to make you understand!"

There was a long, long moment of silence. Winnie, struggling with the anguish of all these things, could only sit hunched and numb, the sound of the water rolling in her ears. It was black and silky now; it lapped at the sides of the rowboat and hurried on around them into the stream.

Winnie comes to appreciate Pa Tuck's message and to become friends with the Tuck family. You can find out more about what happens to Winnie, the Tucks, and the spring of eternal life by reading the entire book Tuck Everlasting *by Natalie Babbitt.*

Author

Natalie Babbitt was born and grew up in Ohio. As a child, she spent many hours reading and drawing. After she had married and raised three children, she started to write and illustrate books. Mrs. Babbitt says her interest in fantasy is the main reason why she writes children's stories. Among the many books that she has written are *Tuck Everlasting,* from which this excerpt was taken, and *Kneeknock Rise*, which was selected as a Newbery Honor Book.

Bird Migration

What Migration Is

Have you ever seen a large flock of birds flying in a V-formation? Did you see them in the spring or in the fall? Did you wonder where they were going?

The birds you saw were probably **migrating.** To migrate, in science, means to move from one place to another in large numbers — and then to return.

Who Migrates

Birds are not the only animals that migrate. Many ocean fish move to freshwater streams to lay their eggs. Then they return to their homes in the sea. Eels, on the other hand, live for most of

A flock of Canada geese flies over Horicon Marsh, a National Wildlife Refuge in Wisconsin.

A herd of caribou at Denali National Park in Alaska migrates to its winter home.

the year in freshwater lakes and rivers. In the fall, they head for the ocean to lay their eggs.

Elk, moose, and caribou move back and forth between summer and winter feeding grounds. Seals and whales swim great distances and return. But the migrators that people see and admire and wonder about most are the birds.

Why Birds Migrate

In the fall, as cold weather approaches, insects begin to disappear. Plants wither and die. Weed seeds are being blown away. The berries and food crops have all been picked or eaten. Fish are moving down to warmer, lower depths. There will not be much food left for birds who live where the seasons change. But the birds' bodies seem to know all this. As the days grow shorter, they prepare for winter.

Almost a third of the world's birds leave their homes each fall and return in the spring. Migrating birds store extra fat in their bodies for the journey. Some birds travel thousands of miles without stopping. They burn the stored fat for energy. The longer the distance a bird has to travel, the more fat it will store before it leaves.

The American golden plover lives in eastern Canada. It flies two thousand miles over the Atlantic Ocean to northern South America before stopping for food. Then it continues on. Its Alaskan cousin does the same thing on the West Coast, but its first stop is Hawaii, three thousand miles away.

This golden plover is resting in its nest in Manitoba, Canada, its summer home.

When the golden plover starts its flight, it weighs about six ounces. It weighs just over three and a half ounces at the end of its flight. The plovers replace the fat quickly before they start out again for their winter homes in Argentina.

Most birds fly from north to south to reach a place where the weather is warm and there is plenty of food. They stay in their wintering places until spring comes back to their northern homes. Since the seasons are reversed below the equator, migrating birds have two summers and no winters.

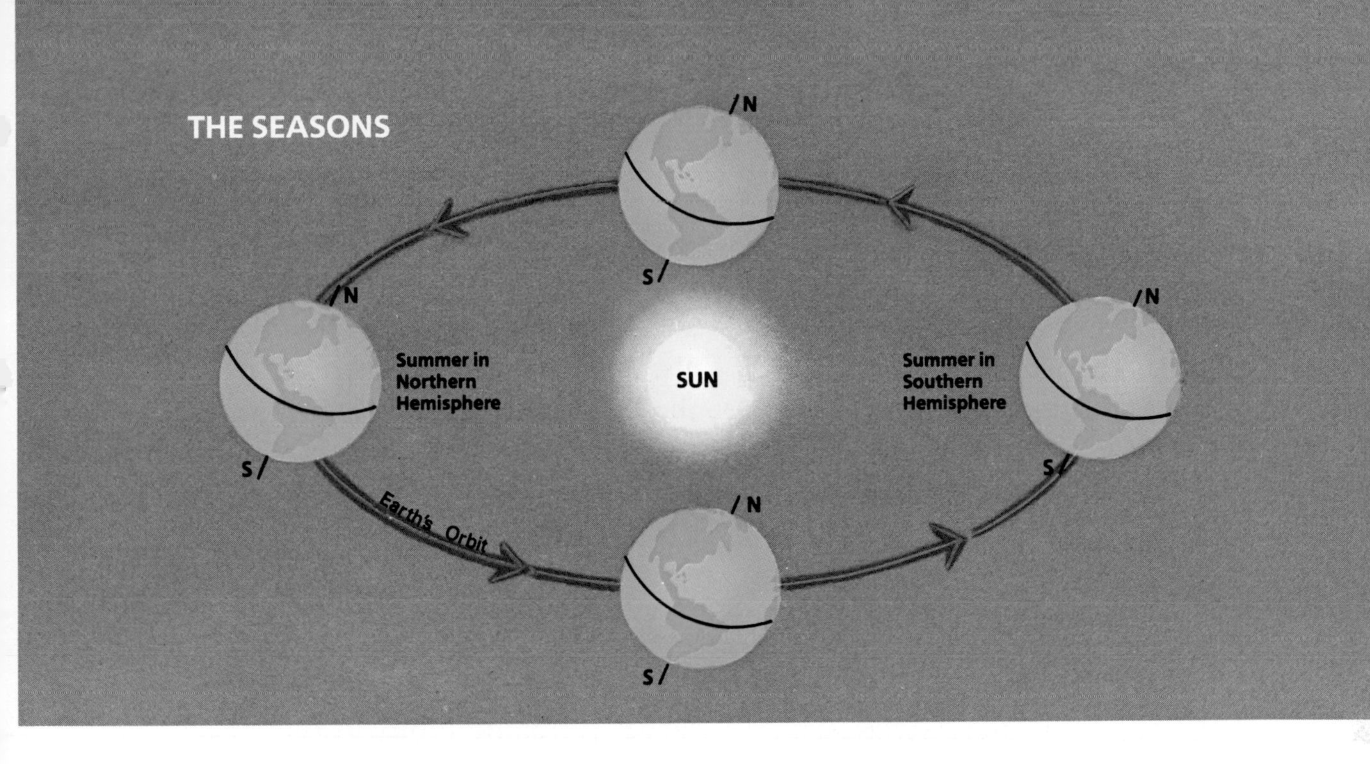

The earth turns around an imaginary line called its axis. Notice that the axis is tilted. This causes the seasons to change.

How Birds Know When to Go

The change of seasons is one reason why birds migrate. As fall approaches, the days become shorter and the nights longer. Do you know why this is? Look at the diagram. Because the axis of the earth is tilted, different parts of the earth receive more direct sunlight as it revolves around the sun. This causes the seasons.

Scientists believe that the length of the days tells the birds when it is time to migrate. Scientists also know that this is not enough to explain what starts the birds moving.

Experiments have shown that birds in cages move to the part of the cage that corresponds to the direction in which they usually fly. No matter how the cage is turned, or how the number of daylight hours are disguised, the birds move to the correct corner and flutter their wings. Something inside is telling the birds that it is time to go.

Many changes take place in birds' bodies before they migrate. Birds store fat to give them enough energy for the long trip. They lose their feathers, or **molt** (mōlt), and they grow a new set. In spring, changes occur that prepare the female bird to lay eggs. All these changes within the bird, together with the seasonal changes outside, seem to trigger the urge to migrate. Scientists believe that birds have an inner clock that works together with the outer clock of the solar system.

The Arctic tern holds the migrating birds' record for long-distance flying. Its powerful wings carry it between the Arctic Circle and Antarctica twice a year. The map shows the routes followed by the Arctic tern.

How Far a Bird Can Travel

The distances that some birds travel are astonishing. The bird that makes the longest journey is the Arctic tern. Look at the map and trace the route the tern travels. Its flight from the Arctic to the Antarctic is a journey of ninety-six hundred miles or more. And the Arctic tern flies that distance twice a year.

The Arctic tern is a large and powerful bird. However, there are tiny birds that also make amazing journeys. The ruby-throated hummingbird is one such flyer. This three-and-a-half-inch bird migrates between Texas

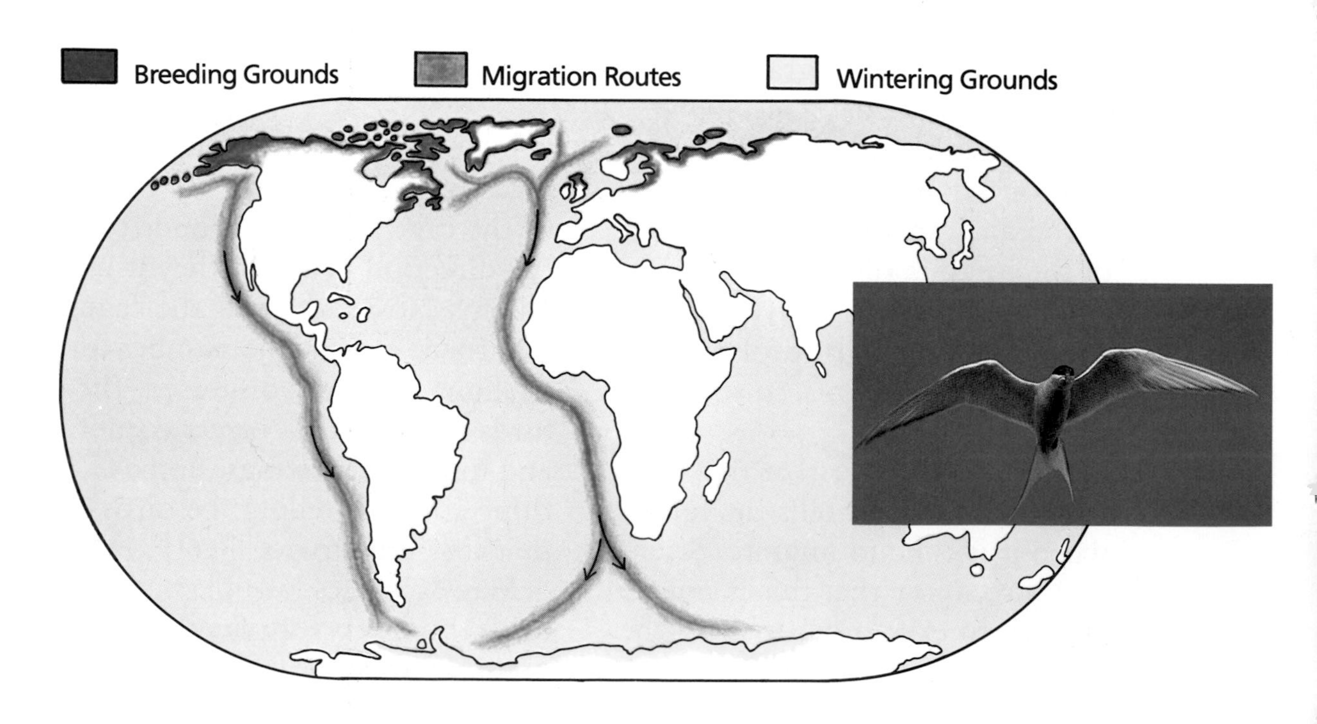

and the Yucatán Peninsula in Mexico. It flies five hundred miles across the open waters of the Gulf of Mexico without stopping to eat or rest. It makes the journey in about ten hours.

The ruby-throated hummingbird may be small, but it manages to fly five hundred miles nonstop twice a year.

How Birds Find Their Way

Perhaps more astonishing than the great distances birds migrate is their ability to find their way back. How do birds keep from getting lost?

Birds have very keen eyesight. Those that fly by day use landmarks to guide them. They follow the coastline. They recognize mountain ridges and rivers. When they are close to home, they may recognize fields, groups of trees, or even buildings. But this is not enough to explain how birds blown off their course, or those flying over water, keep from getting lost.

Do you know what a compass is? People use a compass to tell direction. Scientists think that birds have an **internal compass** — a compass inside their heads. Birds that fly by day use the sun to steer by. When the angle of the sun changes, the bird adjusts its course. Birds that fly by night use the stars. They follow a star that points them home.

How Migrating Birds Are Tracked

How do we know how far birds travel when they migrate? How do we know which routes they take? One way of tracking birds is by **banding** them. Light metal strips, or **bands**, are placed around the legs of millions of birds. (Some banders use nets to capture whole flocks of birds at one time.) A serial number, the place, and the date are stamped onto the band. The birds are then released. Anyone who finds a banded bird can tell how far the bird has traveled and how long the trip has taken.

The route taken by the Arctic tern is known because of banding. Over the years, banded terns have been found in various places around the world. Scientists have thus been able to piece together the tern's travel path. Each recovered bird added another piece to the puzzle.

Banding is done in almost every country on earth. From banding, scientists have learned

- which birds migrate,
- what their flight paths are,
- how long they live,
- if and when flocks move to new nesting places,
- how many of the group survive the flight

People who watch birds as a hobby can be very useful to

A tool called a bird-banding plier is being used to measure and then band the leg of this burrowing owl. The band will help scientists keep track of the bird's travels.

scientists who study birds. Bird watchers help to collect information about birds that live in their area.

Snow geese migrating over the Klamath Refuge in California.

How You Can Help

If you should ever find a banded bird that is not a pigeon, you can help too. Write the serial number and the address that you find on the band on a post card. Also tell where, when, and how you found the bird. Send the post card to

Fish and Wildlife Service
Bird-Banding Section
Laurel, Maryland 20810

You will be sent a reply telling about the bird. The information you supply will be added to the record. This information will give scientists one more piece of the bird migration puzzle.

Every year for all their lives, many birds fly hundreds or thousands of miles to their wintering grounds. Then in spring they fly back home. Each time they return, they build nests or grow bright new feathers, lay eggs, and wait for the chicks to be born. Then when the young birds are strong enough and the days grow short, they set out for their winter homes again.

Scientists have learned many facts about how and why birds migrate, but there are still many mysteries to be explained. Perhaps you can be one of the people who will help to find some of the answers.

An excerpt from

Katzimo, Mysterious Mesa

by Bobette Gugliotta

Carl Bibo was born in 1912, the youngest son of Solomon Bibo, a German-Jewish immigrant, and Juana Valle Bibo, an Ácoma Indian. When he was thirteen, Carl went to spend the summer with his Indian relatives in the pueblo of Ácoma, the Sky City that was built on a mesa. He quickly made friends with Aunt María, her son Wilbert, Aunt Plácida, and her daughter Helen. Helen's brother Horace, who was Carl's age, was another matter. Sometimes, Horace almost seemed to like Carl, but at other times, he seemed to hate him. Carl was determined to make friends with Horace, just as he was determined to climb Katzimo, the huge mesa that towered over Ácoma. Now the summer was nearly over, and both Horace and Katzimo seemed out of Carl's reach. A few days before he was to leave, a race was held as part of a festival. Horace was one of the runners, and he had his heart set on winning. Just before the finish line, however, with the race nearly won, Horace collapsed and was taken home unconscious.

Saukin!

The day after the race there was still no change in Horace. When Carl saw Wilbert for a moment and asked about the sick boy, Wilbert said, "Horace hasn't moved or talked yet."

That evening, when Helen brought food to Aunt María's house, Carl blurted out, "How long can he go on this way?"

And Helen answered, "Until they cure him."

Carl was about to say, why don't you try a doctor in Albuquerque? But he realized it was none of his business. When he became sick the Ácoma relatives had taken him back to San Rafael to be treated with his own kind of medicine.

Now that Horace was ill, they had a right to use theirs. But it was hard to wait for news, be so much alone and having nothing to do.

On the second day Carl began to wander, covering areas on the surface of Ácoma that he had never seen before. In a remote corner, far from the dwelling places of the town itself, he came upon a rock mound, built high with hundreds of tufted prayer sticks wedged in the cracks. He stood there looking at it a long time, then walked down the footpath to the base of Ácoma in search of scrub cedar. When he found some he broke off a branch and whittled a prayer stick. Returning to the place where he had found the rock mound, he carefully inserted the prayer stick into one of the cracks, saying silently to himself that it was for the recovery of Horace. Close by the rock shrine he found a cave with miniature bows and arrows and tiny parcels of sacred cornmeal tucked into its dusky interior. He disturbed nothing. With the exception of Horace's negative attitude, he had been treated with unfailing kindness in Ácoma and he felt that the least he could do was to show respect. He began to understand his mother's gentle ways and her tolerance of other customs and religions.

On the third day Carl spotted the ruins of a cliff house he had never noticed before, on a high rock above the southern portion of the mesa. The climb was such a rough one that it took him a long time to ascend, and when he reached the top it was close to sunset. He flopped down to rest on a ledge covered with ancient grit that was peppered with broken chunks of pottery, thorns, dried corn cobs, and nut shells. It was the most uncomfortable seat he'd ever felt, so he paused just long enough to catch his breath. When he stood up he saw Katzimo in the distance. It looked magic, like a solid mass of gold, the kind of treasure the Spanish conquistadors used to dream of finding. He knew it was only a trick of the sunset,

but he stared at it, fascinated as ever. Then suddenly he felt his temper rise when he realized how many times, since coming to New Mexico, he had gazed in frustration upon this same glorious, unattainable sight.

Picking up fistfuls of dirt he flung them into the air while he shouted, "Katzimo, you're nothing but a bunch of dust and rock! What's so great about that?" Then he hurled a chunk of pottery in the direction of the mighty mesa and watched it shatter into fragments on the cliffs below him.

The only answer he received was that the sun disappeared and Katzimo turned a muddy brown with forbidding purple shadows at the base. He remembered Helen telling him that, for the Ácomas, these were the colors of death and witches. He began to scramble down from the cliff house. All the while he made his way back to Aunt María's, the thread of a plan kept running through his mind.

Early next morning he got up, stuck some bread and jerky in his pocket, and slung a water bottle and rope over his shoulder. Planning to be gone most of the day, he left a note so that if anyone came back to check they'd know he was all right. Counting back in his mind, he realized that this was the fourth day of Horace's treatment. Last night the usual food had been left for him when he returned to Aunt María's house. But since María and Wilbert were away again all night, he had to assume that Horace was still sick and that the family was continuing to maintain the customary vigil by his bedside.

The side of Katzimo that faced Ácoma was less than three miles away. Yesterday Carl realized that he had never really explored the base of the big rock and, although he knew it was impossible for him to walk all the way around in one day, he wanted to be able to say when he went home that he had scouted a portion of it. This was what he told himself anyway when he started out. He had just begun picking his way through the talus when it began to rain. It poured down in bucketsful, with brief intervals between as though water pails were moving from hand to hand, in an old-fashioned fire brigade, before the last man spilled the contents out. He had enough time between torrents to wipe the water out of his eyes, but not enough time to move to shelter before the next one flooded over him. The place he was in had no ledges to stand under, nothing to provide cover. Skidding and sliding through the mud, he tripped over pieces of rock as sharp as knives. He fell down twice, cutting his knee and tearing a hole in his pants. The minute he reached a spot where there was an opening that looked like a cave, the rain stopped.

Standing there, he got the feeling that it was all on purpose. It was another way for Katzimo to tell him to keep his distance. Soggy wet, with hair plastered down around his head, he knew that he looked like a crazy man when he turned and shook his fist at that solid mass of rock. He was glad nobody was there to see him. Seeking the shelter of the cave, he took off his clothes, wrung them out then wriggled back into them, figuring they'd dry faster on than off. He began to walk again, looking up and down the steep sides of the mesa, finally admitting to himself that he was looking for some place where he could make the beginning of a climb.

After a while he began to remind himself of a man he had seen once who trained dogs for the circus. The fellow kept holding up a hoop and, each time, the dog leaped into the air like he was going to sail right through it but he never did make it — at least not while Carl was watching him. Carl would keep seeing markings or ledges, and once a whole series of dark spots that went straight up the side of Katzimo to the top, but as soon as he came near they faded off into nothing or turned out to be shadows changing with the time of day.

It was late afternoon when he worked through to the southern end where he'd never been before. As he stumbled around a curve he suddenly came upon a big gorge or cove, cut like a V upside down into the body of Katzimo. A bell rang in his head and he remembered reading in *Mesa, Cañon and Pueblo* that it was a place like this where a man named Charles Lummis had picked up the ancient trail that led almost to the top, and that it was the last thirty feet of sheer wall that made the climb so difficult. He also remembered that the problem had been solved by using an extension ladder, held by a man on either side and one behind for security, while Mr. Lummis climbed from rung to rung until he reached a point where he could be pushed over the top. But he knew that this knowledge wasn't going to do him any good because he was alone.

At this point Carl told himself that when he had started out in the morning he hadn't said anything like, I'm going to climb Katzimo. He was simply out for a hike because there

was nothing else to do—so what? He turned his back on the big cold rock, took a swig out of his water bottle and tightened his belt, ready to go back to Ácoma. All of a sudden he turned right around, dropped the water bottle, and made straight for the gorge. He crawled about midway up the slope on hands and feet, then, as the going got tough and he looked up seeking a first handhold, he almost lost his balance and fell backward in surprise. There, plastered against the steep wall that led straight to the top of Katzimo, was a rope ladder, sand-colored against sand-colored stone, impossible to detect from the talus below because at a distance it blended into rough rock.

Carl must have stared at it for five minutes, trying to figure out who had put it there and if it had been there a long time. It was getting so dark that he couldn't see if it was fastened at the top or if it only went part way up. Was it rotted so that a person who tried it might drop down and smash into the jagged rubble? He knew there wasn't enough time left in the day for him to find out the answers. Even if he made it to the bottom of the ladder, he'd never get back to the sky city again by sunset and he was afraid somebody might report to the family that he hadn't come home for his supper. He didn't want his relatives to be worried about him with Horace sick, nor did he want anybody to know what he was trying to do. It was hard to leave but he knew he'd better come back at dawn the next morning, fresh after a night's sleep, ready to try again.

Ácoma was quiet as a grave when he got back at dusk. The few people he saw were disappearing into their houses for the evening meal. As he passed Aunt Plácida's house he could see no sign of activity, and when he climbed the ladder to Aunt María's it was the same as before. Nobody was there. Carl was so keyed up that he didn't feel tired, but he was hungry and it didn't take him long to see that food had been laid out and that there was a note placed beside the jug of goat's milk.

Picking it up, he read, "Dear Carl, Aunt Juana and Uncle Solomon sent a message that they have to leave sooner than expected because of business in San Francisco. They'll be coming to pick you up tomorrow at noon. You'd better gather your things together. I'll see you later. Cousin-sister Helen."

As Carl mopped up the gravy from his frijoles, he got the feeling again that every time he came close to doing what he had wanted to do all summer, Katzimo won and he lost out. No matter how early he got up in the morning, there wouldn't be time to make a try up that ancient trail to test the rope ladder, to see if it would hold and be back again ready to leave by noon.

During the course of the last few days either Wilbert or Helen had brought Carl's possessions from Aunt Plácida's to Aunt María's, so when he finished supper Carl began to stack his gear in a corner of the room. Picking up the medicine bowl Helen had made for him, he looked around for something to pad it with so it wouldn't break on the ride back to San Francisco. The minute he touched it his fingers began to tingle. It was the same sensation he had when his hand went to sleep and he felt prickles all over the skin. The bowl felt warm too, almost alive. It was as though it were sending a message to him. He put it down quickly on top of his clothes, afraid he might drop it. As soon as he let go, he knew what he was going to do. There was no other way and no other time. He had to do it now.

Once he made up his mind, he worked fast, not wanting any of the family to catch him before he left. He scrawled a note saying he was camping out and would see them in the morning, then he shot out of the house. There was a full moon coming up and he knew that would be a help. He took the long way round to get to the burro trail, not wanting to pass Aunt Plácida's house, in case any of the relatives might be coming out. When he neared the graveyard he saw people in the distance and heard voices, so he cut behind the church and through the corral where the horses were tethered. There was a high-pitched whinny that faded away as he ran down the trail. Carl knew it was Zutu because he had a funny way of putting a snort at the end of a whinny that was different from any other horse.

When he reached the base of Katzimo, he kept away from the talus and walked around on the plain until he came to the gorge where the trail was. The moon was ascending the sky now, bursting with white light. Even if I don't make the climb, Carl thought, it was worth coming just to see Katzimo. The gorge was bleached to the same silver as the moonlight,

but on either side the big rock had turned to thick black velvet. It looked as though a spotlight had been deliberately focused on the ancient trail.

Carl shook his head to break the spell. Bending over, he started through the talus on all fours, feeling his way with his hands so he wouldn't fall or twist an ankle before he got where he wanted to be. When the rock smoothed out, and he was at the start of the climb where the slope was gradual, he stood up.

"Now," he said out loud. He didn't feel scared because for the first time he thought maybe he could do it. Then it happened. The back of his neck prickled and a chill shot through his shoulders. Something or somebody was standing behind him. He didn't move and it didn't move, but he knew it was there all the same. He waited but there wasn't a sound. At last he whirled around and the two of them stood stock-still, staring at each other.

Carl spoke first. "Where did you come from?"

"From Ácoma, same as you."

"Did you follow me?"

"I was about to mount Zutu when you cut through the corral. Zutu whinnied and I was afraid you were going to see me, but I crouched down until you were gone. Zutu and I picked up your trail, but I stayed way behind so you wouldn't know we were there."

"I thought you were sick."

"I was, but when I woke up this morning I felt good as new and it was all over. The rest of the day we had ceremonies to give thanks because I was well. Nobody in the family leaves until they are over. Didn't you think our medicine men were as good as your doctors? Didn't you think they could cure me, or didn't you want them to?"

Horace hasn't changed a bit, Carl thought. He's as nasty as ever. "Why did you follow me?" he asked.

"I wouldn't follow you anywhere if I could help it. I had my own plans but it wasn't hard to figure out what you wanted to do."

"I don't get it," Carl said. "Listen, why don't you run along back to Ácoma and leave me alone? Get a good night's sleep and maybe your disposition will be better in the morning."

"You've got it all wrong, the way you do with everything, cousin-brother." Horace stressed the last two words sarcastically. "You're the one who's going home. I'm the one who's going to climb Katzimo tonight. That's my rope ladder up there."

Carl took a deep breath, trying to hold his temper. "Why don't we both climb it?"

"No."

Carl tried another tack. "You were pretty smart to make that ladder." When he said these words he couldn't believe the change that came over Horace. He looked at Carl with such fury in his eyes that it was all Carl could do not to turn and run.

"Don't ever say that to me again!" Horace shouted. His thin face splintered and Carl was afraid he was going to cry. Then the whole thing backed up on Carl as he remembered the abuse he'd taken from Horace all summer long.

"Don't scream at me!" Carl screamed back. "It's always me who's trying to keep the peace. You can't even be decent the last night I'm here. Who do you think you are? I said you were smart to make that ladder. So you *weren't* smart. You were dumb, dumb, dumb — "

Suddenly Carl knew he'd better shut up fast because Horace started to cry. It wasn't like other people crying — it hurt to watch him because he was so ashamed of it. He half-twisted his body, turning his face away, putting his hands over his eyes. There wasn't any sound. That was the worst part.

Reaching down, Carl picked up his water bottle. "Okay, you win," he said. "After all, you've been pretty fair at that. You've let me know where I stand ever since I came to Ácoma. Sometimes I used to think you liked me, but then you'd change right back to hating." As Carl buckled the water bottle over his shoulder he realized that even if he had fought Horace and had beaten him so thoroughly that there was no question as to who was the superior boxer, it would have done nothing to fill the empty space inside him that Horace had

created. Carl didn't even turn around to take a last look at Katzimo. He never wanted to see it again. He began to walk away, then paused and called back over his shoulder, "There's only one thing I want to know. Why was it such an insult to say that you were pretty smart to make that ladder?"

This time Horace didn't shout. Carl could barely hear him. "Because that's what *he* said."

"That's what who said?" Carl turned around and took a few steps back so he could hear the answer.

"It's not exactly what he said."

Carl walked up close to Horace. "You don't like me and that's okay, but there's got to be a reason."

"It's not you."

"All right. You don't like Anglos or even half-Anglos."

Then Horace began to talk. "When I was in school in Santa Fe I had a friend in town, an Anglo. We did everything together. We went fishing up the Pecos River, we hunted rabbits. Once in a while another boy would come along, a friend of his, an Anglo too. One day they were waiting for me on the street corner after school. They were talking and didn't see me when I came up behind them. I heard the other boy say, 'If you can't work that problem in your arithmetic book why don't you ask Horace?' and my friend said, 'Well, maybe I will. He's pretty smart — for an Indian.'"

They were both quiet for a while after Horace stopped talking. Finally, Horace said slowly, "I suppose you think that was a stupid thing to get mad at?"

"No, I don't. The half of me that's Anglo is Jewish. The other half's Indian. I've heard remarks like that on both sides. It hurts."

For a long time they didn't say anything more. Then Horace walked a few steps toward the gorge, put his hands on his hips, and stood looking up at the ancient trail.

"I was lying before when I said I was going to climb Katzimo tonight. The ladder isn't fastened. It's just hanging there. I borrowed Zutu because I wanted to ride over to see if it was still here. Before I got sick, I managed to toss it up a ways and it caught on a rough knob of rock. It would take two people to peg it in place. One would have to help the other from below." Horace looked back. His eyes met Carl's and, for the first time, each of the boys knew what the other was thinking.

"Let's go," Carl said. "It's my last chance this summer."

"You first. I'll back you up, tell you what to do, where to put your hands, how to fasten the ladder. You'll have to work holes in the rock before you can push the wooden pegs in. I carved some before the whib race. I've got them in my pocket. I brought a hammer too."

"How come, if you didn't plan to climb Katzimo tonight?" Carl asked.

Horace shrugged his shoulders. "It's hard to explain. There was this feeling — "

"I know, I had it too."

As they clambered up the incline Carl wanted to suggest that he be the one to back Horace up. Horace had been sick and he was so much shorter and lighter that Carl knew that if he slipped back on him, Horace would surely roll over and over down the slope and onto the sharp talus below. But he felt that this was no time to even hint that he, Carl, might be stronger, so he kept quiet. Suddenly a cloud slid across the moon, turning the night so black that for a minute Carl couldn't see a thing until his eyes adjusted. Good old Katzimo doesn't play favorites, he thought. He doesn't want me to climb him, but he doesn't want Horace either.

It seemed to take forever but at last they reached the ladder. Things went along slowly and smoothly at the start. With Horace handing him pegs and hammer in the dark, Carl was tall enough to be able to stand on the slope of the gorge, in relative safety, while he fastened the first few rungs into place. But soon he could reach no higher.

"Now comes the first hurdle," he said to Horace. "Let's see if it'll hold me."

"I'm right behind, backing you up."

Carl tried the first rung gingerly, with one foot, stepped on it, and climbed up to the second. The rungs held. "Now comes the next big test," Carl called back. "You'll have to move onto the first rung or you won't be able to hand me the pegs and hammer. Let's hope the ladder's strong enough for both of us."

Though Horace was light, Carl could feel the additional strain as Horace stepped on. There was the scrunch of wood moving against stone and the rung Carl was on quivered, then sagged, as a peg settled into place. But it stayed firm. Carl didn't realize he'd been holding his breath until he let it out with a whoosh and gulped another. "So far, so good," he murmured to himself.

In this torturous fashion — step by step, rung by rung — they climbed higher. Carl began to breathe a little easier. But when they got within a few feet of the top the thing happened. Suddenly Carl's hands seemed to swell into two big hams without fingers. He felt so clumsy that he was scared he'd drop the pegs down on the rocks below.

"Listen, Horace," he whispered, although there was nobody to hear them, "do you have any extra pegs with you?"

"No, just the one you're holding now and the last one to go on the other side. Why? What's the matter?"

"I don't know for sure. I'm afraid I might drop one of the pegs. If I did, we'd be only a couple of feet short of reaching the top."

"Go ahead," Horace said. "It's got to be all right."

Carl fumbled the peg into the hole, hammered it in, and managed to slip the loop on the side of the rope ladder over it. One more to go. Reaching back, Carl felt Horace put the last peg into his hand.

"Here goes," Carl said. This peg didn't fit in easily. It jutted out at an angle. Carl had to hold it in place with his left hand so he could rap it with the hammer he held in his right. There wasn't much elbow room in the narrow crevice and it was almost impossible to swing with enough strength to drive the peg home. This time Carl wasn't afraid he'd drop the peg but that it might break in two because he couldn't hit it straight on.

It was getting colder. An icy wind slashed along the top of Katzimo and flung dust in his eyes. His hands were slimy with sweat, but he didn't dare wipe them off for fear he might lose his balance. Horace, on the rung below him, was absolutely motionless. Taking a firm grip on the hammer Carl whacked the peg as best he could, then tried it gingerly with one finger. It wobbled in the socket.

"I'm going to have to do it again," he warned Horace, trying to keep a quiver out of his voice. "Hold tight."

The crevice was as dark as a cave. He couldn't really see what he was doing, he could only sense it. This time he was going to have to let fly harder and, to complicate things, he had begun to tremble. Maybe it's the cold, he thought, or maybe it's knowing that this is our last chance. He pushed away the sudden vision he had of the long drop down to the base of Katzimo. During his walk yesterday he had seen the bleached and broken bones of animals wedged between talus as sharp as dragon's teeth. Lifting the hammer, he drove down hard, then, carefully, with thumb and forefinger he tested the peg once more. It didn't turn in the socket. It was firm. He slipped the loop over it and said to Horace, "Let me climb this last rung, get on top. Then I can give you a hand up. I won't feel safe until we're both on solid ground."

In a minute he was sprawled out on the summit, hanging on to a boulder with one arm and reaching down with the other to Horace. They clasped hands, Carl pulled, and, thin as Horace was, he seemed to fly through the air.

They sat there side by side in the dark, breathing hard, waiting for their hearts to stop banging against their ribs.

"How do you feel?" Carl asked.

"Free," Horace said, then "light."

Carl knew what he meant.

"I had to do it," Horace said. "Not like you, just because you wanted to, but because every Ácoma boy must climb Katzimo."

"You mean it's part of a ritual?"

Horace nodded in the dark.

"I didn't know, or I wouldn't have gotten in your way."

"It's a good thing it happened." Horace didn't explain any further and Carl didn't ask him to.

Carl dozed for a while — he couldn't help it, he was so tired. It seemed as though he had just closed his eyes when he felt a tap on the shoulder. Horace stood there in a world that glowed with rose-pink light.

Motioning to Carl, Horace walked to the edge of the mesa. Carl followed him and they stood together watching the day come alive. As the enormous valley yielded its wonders to the demanding light of day, it seemed to Carl that all the mysteries of creation lay revealed before him and that he and Horace were the first men ever to see them. I know there'll never be anything like this again, Carl thought. Even if I climbed Katzimo a dozen times, things like this only happen once. A tinge of sadness touched him and for the first time he knew the sense of loss that comes with the fulfillment of a cherished dream.

"Hold out your hand," Horace said abruptly.

Carl looked at him for a minute, then thrust out his hand.

Horace turned it over, palm up, fished in his pocket, then dropped two rough agate stones shaped like arrowheads in it. "I found them on the other side of Katzimo," he said.

Carl was about to say, I don't have anything for you, but he kept quiet. He could tell by Horace's face that he didn't want anything in return, that he only wanted to give something.

"Thanks a lot," Carl said.

At noon, when Carl's mother and father came to pick him up, the whole pueblo gathered at the base of Ácoma to see them off. As Carl walked down the trail carrying his suitcase, and saw the crowd congregated below, he had the awful feeling that he might bawl like a baby. It came upon him all at once and as soon as he had stowed his bag in the car he scurried around as fast as he could, shaking hands and mumbling good-bye without looking up.

It worked all right until he came to Wilbert and heard him say, "Too bad you can't stay until September second for the festival of San Estevan, the patron saint of Ácoma. But maybe, for this year, it's enough. Besides, it's always good to leave something special for next time. Then we'll be sure that you'll come back. We'll miss you but we'll be waiting for you."

Carl nodded his head, afraid to trust his voice. He tried to put into his parting handshake the gratitude that he felt for all that Wilbert had done for him.

Even his uncles, Edward and Cipriano, were there, overalls splattered with bits of straw and adobe. Carl knew that they had taken time off from house construction to bid him farewell and they urged him to come back next summer when they would have time to take him hunting and fishing in the far reaches of the Ácoma lands, to places he hadn't been before.

He heard Solomon calling, "Come along, Carl, we have to get going."

As Carl hopped into the car, he saw the family up front waving, Horace at one side on Zutu. As the car started to go Zutu snorted, reared up, and lunged forward in pursuit. In no time he was galloping along beside them and Carl heard Horace yell, "Goodbye, cousin-brother. Good-bye, *saukin!*"

Turning to his mother, Carl asked, "What does that word *saukin* mean?"

"It's a good word," Juana replied. "In Ácoma language it means friend."

Author

Bobette Gugliotta is part of the Bibo family, whose lives became linked with the Ácoma Indians in the 1800's. In New Mexico, Mrs. Gugliotta met newfound relatives and taped a conversation with Carl Bibo, who became the hero of her book *Katzimo, the Mysterious Mesa.* Besides her books for young people, she writes for magazines and newspapers.

Houghton Mifflin Literature

In the selections you have just read from *Creating and Accepting Change,* change appeared as many different things. A cat's shape and disposition and the process of bringing a cartoon character to life are just two of the ways change made itself known.

Now you will read two stories in which change happens both mysteriously and powerfully. In *The Girl Who Loved Wild Horses* by Paul Goble, the power of one girl's love changes an entire community, while in *Greyling* by Jane Yolen, a creature pulled from the sea changes the lives of those it touches.

3

A Display of Courage

THE HEROINE OF KAPITI

A Maori Legend
Retold by Shirley Climo

On the south side of the world, where Christmas comes in summer and snow falls in July, are two islands we now call New Zealand. But long ago, before Dutch explorers discovered these islands from their tall-masted sailing ships, the Maori[1] *people had paddled there in their dugout canoes. When the Maoris saw the snowy mountain peaks rising up from the mists of the Pacific Ocean, they named these new-found islands* Aotearoa,[2] *or Land of the Long White Cloud. Here they settled, put out their eel pots, planted their sweet potatoes, and lived happily — or almost happily — because then, as now, people often quarreled among themselves.*

Many tales are told about the battles of those early days, but this legend is based on a true incident and tells of a young Maori woman who lived less than 150 years ago.

Like a school of flying fish, the swimmers skimmed across the water. Then one pulled ahead of the rest with such strong and smooth strokes that her arms scarcely ruffled the surface of the sea.

"Te Rau[3] has won!" called a young girl who was watching the race from the beach. She hugged the baby she was carrying and ran with her to the water's edge.

Te Rau waded to shore, shaking the salty water from her long black hair. She picked up her feather cloak and pulled it about her wet shoulders. Then she took the baby from the excited girl.

"Are you pleased with your mother, my child?" she asked. Her daughter just snuggled against the soft feathers of Te Rau's cloak and closed her eyes.

---

[1]**Maori** (mä ô rē)

[2]**Aotearoa** (ä ô tĕ ä rô ä)

[3]**Te Rau** (tĕ rä o͞o)

The girl danced around Te Rau, scuffing the sand with her toes. "I am pleased," she announced, "and proud to be your sister." She looked scornfully at the other swimmers, mostly men and boys, who were just now coming ashore. "You are the best swimmer on Kapiti Island. Perhaps in all the ocean!"

Te Rau laughed. "The ocean is large. And you forget *mango,* the shark."

"Don't speak of sharks!" cried the girl, catching hold of Te Rau's hand. "I wish I were as brave as you."

Te Rau put her arm around her sister. "Then you must open your eyes to what you can do," she said, "and close your ears to those who would keep you from trying."

Te Rau knew that others were not so pleased with her swimming feat. Some of the men she had beaten grumbled as they passed her. Some of the old women who sat by the sea, soaking the leaves of the flax bush to soften them for weaving, shook their heads.

"Boldness does not become a woman," called one, loudly enough that Te Rau might hear.

"Such foolishness is not fitting," agreed another.

"There is a proverb," said a third. "'A fish in water; a woman on land.'" Then she added more kindly, "Come, Te Rau, you have played the part of fish. Now learn to weave flax."

"So I shall, soon enough," replied Te Rau, smiling down at her sister, "but there are other skills to practice, too."

Then the women muttered among themselves. Te Rau's ways were brash, and she was no longer one of their tribe. She had married a young warrior from the North Island of Aotearoa, four miles away. Now his people and home were hers as well. She had returned to the small island of Kapiti to visit her father, Chief Te Rauparaha.[4] He would choose the right name for her baby daughter — just as he had called her Te Rau-o-te-Rangi,[5] or "The Leaves of the Sky," because her hair was as dark as the midnight sky and her voice as true as the bellbird that sings at dawn.

Now Te Rau looked away from the women and up at the sky. Already the sun was slipping toward its ocean bed. So she climbed the tangled path through the trees to her hut, where she put the baby down upon her mat of ferns.

"Now you, too, must rest," she said to her sister, "for sleep brings strength."

The girl shook her head and shivered, though no breeze blew through the woven reeds of the walls.

---

[4]**Te Rauparaha** (tĕ rä o͞o pä rä hä)

[5]**Te Rau-o-te-Rangi** (tĕ rä o͞o ô tĕ räng ē)

"What troubles you?" asked Te Rau.

"Take me back with you to Aotearoa," begged her sister. "I don't want to stay on Kapiti."

"This is your home," answered Te Rau. "And I cannot return until my little one is named."

"Misfortune comes here," whispered the girl. "I know it. For three nights, I have had a dream, and it is always the same. Evil beings come by sea and turn the waters red. The wind carries the sounds of their wails." Her voice rose, and the baby stirred.

"Sssh!" warned Te Rau. "The god of the sea is our friend. The red of your dreams is but the sun reflected on the water, the cries you hear are no more than the calls of gulls."

Then Te Rau sat, cross-legged, upon the floor and softly sang an ancient charm to quiet her daughter and her sister:

"O eyes that see
be you closed in sleep,
tightly sealed, in sleep, in sleep. . . ."

Lulled by the singing, the children slept; but Te Rau was restless and strangely troubled by her sister's words. She left the hut to walk alone beside the sea. The men had long since left their games, and the women had gone to uncover their earthen ovens for the evening meal. Waves licked lazily against the shore, and the hills of distant Aotearoa looked little larger than pebbles. But when the moon climbed into the sky, its light showed dark shapes moving silently upon the sea.

"Porpoises," said Te Rau aloud. "They, too, race with one another."

She stood still, watching them. Then — suddenly — Te Rau realized these were not ocean creatures at all. War canoes floated upon the waves, waiting for daybreak to attack Kapiti.

Te Rau ran to give warning. Hushed and fearful, the villagers gathered at the shore and stared at the shadows on the sea. Dozens of canoes dotted the water, and each held eighty warriors. Without help from Aotearoa, the people of Kapiti would be destroyed.

Chief Te Rauparaha picked up his greenstone club. "I cannot spare a man to go for help," he said. "Every warrior is needed to protect the *pa*.[6] We must do the best we can."

"Spare a woman," urged Te Rau. "Let *me* go, Father."

The chief shook his head. "They would see even the smallest canoe — and sink it immediately."

"I shall swim."

---

[6]**pa** (pä): A fort or protected settlement.

"Aotearoa is too far, and there are sharks and a strong undertow."

"That is so," agreed Te Rau, "but I, too, must do the best I can."

Some who heard her words raised their voices to protest, and others clicked their tongues against their teeth in disapproval. This was not woman's work. But Chief Te Rauparaha slapped his club upon the earth for silence.

"Go," he said to Te Rau, "and may the god of the sea go with you."

Te Rau hurried back to her hut. Both children were still sound asleep.

"Grow strong, grow brave," she whispered to her sister.

Then Te Rau looked down at her own child. She could not leave her behind. Te Rau took off her feather cloak and wrapped it about her baby. She tied it securely with thongs and hung hollow gourds from the lacings. Should she fail, perhaps her daughter would float safely to shore. Then Te Rau strapped her to her back, walked swiftly to the shore, and stepped into the sea.

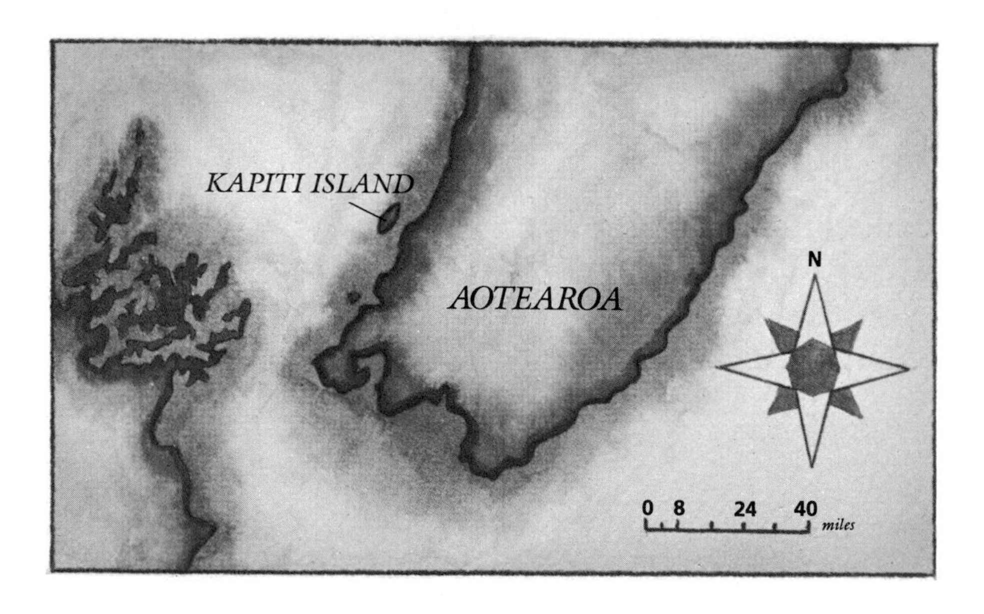

Without a sound, without a splash, Te Rau glided past the enemy canoes. She swam strongly at first, and her baby slept as if rocked in a cradle. But as Te Rau pushed beyond Kapiti's calm lagoon, the current grew greater. Sprays of foam broke over her head and riptides tugged at her legs. Te Rau knew that she must win this race or lose her life.

Soon there was nothing to mark her way through the dark water, for mist hid both the shore behind her and the hills ahead. Then, suddenly, a sea gull circled in the gray above her.

"A good omen!" gasped Te Rau. "The gods have sent a gull to guide me." She swam slowly, following the flight of the bird. Just as dawn reddened the clouds overhead, Te Rau felt the sands of Aotearoa beneath her feet. Struggling for breath, she shouted the alarm.

The night guards awakened the village, and at once warriors in boats set out for Kapiti. As in her sister's dreams, Te Rau listened to their cries borne upon the wind. When the battle noises ceased, she knew the war canoes had been driven off. Kapiti was safe. Only then, with her baby in her arms, did Te Rau sleep upon the sand.

Te Rau swam to save Kapiti in the year 1842. Today the island is a peaceful place, a sanctuary for gulls and other sea birds.

Author

Although she began her career by writing radio scripts, most of Shirley Climo's recent writing has consisted of books and magazine stories based on folklore. After a five-week trip with her family to New Zealand and the South Pacific, she wrote this version of a local legend she heard there.

Zlateh the Goat

from the book *Zlateh the Goat and Other Stories*
by Isaac Bashevis Singer

At Hanukkah time the road from the village to the town is usually covered with snow, but this year the winter had been a mild one. Hanukkah had almost come, yet little snow had fallen. The sun shone most of the time. The peasants complained that because of the dry weather there would be a poor harvest of winter grain. New grass sprouted, and the peasants sent their cattle out to pasture.

For Reuven the furrier it was a bad year, and after long hesitation he decided to sell Zlateh the goat. She was old and gave little milk. Feyvel the town butcher had offered eight gulden for her. Such a sum would buy Hanukkah candles, potatoes and oil for pancakes, gifts for the children, and other holiday necessaries for the house. Reuven told his oldest boy Aaron to take the goat to town.

Aaron understood what taking the goat to Feyvel meant, but he had to obey his father. Leah, his mother, wiped the tears from her eyes when she heard the news. Aaron's younger sisters, Anna and Miriam, cried loudly. Aaron put on his quilted jacket and a cap with earmuffs, bound a rope around Zlateh's neck, and took along two slices of bread with cheese to eat on the road. Aaron was supposed to deliver the goat by evening, spend the night at the butcher's, and return the next day with the money.

While the family said good-bye to the goat, and Aaron placed the rope around her neck, Zlateh stood as patiently and good-naturedly as ever. She licked Reuven's hand. She shook her small white beard. Zlateh trusted human beings. She knew that they always fed her and never did her any harm.

When Aaron brought her out on the road to town, she seemed somewhat astonished. She'd never been led in that direction before. She looked back at him questioningly, as if to say, "Where are you taking me?" But after a while she seemed to come to the conclusion that a goat shouldn't ask questions. Still, the road was different. They passed new fields, pastures, and huts with thatched roofs. Here and there a dog barked and came running after them, but Aaron chased it away with his stick.

The sun was shining when Aaron left the village. Suddenly the weather changed. A large black cloud with a bluish center appeared in the east and spread itself rapidly over the sky. A cold wind blew in with it. The crows flew low, croaking. At first it looked as if it would rain, but instead it began to hail as in summer. It was early in the day, but it became dark as dusk. After a while the hail turned to snow.

In his twelve years Aaron had seen all kinds of weather, but he had never experienced a snow like this one. It was so dense it shut out the light of the day. In a short time their path was completely covered. The wind became as cold as ice. The road to town was narrow and winding. Aaron no longer knew where he was. He could not see through the snow. The cold soon penetrated his quilted jacket.

At first Zlateh didn't seem to mind the change in weather. She too was twelve years old and knew what winter meant. But when her legs sank deeper and deeper into the snow, she began to turn her head and look at Aaron in wonderment. Her mild eyes seemed to ask, "Why are we out in such a storm?" Aaron hoped that a peasant would come along with his cart, but no one passed by.

The snow grew thicker, falling to the ground in large, whirling flakes. Beneath it Aaron's boots touched the softness of a plowed field. He realized that he was no longer on the road. He had gone astray. He could no longer figure out which was east or west, which way was the village, the town. The wind whistled, howled, whirled the snow about in eddies. It looked as if white imps were playing tag on the fields. A white dust rose above the ground. Zlateh stopped. She could walk no longer. Stubbornly she anchored her cleft hooves in the earth and bleated as if pleading to be taken home. Icicles

hung from her white beard, and her horns were glazed with frost.

Aaron did not want to admit the danger, but he knew just the same that if they did not find shelter they would freeze to death. This was no ordinary storm. It was a mighty blizzard. The snowfall had reached his knees. His hands were numb, and he could no longer feel his toes. He choked when he breathed. His nose felt like wood, and he rubbed it with snow. Zlateh's bleating began to sound like crying. Those humans in whom she had so much confidence had dragged her into a trap. Aaron began to pray to God for himself and for the innocent animal.

Suddenly he made out the shape of a hill. He wondered what it could be. Who had piled snow into such a huge heap? He moved toward it, dragging Zlateh after him. When he came near it, he realized that it was a large haystack which the snow had blanketed.

Aaron realized immediately that they were saved. With great effort he dug his way through the snow. He was a village boy and knew what to do. When he reached the hay, he hollowed out a nest for himself and the goat. No matter how cold it may be outside, in the hay it is always warm. And hay was food for Zlateh. The moment she smelled it she became contented and began to eat. Outside the snow continued to fall. It quickly covered the passageway Aaron had dug. But a boy and an animal need to breathe, and there was hardly any air in their hideout. Aaron bored a kind of a window through the hay and snow and carefully kept the passage clear.

Zlateh, having eaten her fill, sat down on her hind legs and seemed to have regained her confidence in man. Aaron ate his two slices of bread and cheese, but after the difficult journey he was still hungry. He looked at Zlateh and noticed her udders were full. He lay down next to her, placing himself so that when he milked her he could squirt the milk into his mouth. It was rich and sweet. Zlateh was not accustomed to being milked that way, but she did not resist. On the contrary, she seemed eager to reward Aaron for bringing her to a shelter whose very walls, floor, and ceiling were made of food.

Through the window Aaron could catch a glimpse of the chaos outside. The wind carried before it whole drifts of snow. It was completely dark, and he did not know whether night had already come or whether it was the darkness of the storm. Thank God that in the hay it was not cold. The dried hay, grass, and field flowers exuded the warmth of the summer sun. Zlateh ate frequently; she nibbled from above, below, from the left and right. Her body gave forth an animal warmth, and Aaron cuddled up to her. He had always loved Zlateh, but now she was like a sister. He was alone, cut off from his family, and wanted to talk. He began to talk to Zlateh. "Zlateh, what do you think about what has happened to us?" he asked.

"Maaaa," Zlateh answered.

"If we hadn't found this stack of hay, we would both be frozen stiff by now," Aaron said.

"Maaaa," was the goat's reply.

"If the snow keeps on falling like this, we may have to stay here for days," Aaron explained.

"Maaaa," Zlateh bleated.

"What does 'Maaaa' mean?" Aaron asked. "You'd better speak up clearly."

"Maaaa. Maaaa," Zlateh tried.

"Well, let it be 'Maaaa' then," Aaron said patiently. "You can't speak, but I know you understand. I need you and you need me. Isn't that right?"

"Maaaa."

Aaron became sleepy. He made a pillow out of some hay, leaned his head on it, and dozed off. Zlateh too fell asleep.

When Aaron opened his eyes, he didn't know whether it was morning or night. The snow had blocked up his window. He tried to clear it, but when he had bored through to the length of his arm, he still hadn't reached the outside. Luckily he had his stick with him and was able to break through to the open air. It was still dark outside. The snow continued to fall and the wind wailed, first with one voice and then with many. Sometimes it had the sound of devilish laughter. Zlateh too awoke, and when Aaron greeted her, she answered, "Maaaa." Yes, Zlateh's language consisted of only one word, but it meant many things. Now she was saying, "We must accept all that God gives us — heat, cold, hunger, satisfaction, light, and darkness."

Aaron had awakened hungry. He had eaten up his food, but Zlateh had plenty of milk.

For three days Aaron and Zlateh stayed in the haystack. Aaron had always loved Zlateh, but in these three days he loved her more and more. She fed him with her milk and helped him keep warm. She comforted him with her patience. He told her many stories, and she always cocked her ears and listened. When he patted her, she licked his hand and his face. Then she said, "Maaaa," and he knew it meant, I love you too.

The snow fell for three days, though after the first day it was not as thick and the wind quieted down. Sometimes Aaron felt that there could never have been a summer, that the snow had always fallen, ever since he could remember. He, Aaron, never had a father or mother or sisters. He was a snow child, born of the snow, and so was Zlateh. It was so quiet in the hay that his ears rang in the stillness. Aaron and Zlateh slept all night and a good part of the day. As for Aaron's dreams, they were all about warm weather. He dreamed of green fields, trees covered with blossoms, clear brooks, and singing birds. By the third night the snow had stopped, but

Aaron did not dare to find his way home in the darkness. The sky became clear and the moon shone, casting silvery nets on the snow. Aaron dug his way out and looked at the world. It was all white, quiet, dreaming dreams of heavenly splendor. The stars were large and close. The moon swam in the sky as in a sea.

On the morning of the fourth day Aaron heard the ringing of sleigh bells. The haystack was not far from the road. The peasant who drove the sleigh pointed out the way to him — not to the town and Feyvel the butcher, but home to the village. Aaron had decided in the haystack that he would never part with Zlateh.

Aaron's family and their neighbors had searched for the boy and the goat but had found no trace of them during the storm. They feared they were lost. Aaron's mother and sisters cried for him; his father remained silent and gloomy. Suddenly one of the neighbors came running to their house with the news that Aaron and Zlateh were coming up the road.

There was great joy in the family. Aaron told them how he had found the stack of hay and how Zlateh had fed him with her milk. Aaron's sisters kissed and hugged Zlateh and gave her a special treat of chopped carrots and potato peels, which Zlateh gobbled up hungrily.

Nobody ever again thought of selling Zlateh, and now that the cold weather had finally set in, the villagers needed the services of Reuven the furrier once more. When Hanukkah came, Aaron's mother was able to fry pancakes every evening, and Zlateh got her portion too. Even though Zlateh had her own pen, she often came to the kitchen, knocking on the door with her horns to indicate that she was ready to visit, and she was always admitted. In the evening Aaron, Miriam, and Anna played dreidel. Zlateh sat near the stove watching the children and the flickering of the Hanukkah candles.

Once in a while Aaron would ask her, "Zlateh, do you remember the three days we spent together?"

And Zlateh would scratch her neck with a horn, shake her white bearded head and come out with the single sound which expressed all her thoughts, and all her love.

Author

One of the last great Yiddish authors, Isaac Bashevis Singer was born in Radzymin, Poland, in 1904. His novels such as *The Magician of Lublin, The Slave,* and *The Family Moskat* are well known for their rich and haunting descriptions of Jewish life. *Zlateh the Goat and Other Stories,* from which this story was taken, was Mr. Singer's first book for children.

An excerpt from

Helen Keller's Teacher

by Margaret Davidson

Helen and Annie, 1894

On March 3, 1887, twenty-year-old Annie Sullivan arrived in Tuscumbia, Alabama to begin her duties as the teacher of a six-year-old deaf and blind girl. Annie came to Alabama from the Perkins Institute for the Blind in Massachusetts, where she had lived since she was fourteen. At Perkins, Annie had learned about the achievements of the deaf and blind woman, Laura Bridgman, who had learned to "talk" using her hands with the help of the famous Dr. Howe. Would Annie Sullivan be as good a teacher as Dr. Howe had been? Would her pupil be able to break through the silence of a world without language? What Annie Sullivan found when she stepped off the train in Tuscumbia was a creature more like a wild animal than a child. Here is what happened when Annie Sullivan began her work with Helen Keller.

The Stranger Arrives

It was the third of March, 1887. Two very tired people sat in a buggy by the little country railroad station of Tuscumbia, Alabama. Kate Keller and her nearly grown stepson, James, were waiting for Annie Sullivan.

James broke the silence. "What if she doesn't come at all?"

"She'll come," Mrs. Keller answered confidently. "She wrote and said she would. Mr. Anagnos said she was trustworthy. Anyway, she's only two days late." She sighed. "Maybe something happened to her train. Oh, James, she *has* to come . . . What will become of Helen?"

Just then James caught the faint sound of a distant train. "The 6:30 is coming in," he said. "That'll be the last train for today."

Mrs. Keller found it difficult to breathe. "Please," she prayed. "Please."

Several people climbed out of the train. Only one of them could possibly be the new young governess.

Helen, age 10

"Looks like a drowned cat, doesn't she?" James commented.

James was right. Annie wasn't looking her best. She'd been wearing the same hot woolen dress for three days and nights. She was red-eyed, low in spirit, and irritated beyond words. It had been such a difficult trip.

She had expected to come winging down here on a fast express. But a stupid Boston ticket agent had sold her tickets for a round-about local that had found its way to every small town between Boston and Tuscumbia.

Well, here she was. She squared her shoulders and smiled gamely at the young man who advanced toward her.

"Miss Sullivan?" he asked.

Something in his greeting made her smile waver. Annie recognized a condescending tone when she heard it. "I'm not going to like him," she thought.

"Yes," she replied coldly.

"This way, please," he continued in an amused tone. "My stepmother's waiting in the carriage."

When Annie saw Kate Keller, her heart lightened. The two young women smiled at each other.

"Why, she's not much older than I am," Annie thought. "It's going to be all right." It was a friendship formed at first sight.

A few minutes later the Keller carriage turned off the road and onto their own land.

"There it is. That's where we live," Mrs. Keller said, pointing to a roomy white house with green shutters, set back in a beautifully tended garden.

Annie was too excited to notice a mere house. As soon as the carriage stopped, she hopped to the ground. "Where's Helen?" she asked eagerly.

Captain Keller came forward.

"How do you do, Miss Annie," he said. "I'm Helen's father."

"Where is she?" Annie repeated, barely acknowledging his greeting.

"There she is." He pointed to the porch. "She's known all day that something was going on. Days for that matter. She's wild with it."

Annie saw Helen for the first time. The child was standing far back in the shadows of the front porch, half concealed by a climbing ivy vine. Her filthy hands were tearing at the vine, stripping it of its leaves. Her hair lay in a tangled mat on her shoulders. Her blouse was misbuttoned, and her dusty brown shoes were tied with white string.

Helen had felt the carriage roll up, and now she was concentrating, waiting, not knowing which way to jump.

"The child looks so neglected!" was Annie's first thought. Later she understood that on Helen's bad days the family could do nothing with her. If anyone approached, she would fly into a violent rage. This was one of her bad days.

Annie Sullivan

Annie suppressed a feeling of dismay and started up the porch steps. At the first footfall on the boards, Helen wheeled around. She knew someone was coming toward her across the porch. She could feel the vibrations increasing through the soles of her shoes.

Helen expected her mother. For the past several days her mother had been gone so much. Helen had no words to express her need. Now she flung out her arms. And Annie gathered her in.

But this wasn't Mother! Helen struggled and strained like a wild animal to get away from the stranger. Annie, taken by surprise, tightened her arms for a moment. This just made Helen wilder.

"Let her go!" James called out. "She'll hurt you."

Annie's arms flew open. She rocked back on her heels and said, "What happened, Helen? What did I do wrong?"

"She doesn't like to be held, Miss Annie," Mrs. Keller explained. "She never kisses anybody — not since her illness. And she lets nobody kiss or caress her either."

"Except you, sometimes," Captain Keller put in.

James sank down on the porch steps. He looked up at Annie quizzically. "Now do you see what you're in for? You were brought here to teach an animal — governess for an animal!"

"James!" Kate Keller exclaimed. "Stop that!"

"Sir! If that is all you can contribute, you may go inside!" Captain Keller added sternly.

Mrs. Keller noticed that Annie was drooping with exhaustion and said quickly, "Show Miss Sullivan to her room, won't you, Arthur? There's time to talk later."

Annie smiled her thanks to Kate and followed Captain Keller up the stairs.

"Helen wasn't a bit frightened," she mused aloud to his back. "I mean, she was startled, all right. She wanted to get away from me. But I didn't scare her at all. She doesn't know much about fear, does she?"

"No, Miss Annie," Captain Keller answered slowly. "And sometimes that's a problem."

He put Annie's trunk down in the white-ruffled guest room that now belonged to her. "I'll leave you to unpack now," he said graciously. Helen had followed them upstairs and into Annie's room. Now Captain Keller made a motion as if to lead her away.

"No, let her stay," Annie said. "She won't bother me. And it's never too early to get acquainted."

Annie made no direct move to be friendly. She just started to unpack. Helen seemed fascinated with everything this stranger did. Her little hands followed Annie's every motion. After removing the sticky fingers from her open case for the umpteenth time, Annie commented, "Persistent little devil, aren't you?"

Just then Helen's hand met Annie's floppy traveling hat. She seemed to recognize it for what it was, for she picked it up and clumsily tied it under her chin. After touching her way over to the looking glass, she stood in front of it and cocked her head first to the right and then to the left.

Annie burst out laughing. "Why you little monkey! You must have felt your mother do that! For all the world as though you could see!" Then Annie stopped laughing and looked a little foolish. She had been talking aloud, as if Helen could hear her. It was going to be hard to remember that this child was so completely cut off.

Suddenly Annie's eyes focused sharply on Helen's fingers, now untying the strings of the hat. Two dirty hands, already fluttering about looking for something new to hold their interest.

"You've learned a lot from those hands, haven't you, Helen?" Annie thought. "You've watched your mother get dressed and put on her hat. And a lot else, I'll wager. They're your eyes, aren't they? And you've seen a fair bit with them, too. But I'll tell you this right now, you haven't seen anything yet. Those hands are going to get quite an education in the next few weeks. Those hands are going to set you free!"

The house grew quiet early that night. Annie had fallen into an immediate, exhausted sleep. Helen, as always, dropped off easily into her dreamless state. But in the big master bedroom, Captain Keller tossed and turned. Finally, his movement woke Kate Keller.

"What is it, dear?" she asked.

He was silent for a few moments. Then he said, "It's that girl. She's so young, Kate. Will she do, after all?"

Mrs. Keller smiled and settled back on her pillow. "Go to sleep, Arthur. She'll do."

On the day before she left Boston, the Perkins students had given Annie a doll. They had pooled their money to buy it, and Laura Bridgman had dressed it in an exquisitely stitched outfit. This doll was the blind girls' gift to Helen. It lay now in Annie's trunk, and was one of the first things that Helen's inquisitive fingers found.

A doll! She recognized its familiar shape. She already had a box stuffed full of dolls in her own room. Helen yanked the toy from the trunk and clutched it close.

"This is as good a starting place as any," Annie decided. She reached for one of Helen's hands, and began to shape the letters D-O-L-L into her palm.

Helen pulled back immediately. But her curiosity was greater than her dislike of being touched, and when Annie picked up her hand again, she allowed it.

D-O-L-L . . . Annie traced the letters over and over again into Helen's hand. Then, by patting the doll's head, she directed the child's puzzled attention to the doll in her arms. Annie repeated the spelling-patting pattern several times while Helen stood transfixed, every bit of her energy focused on those strange movements in her hand.

"Whatever can you two be doing?" Kate Keller came into the room, her arms piled high with laundry. She smiled at Annie. "Tell me just a bit of what you're doing, and I'll be satisfied to keep quiet as a mouse. I promise."

Annie smiled back. Odd, she thought, how quickly she and Kate had been drawn to each other. She was very glad of this friendship, for already she understood that the others in this house — Captain Keller, James, and the captain's other younger son, Simpson — looked upon her as a sort of half-servant. Certainly not as a friend.

"Watch, now." Annie picked up Helen's hand, and again she began tracing the letters. "I'm shaping some of the letters of the alphabet into Helen's palm — or shapes that stand for the letters. This is the manual alphabet."

Annie held out her own hand, and her fingers began to flutter through a series of fast movements. "I'm spelling,

'How are you today? It's a pleasant day for a walk, isn't it?'"
she explained to Mrs. Keller.

Annie turned toward Helen. "Helen will have to rely on her hands for almost everything — they'll have to be her eyes and her ears.

"This morning I've been tracing the letters D-O-L-L into her palm and getting her to make the letter shapes back. Then I direct her attention quickly to the real doll she's holding in her other arm. I'm trying to connect these things in her mind.

"See! She's going through the motions now. There! She's making the letters D . . . and O . . . and L . . ." Annie stooped down. "And one more L," she murmured, as she helped Helen's fumbling fingers shape the last letter of the word.

Looking up, Annie caught the glimpse of hope on Mrs. Keller's face.

"Of course, it's not the real thing," she hastened to explain. "It's just mimicry — excellent monkey work. Helen can make the symbols of the word "doll" now, but she doesn't have the remotest idea that those particular finger movements stand for all the dolls in the world. I've got to get that across to her. I'll have to repeat and repeat and repeat, over and over again. word, object — word, object. And one day she'll connect them for herself. Won't you, Helen?"

Annie stopped. She wanted to gather just the right words for what she had to say next. "Once Helen has learned this much," she spoke slowly, "the rest won't be easy. But it will be possible."

Annie turned back to Helen. "Come on there. Let's carry this game a bit further!" And with that, Annie reached down and took the doll away from Helen. She wanted Helen to spell "doll" on her fingers, and then she would give back the doll. She wanted to reinforce the connection between the word and object.

Helen and her dog Jumbo

Helen couldn't know this. All she knew was that the stranger was taking the doll away from her. A weird growl began to grow in the back of her throat. Her face turned red. Her hands locked into fists. In an instant she became a fury. Now she came whirling at Annie.

Annie tossed the doll out of the way and turned toward the charging child. She grabbed her flailing hands and held on for dear life.

"Give the doll back to her, Miss Annie," Kate Keller begged.

"No," Annie answered. "Then she'll think she can get her way with me any time. And that won't do. If she flies off the handle like this, how can I teach her anything?"

"But it's the only way to quiet her: give her what she wants!"

"No," Annie replied, still struggling with Helen. "There's another way: obedience."

"But Miss Annie, Helen doesn't know anything about obedience. How could we ever teach her to mind?"

"I've got two jobs then," said Annie. "First to gentle her, and then we'll get on with the words."

Helen and Annie struggled on, neither giving an inch. Finally Helen went limp in Annie's arms.

"So," Annie thought, "you give up!"

No such thing! As soon as Annie relaxed her hold, Helen wrenched free and raced from the room. Annie looked after her ruefully. "Well! I wonder who won that one," she thought. "Maybe I went too fast for her. I'll have to be firm, but not too firm. I'll have to move more gradually. Yes — it's as simple as that."

But there was nothing simple about Helen — a fact that Annie was forced to appreciate fully in the next few days.

"Heavens!" she thought after another tussle, "What was I expecting?" And then she began to chuckle. For she knew what she'd been expecting. Another Laura Bridgman, that's what — sweet, pale, and pathetically grateful for deliverance from the silent darkness of her life. Instead here was Helen, this wild thing who fought her at every turn.

"She's badly spoiled," Annie thought. Which was certainly true. Out of their pity, the family had indulged Helen's every whim for five years. Now she was a little tyrant, ruling through her rages.

But there was another reason for the tantrums she continued to throw with Annie: fear. Helen came quickly to fear the stranger. For she soon sensed that Annie was chipping away at the only way of living she had known in her five years. Maybe it wasn't much, that no-world of hers, but it was all she had. And no one could reach in to her to explain that a fuller life was waiting for her now.

So Helen fought for her dark, silent, empty, little life. She fought hard, and without rules. She fought by hiding. She fought by screaming and raging. She fought with her fists. But Helen's favorite way of fighting was with her animal-sharp wits. In her own primitive way, Helen was very cunning.

One day Mrs. Keller handed the child a bundle of towels, indicating through signs that these were to be taken to the stranger. Helen trotted off obediently. Halfway there, she stopped. She laid down her bundle and crept the rest of the way down the hall to Annie's door.

The stranger was in that room. She knew it. Now Helen's hand fingered the door until it came to the keyhole. Ah! The key was in the lock.

Quickly, Helen turned the key, yanked it from the door, and fled with it down the hall. She stopped only for a split second to shove the key under a heavy bureau; then she was gone.

Annie heard the telltale sound. She was over to the door in a flash. Too late. The stout old door was locked. Annie hollered. Kate Keller and the cook, Viney, came running.

"What's happened, Miss Annie?" Kate called out.

"She's locked me in!"

Neither woman standing in the hall outside bothered to ask who. They knew.

"It just doesn't seem she could have done it, with that innocent little face of hers," Viney commented.

"Well, she did," Annie returned dryly from the other side of the door. "What that child needs is a good spanking. Isn't there another key for the door?"

But there wasn't. Captain Keller had to be sent for, and when he arrived he was not amused.

"We pay her twenty-five dollars a month. You'd think she'd have the sense not to get locked in her room!"

"Yes, Arthur," Mrs. Keller took care to agree. "But meanwhile what do we do? Her room's on the third floor!"

Captain Keller got a ladder from the barn and clambered up to Annie's window. He scooped her into his arms and carried her safely to the ground.

Annie was burning with embarrassment and fury. Here she was, a grown woman, being carried down the side of the house like a bale of cotton! The yard was now crowded with grinning house servants and field hands. It was too much.

Indeed the whole incident was funny, though it would be some time before Annie saw it that way. Even Captain Keller presently began to see the humor in Annie's recent plight. With a chuckle he asked, "Well, what do you think of our Helen now, Miss Annie?"

"I'll tell you one thing I'll never worry about again," Annie replied tartly.

"What's that?"

"Her brain, Captain Keller. When I first came here, I was worried that Helen's illness might have caused some damage to her brain cells. But she's fully equipped. Yes indeed, she's smart enough for ten children — if you like them tricky!"

And with that Annie turned on her heel and fled into the house.

And so the conflict of wills deepened. Sometimes it was funny. More often it was trying. But Annie remained reasonably full of hope. "Just a little more time. I'm sure she'll respond," she would tell herself.

Then came the battle of all battles. The one that couldn't be ignored or laughed away.

It began at the breakfast table. Helen had terrible table manners. She knew full well how to use a knife, fork, and

Helen reading, age 8

spoon, but she refused to do so. She preferred to use her hands. And not only in her own plate.

Although she would begin each meal in her own place, soon she would slip out of it and begin to roam about the table. Annie watched with fascination as Helen's wriggling nose sorted out the different smells of a meal. She watched with growing horror as Helen's grubby hands dipped and smeared across other people's plates, taking what she wanted, ruining the rest. Yet as long as Helen stayed away from her, Annie said nothing.

Then came the morning that Helen stopped beside Annie's chair. Her nose informed her that sausage lay on the stranger's plate. Helen adored sausage. But this was the stranger, and she hesitated to come closer.

With a little shake of her head, Helen sniffed her way around the table once again. Her nose informed her that nobody else had any sausage left on his plate. Here she was back at that tantalizing smell again. Back at the stranger's place. Was it worth it? One last sniff, and the balance tipped. Out flashed Helen's hand.

Down came Annie's hand. Helen jerked back in surprise, but she couldn't pull free. She was pinned to the table. Slowly Annie began peeling the little fingers away from her sausage.

"Just what do you think you're doing, Miss Sullivan?" Captain Keller asked.

"I'm taking my sausage back," Annie replied coldly.

"Miss Sullivan, that is an afflicted child," Captain Keller pointed out, as if talking to a simpleton. "We have always made allowances for that."

Annie took a long breath and tried to contain her rising temper. If only the Kellers would stop interfering!

"Captain Keller, I know Helen is desperate and frustrated and handicapped. But she's also terribly spoiled. And that doesn't have to go on!"

Captain Keller half rose out of his chair. "No child of mine is going to be deprived of her food in my house!" He was furious.

So was Annie. "And no child in my care is going to help herself to food from my plate!" she shot back.

James choked back a laugh, and gazed at Annie with a new appreciation in his eyes.

"Do you have something to say, James?" Captain Keller asked ominously.

"Nothing, sir," the young man answered hastily.

"Now, to make myself completely clear, Miss Sullivan," Captain Keller went on. "I will repeat once more: as long as I am at the table, Helen will not be interfered with."

"Then perhaps it would be easier if you all left the room," Annie snapped.

That did it. "Miss Sullivan, I am sorry to tell you . . ." But before he could finish his threatening sentence, Kate Keller had thrown down her napkin and was at his side, urgently whispering in his ear.

"Come, dear. You promised that Miss Sullivan could have a free hand with Helen. You know you did. I understand what she's doing. Truly I do."

Annie winced at her next words. "It's not as cruel as it looks. Really it isn't. It's for Helen's good. Come, let's do as she asks. Let's go outside onto the porch. I'll explain it all. Come, dear. Come, James." Gently Kate Keller ushered the family out.

So they were alone, phantom and the stranger — just the two of them.

Annie got up and locked the dining-room door. Pocketing the key, she side-stepped Helen, who was rolling and raging on the floor, and returned to her seat.

"This is going to choke me!" thought Annie, as she picked

up her fork. But she wanted to impress on Helen that life would go on as usual, tantrum or no tantrum. So now she began to chew slowly on her cold breakfast.

That next half-hour dragged for both of them. Annie went through the motions of eating. Helen continued to pound away on the floor. Finally she got bored. Where was everybody? Why were they ignoring her? Curiosity slowly got the better of rage, and as suddenly as it had begun, the tantrum stopped.

Now Helen picked herself up and wandered over to see what the stranger was doing. So the stranger was eating, was she? One hand patted Annie's arm, as the other hand crept out toward her plate. Annie pushed the hand away. But Helen was hungry and determined. Her hand came forward again — this time with more speed. And again Annie pushed it away — this time a little more roughly than before.

Now Helen exploded into a small rage. She pinched Annie cruelly on the arm. Without a moment's hesitation, Annie slapped Helen's hand as hard as she could.

Helen jerked back. That had hurt! But it was something she could understand. She reached forward and pinched Annie again. And Annie slapped back. Pinch, slap — pinch, slap. Each time Helen pinched, a stinging slap would come sailing out of the dark.

Suddenly Helen veered off and made a quick tour of the table. All the seats were empty! She dashed across the room. She yanked at the door, but it wouldn't open. Her fingers sought the key, but the keyhole was empty and the door was locked. For the first time she seemed to realize that she was alone with the stranger. Locked in with her enemy, and all the understanding arms gone!

"Oh, Helen, I won't hurt you," Annie murmured, as she watched Helen flatten herself against the door. With strange animal movements, the child began to inch around the walls, keeping as much distance as she could between herself and the stranger.

Annie sighed and rested her head in her hands. Perhaps she'd better unlock the door . . . perhaps it was too much to expect. But no! "I'll see this through, no matter what," Annie decided, and she picked up her fork again.

As time passed, Helen got hungrier and hungrier. The stranger was still at the table. Dare she go close? More time passed, and the hunger grew stronger. Finally, making sure not to touch the stranger on the way, Helen returned to her seat and began to eat her oatmeal — with her fingers.

"Oh no!" Annie sighed. "I thought we'd won. You know what you're doing, Helen. I know you do. You're just defying me again. And I can't let you get away with it. Not this time." So Annie got up and handed Helen her spoon.

Helen held the spoon for a moment. Then she flung it to the floor. Forcing Helen out of her chair and down to the floor, Annie made her pick up the spoon. And then she plunked Helen back into her seat. She held her hand, and with steely strength forced the child to scoop up some cereal and carry it into her mouth.

One bite. Then two. Good. Annie began to relax her hold. But too soon. For in that instant Helen took aim and hurled the spoon at Annie.

Annie ducked. The spoon clattered to the floor. And the whole process began again. Helen screamed and kicked. Annie held on firmly, and just as firmly she forced Helen through the motions of polite eating. This time, when Annie finally relaxed her hold, Helen kept right on eating. How hungry she was. And oh so tired! She finished her breakfast without further battle.

"It's almost over, it's almost over!" Annie sang to herself, as she watched the food disappear. But not quite. For as soon as

Helen scraped the last of the food from her plate, she yanked the napkin off her neck and threw it to the floor.

"My, you do like to throw things, don't you?" Annie whispered. "Well, throw away. You're stubborn, but I'm just as stubborn. You're strong, but I'm a little stronger — thank God! You hate it now, but that little edge of strength will save us. So I can't let you go just yet. I can't let you leave before you fold that napkin. Come on . . ."

And so they fought one more battle that morning — over a properly folded napkin. It lasted another full hour. Helen fought like one possessed, and so did Annie. At last it was over. A tiny shiver shook Helen's body, and she went limp.

Now her fingers followed Annie's promptings — fold, fold again, and fold once more. There. A properly folded napkin. With a sigh, Helen sank back in her chair. It was all over.

"And so is the morning," Annie realized with dismay, as she unlocked the door and led Helen out into the garden. "We spent the whole morning in that dining room!" For the sun was overhead, and Annie could hear the sounds of lunch being prepared in the back kitchen.

"But not for me," she breathed. "I may never be able to eat again." She looked down at Helen sitting listlessly on a bench. "And I bet poor Helen won't either."

Annie left Helen in the garden and walked back toward the house. Wearily, she climbed the steps to her room. With a great sigh of relief, she loosened her skirts and flopped down across the bed. For a few seconds everything was quiet. Then the tears came pouring out.

Kate Keller was sitting on the vine-shaded side porch, with a basketful of socks. But it was hard to concentrate on darning. Her thoughts were too troubling.

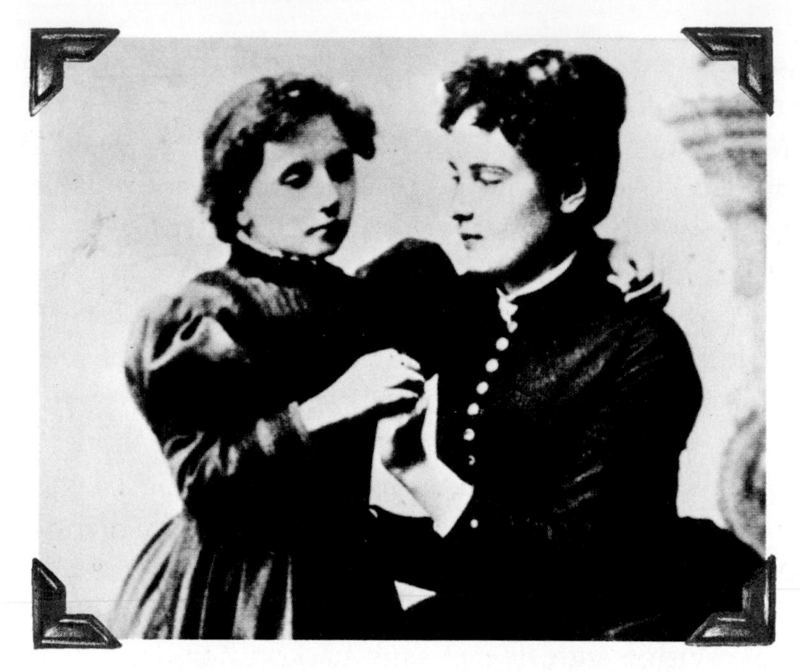

Helen and Annie "talking," 1890

She had been severely shaken by the wild sounds coming through the dining-room door all morning. Had she been wrong about Annie Sullivan? Was she simply allowing poor Helen to be senselessly tortured?

That's what Arthur had said. The sounds in there had driven him straight out of the house. He hadn't returned yet, but she knew what he'd say when he did: "Send her packing!"

And yet . . . James took just the opposite tack. Strange, too, since in the beginning he had been so skeptical of the new teacher. Now he was saying that this was the best thing that had ever happened to Helen . . . that it would be the saving of her — if the family allowed it.

What did *she* think?

"I don't know," Kate thought in despair, as she pricked her finger with the darning needle for what seemed like the hundredth time that afternoon. Just as she put the basket aside, Annie appeared at the door.

"May I come out, Miss Kate? I've been looking for you everywhere."

"Yes, do," Kate replied. "I've been wanting to talk to you too."

Annie was too impatient to listen. The words poured out. "Miss Kate, I've been upstairs in my room for hours, thinking. There's no other way. I tried and tried to think of another — but there isn't one. I've got to take Helen away from here. Now. I've got to separate her from the family, or I'm going to fail."

"What are you saying?" gasped Helen's mother.

Annie struggled frantically to find the right words — soft words — for what she had to say. Finally she used the only words there were. Words of truth.

"Miss Kate, before I came here I studied Laura Bridgman's records. I felt ready to teach Helen to communicate. When I got here, I soon realized that teaching Helen could only come second. She's completely wild! And that's my first job: to tame that wildness — the wildness nobody else has controlled in five years!"

Kate's lips began to move, to protest. But Annie hastened on.

"I know you did it out of pity. That's why you gave in at every turn. But Miss Kate — I'm sorry — it was a mistake. Those five years of pity have made her into a little tin god. She will or she won't, and that's the end of it. Please try to understand. That willfullness of hers is a kind of not listening. And I've got to have her listening to me, or how can I teach her anything?

"A few more sessions like this morning's, and one of two things is bound to happen. Either she'll go completely wild, like some maverick animal, and never let me near her again, or she'll learn to mind . . . Oh, yes. But the wrong way — not through understanding and warmth, but because I've broken her will. Why then she'll be of no more value to herself than one of Captain Keller's horses!"

Kate winced. "But what can we do?" she cried out. "You make it sound as if there's so little hope!"

"Oh yes, there is hope — some." Annie spoke softly now, persuasively. "But not if we stay here. If we stay here, she'll just keep on turning to you and fighting me. Soon she'll start hating me. Then it'll be all over. I'll have to pack up and go home.

"But if I can get her away somewhere, where we're alone. Just for a little while, Miss Kate. Just till I make some kind of calm contact with her. Just till she learns to depend on me. Please . . ." Annie leaned forward in her chair, frankly begging now.

Mrs. Keller looked dubious.

"It's our only hope, Miss Kate."

Finally Kate nodded. "All right." Then she added grimly, "Captain Keller won't like this. He'll hate it, in fact. But I'll talk him around."

"Thank you, Miss Kate! You'll see, it will be all right." Annie's spirits soared. "Where can we go?"

"Well . . . there's a little garden house near here. That might do. It has one room, but it's quite lovely."

"It sounds perfect! That's all we need, Helen and I — one room to be together."

As Kate had said, Captain Keller wasn't happy about the idea. He'd come home, in fact, raring to fire the Yankee snippet. Now this!

Kate kept repeating Annie's words: "It's our only hope. It's our only hope." She reminded him that there was only one other place for Helen to go . . . Surely the garden house was not as bad as that. At last, reluctantly, Captain Keller agreed.

"But only for two weeks! Do you hear me, Kate? Two weeks — that's all the time I'll give her. And we've got to be able to see Helen every day."

"Two weeks! Not long enough," Annie thought. But she wouldn't dwell on it. Two weeks would have to do. Captain Keller had been firm about that.

Annie was equally firm. The Kellers could see Helen every day, but the child must never know they were near. They could watch her to their hearts' content through the window of the garden house, but they could come no closer.

The next day the experiment began. At first it seemed that nothing would be accomplished. Helen fought Annie at every turn, to the point of exhaustion. Then she huddled for a while, gaining strength for another bout. After three or four days the pattern began to change. The tantrums were still violent, but they became fewer and fewer. Helen's attention span was lengthening, too. She was learning to mimic more and more words each day. One day there were no temper squalls at all. And then there came the moment when Annie reached out to touch Helen, and Helen didn't shrink away. The experiment was beginning to work!

Captain Keller saw this too. One morning he stood outside the window, watching his daughter string beads onto a length of thread. First a big rough one, then two small smooth ones, then one with three sharp corners. Over and over Helen repeated the pattern. Her interest never flagged. Her fingers never made a mistake.

"How quiet she is," Captain Keller murmured. Had he been wrong all the while about this Yankee girl? Did she really know what she was doing?

The little savage had learned to obey. It was a great step forward. But Annie was only half satisfied. All her attention

The Kellers' garden house

now focused on the second goal: to reunite Helen with the world outside.

Hour after hour, Annie sat beside Helen and spelled words into her hand. Hour after hour Helen traced the shapes back into Annie's waiting palm. How Helen concentrated! She could spell back twenty-one words — eighteen nouns and three verbs: doll, mug, pin, key, dog, hat, cup, box, water, milk, candy, eye, finger, toe, head, cake, baby, mother, sit, stand, walk. But though she learned the words faster and faster, she still did not understand that they had meaning.

"Hurry up, Helen. Hurry!" Annie begged over and over. For the two weeks' time in the garden house was running out. How much she wished to lead a different Helen out of here — a Helen who grasped the meaning of words.

The last afternoon came too soon. "Miss Annie . . ." Captain Keller came walking into the room. "It's time to go home. If we hurry, we'll be in good time for supper."

Helen had been playing across the room by the fireplace. Suddenly she felt the strange vibrations. She raised her head and sniffed the air. That was her father's smell! With a cry of joy, she flung herself across the room and into his arms.

Father and daughter hugged each other hard. Then Helen raised her head and began to sniff again. Another smell? She recognized this one, too. Her father had brought his hunting dog with him. Helen felt her way around the room until her hand met up with the furry coat of her old friend, Belle.

Annie turned toward Captain Keller again. "Just give us a few more days, sir," she begged. "You can see how happy she is. And oh, she's learning so fast. You wouldn't believe it. Just a few more days of concentration, and I'm sure a breakthrough will come."

"Well . . ." Captain Keller wavered.

"He's going to agree!" Annie thought jubilantly.

Just then Captain Keller asked in a puzzled voice, "What's she doing now, Miss Annie?"

Helen was sitting cross-legged on the floor, holding one of Belle's paws in her hand. With her other hand she was pushing the dog's claws back and forth. Then she dropped Belle's paw and began to shape some letters with her hand.

Annie began to laugh. "Why, she's trying to teach Belle how to spell."

They shared a laugh. Then Captain Keller grew sober. "It's all well and good," he said heavily. "But we know dogs can't learn English. Can Helen?" And he made them pack up and come back to the house.

One morning soon after their return to the big house, Helen and Annie were sitting side by side on the bedroom floor. Annie had Helen's hand imprisoned in hers — spelling, spelling, spelling more shapes into it.

M-U-G she spelled. Then she guided Helen's hand over her own breakfast mug. M-U-G. Helen shaped back obediently. M-U-G . . . M-U-G. But her heart wasn't in it. Not today. This weary game of shapes was fast losing interest for her.

The smells of spring were pouring in through the open window. She tugged at Annie's sleeve. Clearly she was asking to go outside.

"Not yet, Helen," Annie spelled. "Just a few more minutes. Then the lesson'll be over and we can go outside."

Helen felt the strange shapes of Annie's speech being formed in her palm. But she still didn't know that the shapes were words, that they held meaning. It was this that was building up her frustration now. For there was a dim awareness inside of her: the stranger wanted something from her — something she simply didn't know how to give. And besides, those smells! The outdoors was calling too strongly. Helen jerked again at Annie's arm. Much harder this time.

"Oh, no!" Annie exclaimed, as she saw the telltale signs of rising temper. "I'm simply not equipped to handle it this early in the morning! Come on!"

Annie led Helen outside. As soon as Helen felt the sun on her face, she began to skip and dance. She was getting her own way! The lesson must be over!

The two of them rambled through the middle of the garden, Annie letting Helen stop whenever she wanted to smell the flowers or roll in the grass. It seemed for all the world as if they were out for a casual stroll. But stubborn Annie still intended to salvage something from the morning.

She led Helen down to the old well house that stood at the foot of the garden. Helen loved to play in its cool dampness, so now she scurried cheerfully inside. Annie took a deep breath and followed.

She began to bang the pump handle up and down, and soon a stream of water poured from its lip. She grabbed Helen's hand and stuck it under the icy flow, and in the same instant began to spell W-A-T-E-R into the wet palm.

Helen went rigid and pulled wildly toward freedom. But Annie held on. W-A-T-E-R . . . W-A-T-E-R . . . W-A-T-E-R — she drummed the word faster and faster into Helen's hand.

Suddenly Helen stopped struggling. Or breathing. Or doing anything except concentrating on the shapes in her palm. W-A-T-E-R . . . she felt the word burn down through her hand and into her brain. W-A-T-E-R . . . a light flooded across her face.

W-A-T . . . she began to spell the word back to Annie. And with each movement of her own fingers, the namelessness retreated. She understood! These movements stood for the cold liquid that was pouring over her hand! They *always* stood for that, and nothing else! She understood!

Life came rushing in on Helen. Now she dropped to the ground and struck it with her fist. Laughing, crying, Annie knelt down and hugged her. But Helen had no time for this! She pushed Annie back, and again struck the ground. "Name it!" she was demanding. And Annie did.

Helen paused for a moment to absorb the shapes. Then she wheeled round and hit the pump. P-U-M-P . . . Annie fluttered off on her fingers. Helen stood on one leg, concentrating on this, her third word in as many minutes. With a short nod she added it to her growing pile. Then, with ever-increasing speed, she whirled around and around the well house, demanding the names of everything she touched.

After six or seven more words, she stopped. She cocked her head, and it was clear to Annie that she was puzzled. There was something she wanted to know. Helen frowned as if she were heading into another rage. But she wasn't. It was the effort of shaping thought without words. Now she took her fist and banged herself across the top of the head.

Annie burst out laughing. "So that's it!" she exclaimed. "Come, rascal, give me your hand."

H-E-L-E-N, she spelled slowly into it.

It didn't seem possible, but the light grew brighter in Helen's eyes. She stood very still for a moment, with her face raised toward Annie. She had a name.

Now she took Annie's hand and very gently patted her on the arm. Annie thought she was saying "Thank you." But Helen wanted something more. She patted Annie's arm again.

"Oh," said Annie, as she knelt beside Helen and spelled T-E-A-C-H-E-R into her hand. Now the two of them had names.

So it happened that a few minutes later two entirely new people walked out of the well house. Teacher had come to take the stranger's place. Phantom was gone too; instead there was Helen.

Full of the joy of understanding, Helen continued to reach out for Teacher, begging for new words. Before bedtime that evening, Helen had learned to spell more than thirty words. More words in one day than she'd learned in all the five weeks since Annie had come — and she knew their meanings too!

Now her fingers were trembling with exhaustion. She fumbled the shapes, and her eyelids drooped. "Enough's enough," Annie thought, as she tucked her in the bed they now shared.

Helen settled down happily, but Annie had to laugh as she watched her hands. "There'll be time for that tomorrow, Helen!" she murmured. "There'll be a lot of tomorrows now." And she reached down to quiet the fingers which were still moving against the sheets.

Annie stood beside the bed, realizing for the first time that day just how tired she was. Quickly she slid into her

the water pump

nightgown and climbed in beside Helen. No face washing or teeth scrubbing tonight.

"Ah, the end of a wonderful day," she thought, and wriggled her toes against the cool sheets.

But the day wasn't quite over. For Helen was still awake, and now she came stealing over to Annie's side of the bed. After dropping a damp kiss onto Annie's cheek, she snuggled down in the crook of her arm and fell asleep.

Annie lay there, holding the sleeping child. Then she bent down and kissed Helen back.

Author

Born and raised in New York City, Margaret Davidson says that her love of reading as a child is the reason she writes today. Ms. Davidson has authored numerous biographies for children, including books about Thomas Edison, Louis Braille and Eleanor Roosevelt. For her book *Helen Keller's Teacher,* from which this selection is excerpted, Margaret Davidson received the Junior Book Award from the Boys' Clubs of America.

An excerpt from

Mister Stormalong

by Anne Malcolmson and Dell J. McCormick

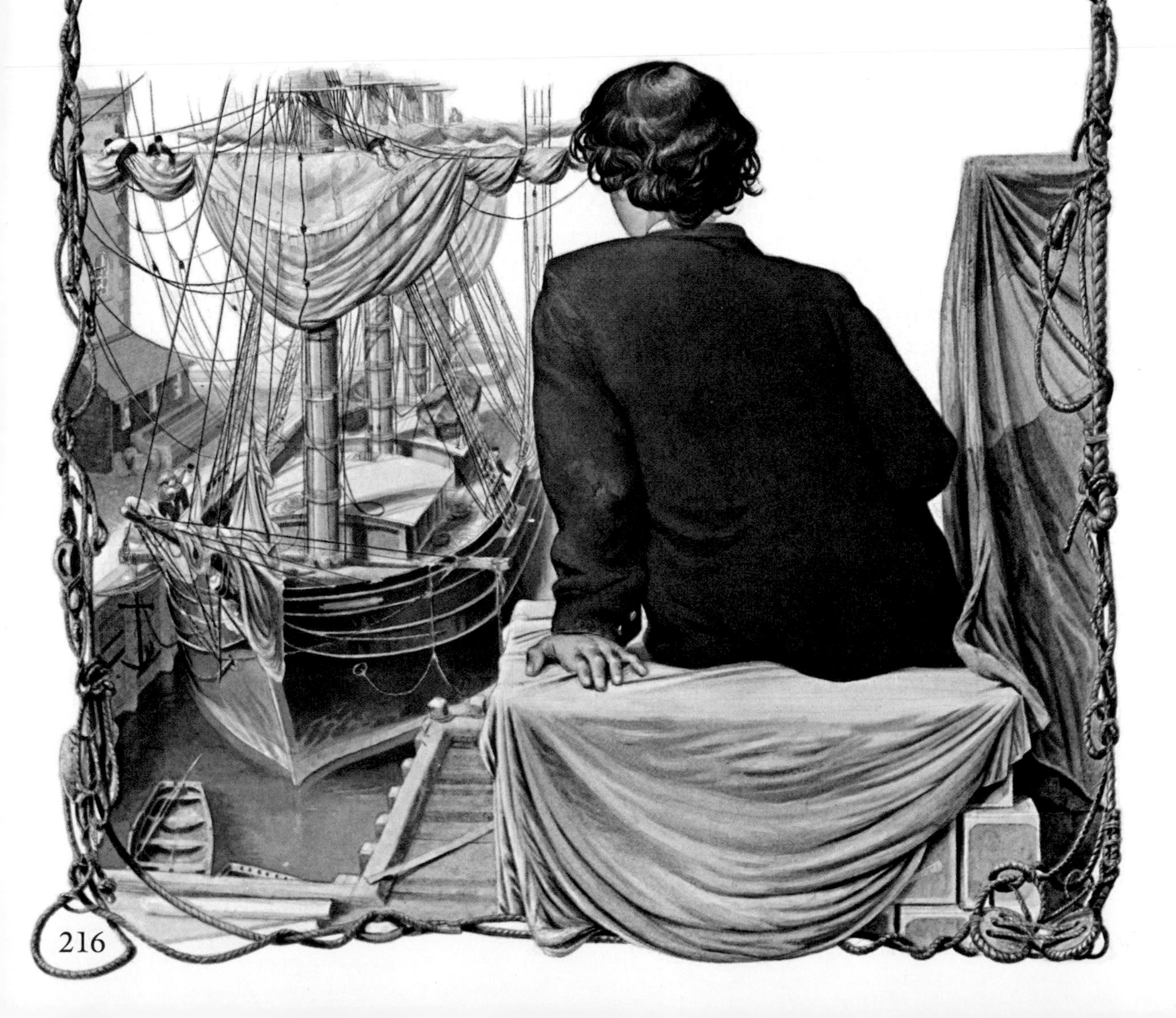

Captain Snard looked up at the Blue Peter, the flag which proclaimed to the whole of Boston Harbor that his ship, the *Silver Maid,* was ready to leave for China. Her hold was filled with hides, beaver skins, and good English coal. But everything was going wrong! The cabin boy was at home, sick with the measles. The shrouds and rigging lines were hopelessly tangled. The anchor was stuck. Captain Snard paced the afterdeck, fidgeting and looking at his watch.

His men tiptoed about their duties and whispered among themselves. They knew enough not to cross the Captain when he was in a temper. But they, too, knew that it was time to leave. The tide was running out. Still, the Mate had not returned from town with a new cabin boy. The lads in the rigging were getting nowhere. And, strain as they might, the hands at the capstan could not budge the anchor chain.

Suddenly from the dock the Mate's voice was heard, as he ran to the ship. "Captain! Captain Snard!"

The Captain leaned over the rail. "Have you got a cabin boy?" he shouted.

"No!" hollered the Mate. "There's not an experienced cabin boy to be had in Boston, sir."

"Then come aboard," roared the Captain. "From here to Canton *you'll* be my cabin boy!"

Neither the Mate nor the Captain had noticed a group of schoolboys sitting on the piles of the wharf beside the ship. Every Sunday the lads gathered on the docks to watch the ships sail, and to dream of the time when they, too, would be sailing. Among them was a youngster who had heard the Mate's call and the Captain's answer. This was his chance! He had always wanted to go to sea. The *Silver Maid* needed a cabin boy! With a light leap he cleared the wharf and landed on the starboard deck, right under the Captain's nose.

The vessel gave a lurch. Its topmast crosstrees brushed the roof of the warehouse on the pier. The *Silver Maid* listed dangerously to starboard.

"What is the meaning of this?" bellowed the Captain, who had had enough to irritate him already.

"Excuse me, sir," said the schoolboy, "I hear you need a cabin boy."

The Captain clung to the wheel to keep from slipping into the arms of the youngster who had jumped aboard. The latter was large for his age. He stood five fathoms, or about thirty feet tall; to judge from his appearance, he weighed several tons. No wonder the *Silver Maid* was listing!

"If you don't shift your weight more to the port side, I'll need a salvage crew more than a cabin boy!" roared Captain Snard.

Stormy, the little fellow who was causing the trouble, blushed with embarrassment. "I'm sorry, sir," he stammered, and carefully placed one foot beside the port rail. The ship creaked and righted itself.

"Well!" said the Captain, wiping his brow and looking up at the lad. "What makes you think you can be a cabin boy?"

Tears came to the young boy's eyes. "The sea is in my blood, sir," he said simply. "All my life I've wanted to join the China trade."

"And how long is that?" The Captain meant to snap out his question, but the words came weakly.

"Thirteen years, sir," answered the little fellow politely.

"You're large for thirteen years," conceded the Captain, relaxing a bit. "Have you had any previous experience?"

"Oh, some, sir," Stormy replied, and proceeded to tell his story. The words tumbled out of his mouth as he spoke. His recital was full of gushes and pauses and "I-mean-sirs" and "You-see-sirs", which were perfectly natural in a boy of his age at an exciting moment.

Alfred Bulltop Stormalong, aged thirteen, was born in Kennebunkport, Maine, of a long line of seafarers. His mother's great-great-great-great-great-great-great-great-great-great-grandfather was the naval architect who designed Noah's Ark. His father's grand-grand-grand-grand-grand-granduncle sailed with Odysseus from Troy to the lands beyond the Cimmerian Seas. One of his ancestors, Leif Ericson the Viking, was credited with the discovery of America long before Columbus, who, incidentally, was related to the family through a cousin on his mother's side. Stormy's own father had been the first Yankee skipper, whom Captain Snard himself had known, more by reputation than personally.

Stormy really did have the sea in his blood. His veins and arteries were filled with salt water, which shone out in the bright sea blue of his eyes. He had cut his teeth on whalebone, and, in the days when he was too young to walk, he had been cradled in a dory. On one occasion he gave his mother fits when he tied his diaper to his teething rattle, used it for a trysail, and headed out to sea while she was preparing a formula of clam chowder for his evening bottle. At the age of five he could handle any sailing vessel in the Kennebunk estuary.

It was not until he started school, however, that he truly learned to love the sea. Because of a shortage of primers, his teacher taught him to read from Bowditch's *Practical Navigator*. That set the course for his whole future life. Kennebunkport was a small town, and there were very few boys of his own age to play with. Stormy soon fell into the habit of swimming down to Gloucester or Provincetown, or sometimes Nantucket, after school to play. His mother knew he was perfectly safe and could handle himself in any sort of a squall. Her only objection was that the long swim increased his normally large appetite.

She did become angry, however, the fourth time he tried to stow away on a whaler at the age of eleven. Fortunately, from her point of view, Stormy was so large for his age (he had already reached a height of three and a half fathoms) that he was unable to hide himself successfully in a lifeboat. He was discovered before the whaler put to sea. As she told her friends later, she was cross because she worried that her son might be mistaken for a whale and cut up for oil and ambergris.

When the family moved to Boston, his mother knew that Stormy's days at home were numbered. She gave him her blessing, along with a note which he dutifully showed to Captain Snard, explaining that her son, Alfred Bulltop Stormalong, had her permission to join the crew of any vessel which would give him a berth.

The Captain was the father of seven daughters. Before Stormy had finished his tale, he had taken the boy to his heart. The Captain, however, had to maintain discipline aboard his ship. He could not take on a new hand for whimsical reasons. The crew had gathered in a circle to hear the amazing tale of the young stranger. Therefore, Captain Snard felt forced to put the boy through a series of tests.

"Your background is fitting for a life on the sea, my lad," he said. "But I'll have to ask you a few questions to test your seamanship. What are the Horse Latitudes?"

Stormy's eyes shone at the chance to prove himself. "A belt of calms, sir, to be found thirty degrees north latitude, and another thirty degrees south."

"What is the difference between a barque and a brigantine?"

"That is quite simple, sir," replied Stormy. "A barque is a three-masted vessel, with foremast and mainmast square-rigged, and mizzenmast fore-and-aft-rigged. A brigantine is a two-masted, square-rigged vessel which does not carry a square mainsail."

"Fair enough," said the Captain. "Now, can you recite the sails of the mainmast of the *Silver Maid,* from the bottom to the top . . . and with your eyes closed, of course!"

Stormy covered his eyes with his hands. "Main course, main lower topsail, main upper topsail, main lower topgallant, main upper topgallant, main royal, main . . . main . . . main . . ." Stormy paused and a wrinkle appeared in his forehead. He seemed to be stuck. A snicker ran through the crew. The Captain held his breath. Then Stormy's forehead cleared; he grinned from ear to ear. "Main skysail, sir! Of course, I knew it all the time!"

"Good boy," sighed the Captain, relieved that Stormy had passed the test. He stroked his chin for a moment. Then he held up a length of line for the little giant. "Show me what you can do with a piece of rope."

Stormy took the line between his fingertips, like a lady knotting a silken thread for her tapestry. He rubbed his thumb and ring finger together. Without further ado he held out his handiwork for the Captain to see. In the ten-foot length of cordage, Stormy had tied three perfect knots — a Bowline with a Bight, a Studding-sail Halyard Bend, and an Englishman's Tie!

"This is all very fine," agreed the Captain, trying not to show his enthusiasm for the boy. "However, theoretical knowledge is not enough at sea. You look to me as though you might be pretty clumsy. Do you think you can climb the rigging?"

"Aye, aye, sir!" Stormy was out of his jacket and halfway up the mainmast before the Captain could close his mouth. Up, up, up he went, hand over hand, until he was perched dangerously on the topmast crosstrees. His curly black hair, blown by the wind, fluttered out from the skysail yard like a shiny dark pennant. "Captain, oh, Captain, sir," he called down from his perch aloft. "It looks to me as though the lines

are tangled. With your permission, sir, I'll straighten them out."

Captain Snard picked up his megaphone and shouted. "Be smart about it, son! And see that you don't make things worse!"

"Aye, aye, sir!" came the reply. From the deck the Captain and his crew could see the little fellow reaching out to right and left, deftly unwinding the snarl of ropes which formed a spiderweb around him. One by one the lines fell into their proper places. Flushed with excitement, Stormy forgot himself. One last tangle remained at the port reach of the main royal yard. Without thinking, he hitched himself along the yard in order to get a better purchase on the line. Oooooops! Slowly, as his weight shifted, the *Silver Maid* heeled over to port. The gaping members of the crew skidded down the deck to the port rail. The Captain grabbed the binnacle to keep himself upright.

"Ahoy there! None of your tricks! Come down from that rigging before you ruin the ship," shouted the Captain.

Stormy caught himself just in time. He scrambled back to the main mast. The ship righted itself. Phew! said Stormy to himself, That was a close one! Then, since he was an obedient boy, he grabbed a mainstay and zipped to the deck like a fireman down a brass pole.

Unfortunately, just as he started down, Porky the Cook emerged from the galley carrying a kettle of hot shark soup to cool on deck. As luck would have it, Porky and his chowder reached the exact spot at which Stormy landed at exactly the same moment. Cook, kettle, and Stormy disappeared behind a great splash of soup. The scalding, greasy liquid splattered the ship in all directions, ran over the decks and down the companionways and hatches. The crew, who had spent the morning polishing the deck and the brasses, roared in dismay.

Porky was speechless with surprise and anger. Only Captain Snard, who was protected from the splash by the large wooden circle of the wheel, thought it was funny.

"That was a hot one!" he exclaimed to no one in particular. Then, struck by the wittiness of his own pun, he slapped his knee and felt very pleased with himself.

Stormy, of course, expected to be ordered off the ship. The Captain, however, looked at him with indulgent affection as the lad apologized. "Boys will be boys!" was all he said. For no particular reason, the Captain suddenly pictured his seven little daughters at home, properly working their samplers and learning their manners. What we need aboard this ship, he thought to himself, is a little liveliness.

The Captain would have hired Stormy then and there. The crew, however, were still angry about the soup. One further test was necessary to make them accept a new hand. Sailors need knowledge and agility, but they also need physical strength. It was obvious, looking at the boy, that he had strength, but it was difficult to know what kind of test would appease the disgruntled crew. The only thing the Captain could think of was the stuck anchor. He had no hope that Stormalong could raise it, but the lad might be able to budge the chain. That at least was worth trying.

"Man the winches, lad," the Captain cried to Stormy.

"Aye, aye, sir!" Stormy answered to the Captain's order. The Captain watched solicitously as the boy pushed and strained against the capstan bar. Slowly, slowly, the heavy iron chain moved a little. There was a rumble as the anchor budged in its bed. Inch by inch, the chain clanked up around the capstan. Little by little, the stone that held the anchor gave way. Without warning, the resistance disappeared. Stormy, with one hand, turned the capstan. The anchor chain coiled up as though it had been woven of daisies.

A cheer went up from the crew. The men ran to the foredeck to watch the little giant wind the capstan. Without thinking, they burst into an old chantey:

"A Yankee ship comes down the river,
Blow, boys, blow!
A Yankee ship and a Yankee skipper,
Blow, my bully boys, blow!

"And how do you know she's a Yankee clipper?
Blow, boys, blow!
Because her mast and yards shine like silver,
Blow, my bully boys, blow!"

The *Silver Maid* strained and snapped her painters as the anchor lifted. Suddenly she was drifting out to sea with the tide.

"Unfurl the main course!" shouted the Bosun.

"Haul down the blue peter," shouted the Captain. "We're off to Canton!" The men cheered as they raced to their posts. The *Silver Maid* put out to sea.

It was too late now for the Captain to dismiss the new cabin boy. He ordered the Mate to bring out the ship's ledger, and told Stormy to write down his name. Stormy, boy that he was, felt very grown-up. He had got the job he wanted and was finally a member of a ship's crew. Therefore he wrote himself down in the most grown-up way he could think of. Stormalong, A. B.!

Captain Snard took one look at the signature. "Stormalong, A. B.," he mused. "There's an able-bodied seaman for you," he commented to the Mate.

That is how Stormy got his first berth in the China trade. Ever since that day sailors in the merchant marine have written themselves down as Able-Bodied Seamen, with the initials *A. B.*

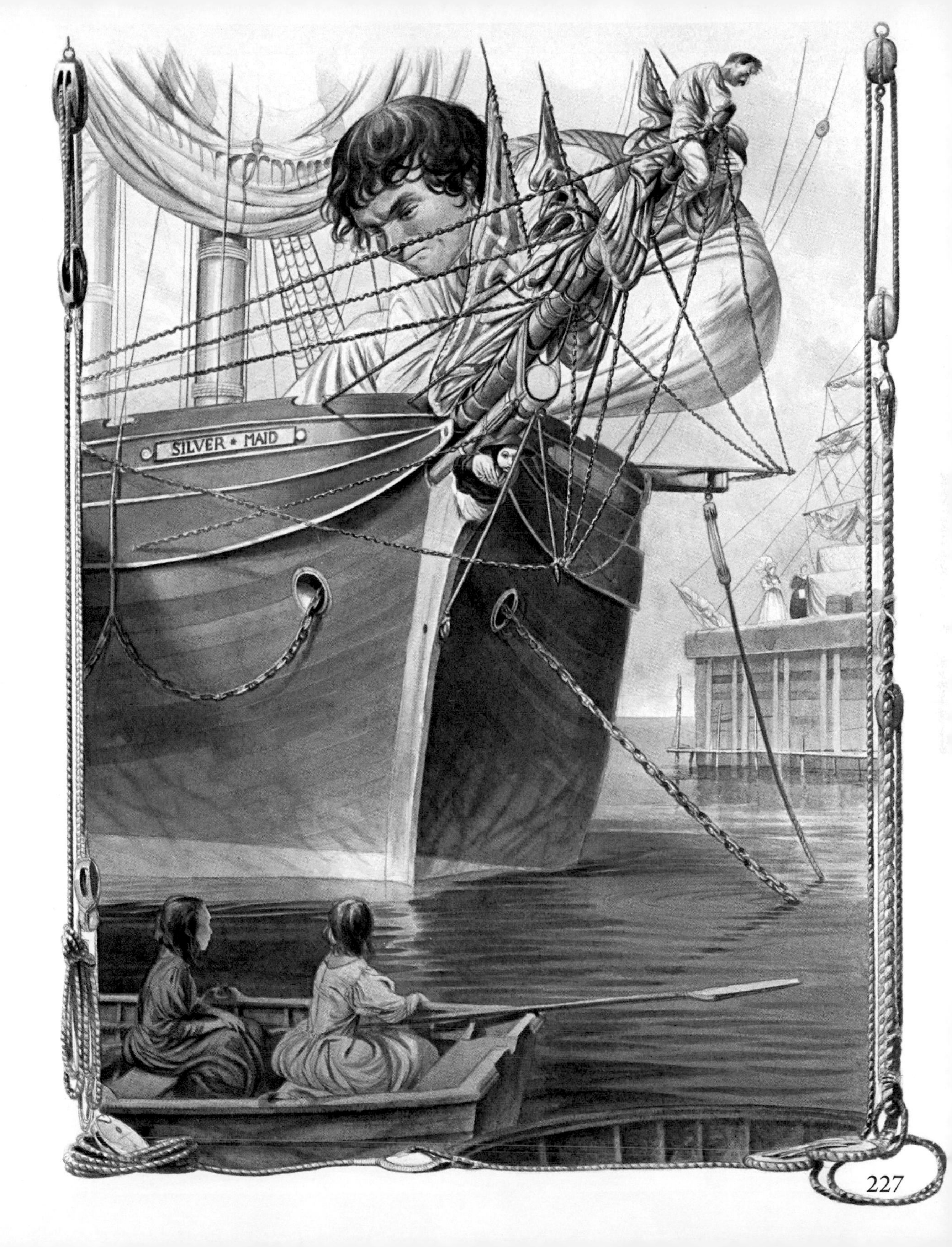
SILVER * MAID

This poem, from the movie-musical The Wizard of Oz, *is spoken by the Cowardly Lion as he prepares to visit the Wizard with Dorothy, the Tin Man, and the Scarecrow. Dressed in a crown and velvet cape, the Lion has just proclaimed himself "King of the Forest." When his friends ask if he understands the meaning of bravery, this is the Lion's reply.*

What makes a king out of a slave?
    Courage!
What makes the flag on the mast wave?
    Courage!
What makes the elephant charge his tusk
In the misty mist, or the dusky dusk?
What makes the muskrat guard his musk?
    Courage!

What makes the Sphinx the seventh wonder?
    Courage!
What makes the dawn come up like thunder?
    Courage!
What makes the Hottentots so hot?
What puts the ape in apricots?
Whadda they got that I ain't got?
    COURAGE!

Houghton Mifflin Literature

In the selections you have just read from *A Display of Courage,* the main characters displayed courage as they found themselves in trying circumstances.

Now you will read a collection of "tall tales" in which you will meet Johnny Appleseed, planter; Paul Bunyan, legendary woodsman of the North Country; and Pecos Bill, the cowboy to beat all cowboys. Unlike the quiet, dignified displays of courage in the stories you have just read, these tales boom and thunder with the daring deeds of their bigger-than-life heroes.

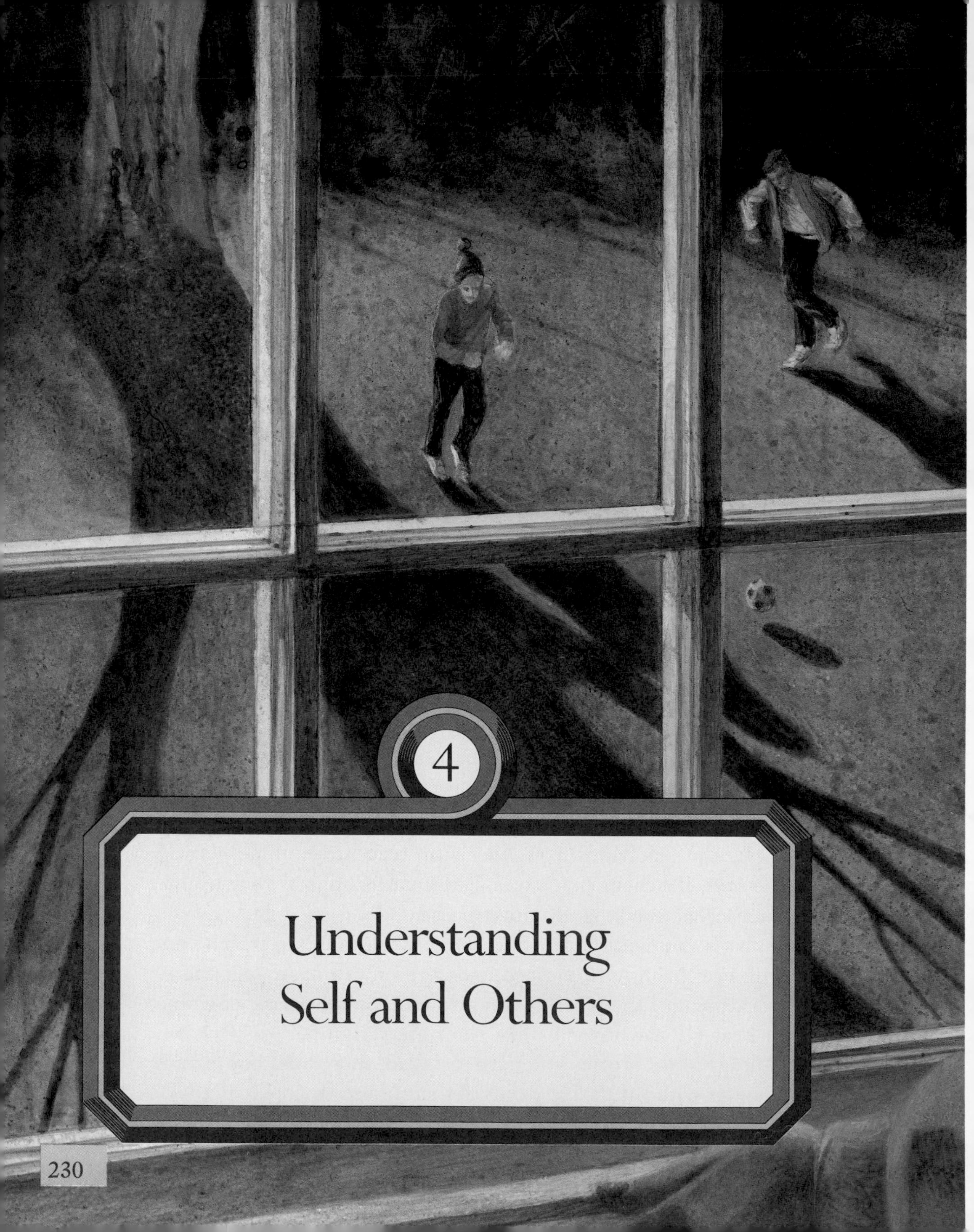

4

Understanding Self and Others

An excerpt from

Philip Hall likes me. I reckon maybe.

by Bette Greene

Eleven-year-old Beth Lambert has a crush on Philip Hall, "the cutest boy in the J. T. Williams school." However, this doesn't prevent her from beating him at catching turkey thieves and from challenging him to a calf-raising contest. These are only two of the warm, funny episodes in Philip Hall likes me. I reckon maybe., *which traces a year in the life of this Arkansas farm girl. During this year, Beth learns to accept things in life that she cannot change. In the excerpt that follows, Beth learns to deal with an unasked-for allergy.*

I never asked for no allergy.

Mr. Barnes stopped the school bus along the side of the highway just at that spot where the dirt road leading to our farm meets the blacktop. First Philip Hall got off. Then I jumped off in front of the faded black-and-white sign at the intersection which read:

> 1 MILE TO LAMBERT FARM
> GOOD TURKEYS GOOD PIGS

As I took a flying leap across the frozen drainage ditch that separated the road from the field, I heard Philip calling me.

"Hey, Beth!" He was still standing on the blacktop just where the bus left him. "You oughtna be going through the field. You might step into an ice puddle."

Of all days to have to stop and start explaining things to Philip Hall. But at any other time I'd be thinking that he wouldn't be fretting about my feet if he didn't really like me.

Now would he? "Frosty feet ain't nothing," I told him. "When you have a spanking new puppy waiting to meet you."

"What if Mr. Grant wouldn't swap a collie dog for one of your pa's turkeys?" asked Philip, grinning as though he hoped it was so.

"That's all you know! When I left the house this morning, my pa was picking out six of our fattest turkeys for swapping." I turned and began running across the field.

"Well, one collie dog is worth more than six of your old turkeys," called Philip.

I kept on running, pretending not to hear. And, anyway, everybody loves to eat turkey. Don't they?

When I reached the rise in the field, I could see our house a nice pale green. It always surprised me a little to see the house painted because until last year the weathered boards had never seen a lick of paint.

That was the year Pa sold mite near three hundred turkeys not even speaking about the forty-two pigs. And that was when Pa asked Ma what it was she wanted most. And she said that all her life she had wanted to live in a painted house. Especially in a house that was painted green.

As I came closer, I could see the chocolate brownness of my mama against the paleness of the porch. She was hanging work-worn overalls across the porch clothesline. Ma used to always be finished with the laundry by this time of day, but she says that carrying a baby inside tends to slow a person down a mite.

I tiptoed up behind her and threw my arms as far as they would go, which was about half the distance around her ever-widening waist.

"Ohhh!" She jumped. "What you mean scaring me clear out of my wits, girl?"

"Where is he?" I asked. "Where's the collie?"

She put on her I'm-not-fixing-to-listen-to-any-nonsense face and said, "I don't know nothing about no collie."

"Did Pa make the swap? Did he?"

"Get out of here, girl. Go on into the kitchen."

"Tell me if Pa got the collie," I pleaded. "Now did he?"

Her mouth was still set into that no-nonsense way of hers, but it was different with her eyes. Her eyes were filled up with pure pleasure. "And I told you," she said, "to get on into the kitchen, didn't I?"

Suddenly I understood. I threw open the screen door and, without waiting to close it gently behind me, ran in a straight line through the living room and into the kitchen.

And then I saw him. There in a cardboard carton next to the cookstove was a reddish-brown puppy with a circle of white fluffy hair ringing his neck and spilling down to his chest. I dropped to my knees and showed my open palms. "Hi, puppy. Beautiful little collie puppy."

"He's beautiful, sure enough," said Ma from behind.

The collie just looked at me for a few moments. Then he got to his feet and trotted over.

"And you're friendly too," I said, patting his back. "Hey, that would be a good name for you."

"Friendly," said Ma, smacking her lips like she was word tasting. "That's a right good name."

I gave Friendly a hug and a kiss. "I will now name you — *ah-choo!*" I tried again. "I will now name — *AHHHH-hhhhh-choo!!*"

Ma shook her head the way she does when she catches me at mischief. "You done gone and got yourself a cold, now, didn't you?"

"AHHHHhhhhhh-ha-ha-ha-choo! I now name you Friendly," I said at last.

By bedtime I was sneezing constantly and water kept pouring from my sore, itchy eyes. But, thank goodness, all my sneezing didn't seem to bother Friendly, who slept peacefully in his cardboard carton at the foot of my bed.

I could hear my folks in the kitchen talking about what they were always talking about these days — names for our soon-to-be-born baby. When they finally tired of that topic, Ma said, "Beth got me worried. All them wheezing sounds coming from her chest."

"I seen Doc Brenner in town this afternoon," said Pa. "He asked me to kill and clean one of our twenty-pound birds. Said he'd stop by this evening to pick it up."

"When he comes by," said Ma, "ask him to kindly take a look at our Beth."

I climbed out of bed to take off my raggedy tail of a nightgown and put on the one that Grandma had given me last Christmas. She had made it out of a sack of Fairy Flake flour, but she dyed it a bright, brilliant orange. It was nice.

Friendly started to bark.

"Don't you be frightened, little Friendly, it's only me, only Beth."

While I patted my new pet, I told him how glad I was that he had come to live with us. "You're going to like it here, you'll see. I'm going to bring all my friends to meet you. Philip Hall, Susan, Bon — *ahh-choo-whoo! Ahh choo!* Bonnie, Ginny, Esther. You're going to like all my friends, Friendly, but you're going to like me best of all . . . I reckon maybe."

Ma called out, "Is you out of bed, Beth?"

I jumped back into bed before answering. "No m'am, I'm right here. Right here in bed."

I kept my eyes open, waiting for the doctor to come, but after a while my eyelids came together. Sleep stood by waiting for me to fall . . . fall asleep . . . sleep . . . sleep.

"Let me take a look at my old friend, Beth," said a big voice.

My cheeks were being patted. "Doctor's here, Beth honey," Ma was saying.

I pulled myself up to sitting and looked into the face of Dr. Brenner, who said, "This won't hurt," as he placed a freezing stethoscope to my chest.

I jumped. "It's cold."

He rubbed the stethoscope warm with his hands. "That doesn't sound much like the Beth Lambert who caught those turkey-thieving Cooks with only a" — Doc Brenner commenced laughing — "with only a . . ." But again his laughing interfered with his talking so I just said, "With only a toy gun," while the doctor laughed all the harder.

After wiping away all the tears that his laughter shook loose, Doctor Bernard M. Brenner became fully professional. "Just breathe naturally," he said as he put the warmed tube back to my chest. He listened quietly without saying a word. Then he took the stethoscope from his ears. "I heard some wheezing sounds coming from your chest. Tell me, how do your eyes feel?"

"They feel like I want to grab them out of their sockets and give them a good scratching. They're so . . . so itchy."

"Uh-hun," answered Dr. Brenner, as though he knew all about itchy eyes. "Beth, can you remember when all this sneezing and wheezing began?"

Across the room, my sister turned over in her bed and let out a groan without once opening her eyes. It was as if Anne was making a complaint that her sleep was being disturbed by inconsiderate folks.

"Yes, sir," I told the doctor. "It all started when I met Friendly."

Friendly must have heard his name called 'cause he jumped out of his carton and jogged floppily on over.

"Hi, little Friendly, little dog." I picked him up and gave him a hug and a kiss. *"AHHHHhh — choo! Ah-choo!"*

"Beth," said Dr. Brenner, running his fingers through his silver hair. "I'm sorry to do this, but I'm going to have to tell you something. Something you're not going to like hearing. I believe you have an allergy to Friendly."

"Oh, no sir, I don't!" I cried. "I don't have one, honest. I never asked for no allergy. Why, I don't even know what that means."

Dr. Brenner took my hand. "It simply means that Friendly's dog hair is making you sick. And, furthermore, it means that he must be returned to wherever he came from."

"But Friendly is *my* dog. He belongs to me. And he's never *never* going to go back to that kennel!" I felt tears filling up my eyes. "I love Friendly; Friendly loves me."

"I know you love one another," agreed Dr. Brenner. "But all this sneezing, wheezing, and red eyes is your body's way of telling you something."

I shook my head no.

Doc Brenner nodded his head yes. "Bodies don't need to say fancy words like allergic rhinitis — or any words at all,

Beth. When your throat is dry, you don't wait to hear the word *water* before taking a drink. And do you really need the school's lunch bell to ring before you know when it's time to eat? Well, now your body is saying something just as important. Listen to it!" he said, cupping his hand around his ear. But the only sound in the room was the hissing noise coming from my own chest.

When the morning sun came flooding through my bedroom window, my eyes opened and I remembered about the allergy. Was it real or only a dream?

"Friendly," I called. "Come here, little Friendly."

But Friendly didn't come and I didn't hear him either. I jumped to the foot of my bed. The cardboard box was empty. They've taken him back to Mr. Grant's kennel!

I was just about to shout out for Friendly when outside the kitchen window I heard Luther's and Anne's voices: "Get that ball, Friendly. Friendly, you going to get that ball?"

Ma laughed. "That dog ain't fixing to do nothing he ain't a mind to do."

I went out the kitchen door still wearing my orange nightgown and sat down on the back steps next to her. She put her arm around me and gave me a quick squeeze. "How you feeling, honey babe?"

I thought about her question. My chest felt as though it was still filled up with old swamp water, while my head carried around last night's headache. Finally, I gave my answer, "I'm okay, Mama. I reckon."

"After you come home from school, I want you to take a little nap. Never mind the chores; just put your head down on the pillow and nap. 'Cause you spent half the night crying into your pillow."

"About what the doctor said . . . about taking Friendly back to the kennel. We're not going to listen to that, are we?"

She looked past me, out to where Luther and Anne were playing with Friendly. "Life don't always be the way we want it to be. Life be the way it is. Nothing we can do."

"You *can't* take him back!" I shouted. "Besides, Mr. Grant's probably eaten up all the turkeys."

"If he did, he did," answered Ma.

"You don't understand," I said, bringing my voice back down to size. "I *need* Friendly! Luther was three and Anne was two when I was born, so they had me; but I never had anything little and soft to — "

"And I told you," she said, "that life be the way it be. Ain't nothing we can do. But if you misses that school bus, there is something I can do. So *get!*"

At school I felt better and worse. Better because I didn't sneeze or wheeze and even my eyes stopped itching and watering. And worse because tonight, after supper, Friendly was going back to Mr. Grant's kennel.

If only I had some magic. One time I remembered my teacher, Miss Johnson, pointing to shelves of books and saying that they held many secrets. Could one of her books hold the secret of making the allergy go and the dog stay?

At recess, she stood on a three-step ladder to bring down a heavy book from the top shelf.

"This book may have the secret we're looking for," she said, pointing to a page. "Right here," she whispered, the way people do when they're telling secrets. "It says that people who have an allergy to long-haired dogs, like the collie, might not have an allergy to a short-haired dog, like the chihuahua."

At the kennel, I held Friendly close to me while Pa explained about the allergy to Mr. Grant.

"We don't breed chihuahuas," said the kennel owner. "But we happen to have one that I got in trade from a customer in

Walnut Ridge. So you sure are welcome to swap," he said, reaching out for Friendly.

"Wait!" I said. "A person has got to say good-by, don't they?" I looked into Friendly's eyes and wondered how I could make him understand. "I never wanted to get rid of you, Friendly. I only wanted to get rid of the aller — *Her — her — choo!* — of the allergy."

He licked my ear almost as if to tell me not to worry because any dog as friendly as Friendly would get along just fine.

Again Mr. Grant reached out, only this time I gave him my Friendly. As he took him away, I heard him say, "Rest of the collies going to be mighty happy to see you again."

When he returned, Friendly wasn't with him. "An allergy sure is a bothersome thing," said Mr. Grant. "Reason I know that is because I've had an allergy ever since I was about your age."

It was so hard to believe. "You got yourself an allergy to collies too?" I asked.

"Nope." Mr. Grant pointed to the bend in his suntanned arm. "Tomatoes — that's what gets my allergy going. One tomato and my arm breaks out like a strawberry patch."

"Tomatoes don't bother me a bit," I said proudly.

"Reckon that's what an allergy is," said Mr. Grant. "It's what don't bother some folks, bothers other folks a whole lot."

When we stopped in front of the chihuahua's run, a tiny fellow came rushing to the gate, barking. "That's the dog for me," I said.

On the drive back home I held the chihuahua in my lap while my folks went back to trying to pick out a baby name. I was hoping they'd find a better name for the baby than they found for me.

When Pa turned off the highway onto the dirt road leading to our farm, the puppy jumped off my lap. He stood on his toes, pressing his nose against the truck's window. I hollered, "Looky there! Look at Tippietoes!"

"Ohhhh," said Ma, turning her head. "Now ain't that something? And what a fine name for him too."

I put my hands against the little dog's cheeks and gave him a kiss between the eyes. "I now name you — *ah-ah* ——I now name you ——*ah-ah-ah-choo!*"

"Oh *no!*" said Ma and Pa at exactly the same time.

But finally I was able to say, and say proudly, "I now name you Tippietoes."

By the time I crawled into bed, my eyes were red and itchy. My nose was sneezy and my chest was wheezy. Ma stood at my doorway. "Tippietoes going to sleep next to the cookstove tonight, but tomorrow evening we're going to take him back."

I shook my head no. "Mama, don't say that. I don't care nothing about no little allergy, cross my heart I don't. All I care about is my little dog. My own little Tippietoes."

"Girl, you ain't talking nothing but a heap of foolishness. I ain't about to let you walk around sick. Not as long as I'm your mama, 'cause I ain't that kind of mama. Now you get yourself to sleep."

At first recess, I told Miss Johnson about having an allergy, not just to long-haired dogs but to short-haired ones too.

"Maybe I can find still another secret in that book," she said, bringing down the big book again. She fingered through a lot of pages before she finally began to read aloud: "People who have an allergy to both long-haired and short-haired dogs might not have an allergy to poodles, as they are the only dogs that never shed hair."

Pa explained to Mr. Grant what I had learned from the book. "So we'll be much obliged if you'll kindly swap Tippietoes here for one of your poodles."

"Fine with me," said Mr. Grant, reaching for Tippietoes.

"Wait!" I said, holding onto the little one for another moment. "A person still has to say good-bye." I patted his chin. He licked my fingers. "Good-bye, little boy, little Tippietoes. I'm sorry you couldn't be my dog."

I closed my eyes as I gave him over to Mr. Grant, who took him away. When he came back he said, "Come along folks. Let me introduce you to my poodles."

We followed him until he stopped at the gate of a chainlink fence. "Poodles may be just the right dog for a girl with an allergy," he said, pointing to two white dogs that looked more like fluffy powder puffs than real dogs. "Because they never have dandruff or a doggy odor. And the book is right. They never shed a single hair."

He unhooked the gate and I walked in saying, "This time I'm going to be lucky. This time I *hope* I'm going to be lucky."

"Hope so," said Ma and Pa at exactly the same moment.

Both poodles walked over to say hello. They were quite polite. I bent down and one of the puppies came closer. "Is it you?" I asked him.

He took one step closer, resting his fluffy little head in my hand. I whispered, "I'm going to take real good care of you."

Inside the crowded cab of the pickup truck, I held the poodle puppy on my lap as Pa turned on the headlights and started for home. My patting must have relaxed the little dog 'cause he closed his eyes and went to sleep.

After a while Ma said, "I think we ought to name the baby after my great-aunt Alberta."

Pa's nose crinkled. "What you want to name our baby after her for?"

Ma's nose climbed. "Ain't she my grandma's sister? The oldest living member of my family?"

"That nosy old lady!" said Pa.

"Aunt Alberta ain't one bit nosy," Ma corrected. "What she is, is interested. I'm disappointed in you, Mr. Eugene Lam — "

"Have you all noticed," I asked, hoping that my interruption would stop an argument from starting, "that I haven't sneezed even one time?"

Ma smiled. "Ain't it the truth."

"And Puffy will never have to go back to Mr. Grant's," I said.

"Puffy?" asked Pa, surprised.

"Don't you see," I asked, "how he's all puffy like cotton candy?"

Ma turned to look at Pa. "Beth has thought up three good names for three dogs while we is still fussing over one name for one baby."

Puffy opened his eyes and looked around. "You're here, Puffy," I said, putting my face into his white fluffiness. "And you're always going to be . . . my . . . my ——*choo!* My ——*ahhhhhhh — ey!*"

"Lord, don't go telling me I heard what I think I heard," said Ma, fixing her eyes on the ceiling of the truck.

"It ain't what you think," I said quickly. "I really — *ahhh-choo! Ah-choo-who!* I really think I'm catching Billy Boy Williams's cold. He had one at school today. Sneezed all over the place ——choo, choo, choo, like that! Spreading his germs about."

Pa drove the truck over to the side of the road and turned off the engine. "Beth, I is sorry to disappoint you. I know how much you wanted a pup, but there ain't nothing I can do."

"If you take him back," I warned, "I ain't never going to live home again. For the rest of my life I'm going to live in the kennel with Puffy."

My mama patted my hand. "In this life you got to be happy about the good things and brave about the bad ones."

"I don't want to be brave," I shouted. "All I want is my little dog."

Pa started up the truck, made a U-turn on the highway, and headed back toward the kennel. "Ain't nothing in this wide world we can do," he said, shaking his head.

The next morning I asked Miss Johnson to bring down the book again. But after a while we stopped reading. It didn't have any more secrets to tell. I walked away 'cause I didn't have a single word for a single solitary soul. But later in the afternoon I told her, "I guess it's nobody's fault. But I reckon I'm learning to be brave about things I don't like."

"And I want you to know," said Miss Johnson, taking off her glasses, "that I think you're learning very well."

When the school bus stopped in front of our sign, I jumped off and with a running leap crossed the ditch.

"How come you shortcutting through the field again?" called Philip Hall. "Ain't no dog waiting for you today."

"Guess I know that," I said, wondering how I could have forgotten. And yet for some reason I really was in a hurry to get home.

When I reached the rise, I could see the chocolate-brown outline of my mother. But it didn't look like her, not exactly. After I passed the vegetable garden, I could see that it wasn't her. It was . . . my grandmother.

I started running my fast run. "Grandma, Grandma! Hello!"

"Howdy there, Beth babe," she called back.

I ran into her arms as she closed them around me. "How come you're here? All the way from Walnut Ridge?"

Grandma smiled. "I came to see my new grandbaby. Born this very morning, a few minutes after nine."

"Where are they?" I asked.

"Shhhhh," she said, pointing to the inside of the house. "They are both real fine, but they're resting just now."

I asked, "Is it a . . . is it a brother?"

"A brother for you; a grandson for me," she said, hugging me some more.

I danced a circle around her. "My own little brother. He's going to be fun to take care of and fun to play with.

Sometimes boys are almost as much fun to play with as girls. I've noticed that."

"Reckon I've noticed that too," said Grandma, joining my dance.

"What's my brother's name?"

Grandma stopped dancing. "Your folks ain't come to no decision on that," she said.

"Don't fret about that," I told her. "I happen to be good at names."

Then I heard Pa calling from inside the house, "Beth, come on in and meet up with your brother."

I closed the screen door quietly behind me the way I always remember to do when there is a visitor in the house. Pa stood at the door of his and Ma's bedroom and waved me on. "I want you to see something real pretty," he said.

Ma was sitting up in bed, propped up by two pillows. She was wearing her "sick" nightgown — the pink one with the lace running around the neck and collar. When I used to remind her that she ought to get some wear out of it 'cause she's never been sick a day in her life, Ma always said, "We'll see."

As I came closer, I saw something in her arms that I had never seen there before. A baby.

Ma said, "Fold your arms."

"Like this?" I asked.

"Just like that," she said, placing my soft little brother in my arms.

"Ohhhhh," I said, touching my lips to his warm head. "You are a beautiful baby brother. Baby brother Benjamin."

"Benjamin?" asked Ma. "Benjamin? *Benjamin!* — Oh, Lordy, yes. That's it. That's the name!"

Pa smiled. "Benjamin is a good strong name for a boy."

"Finally," said Grandma, coming into the room. "A name for the baby."

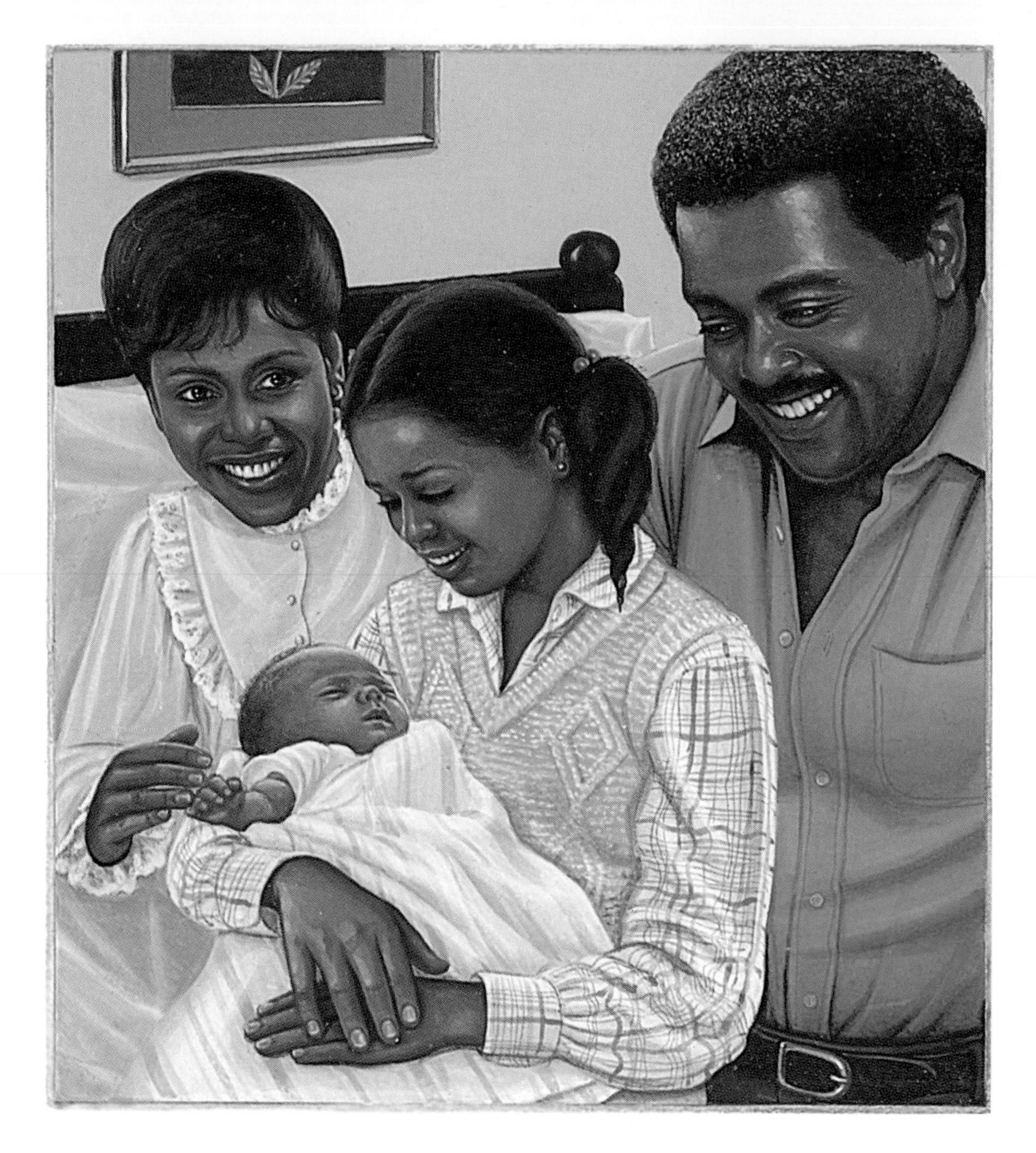

I put my face next to Baby Benjamin's and breathed in deep. I didn't sneeze. "You're always going to be our Baby Benjamin," I whispered in his ear. "And anyway, Mr. Grant wouldn't know what to do with a real baby."

Author

Bette Greene grew up in a small Arkansas town and in Memphis, Tennessee. She studied in Paris for a year, then attended Columbia University in New York. Her first book, for junior and senior high schoolers, grew out of her childhood experiences in Arkansas. It won several awards.

Her second book, *Philip Hall likes me. I reckon maybe.*, from which the excerpt you have just read was taken, was also set in rural Arkansas. Mrs. Greene says, "Without the memory of childhood sights and feelings and events, I'd be a writer with nothing to say." That book, too, won several awards. A sequel is *Get on out of here, Philip Hall.* Mrs. Greene has also written short stories and newspaper and magazine articles.

An excerpt from

Felita

by Nicholasa Mohr

Best Friends

A wonderful thing happened this new school year. Gigi, Consuela, Paquito, and I were all going into the fourth grade, and we were put in the same class. It had never happened before. Once I was in the same class with Consuela, and last year Gigi and Paquito were together. But this — it was too good to be true! Of course knowing Gigi and I were in the same class made me the happiest.

Our teacher, Miss Lovett, was friendly and laughed easily. In early October, after we had all settled into our class and gotten used to the routine of school once more, Miss Lovett told us that this year our class was going to put on a play for Thanksgiving. The play we were going to perform was based on a poem by Henry Wadsworth Longfellow, called "The Courtship of Miles Standish." It was about the Pilgrims and how they lived when they first landed in America.

We were all so excited about the play. Miss Lovett called for volunteers to help with the sets and costumes. Paquito and I agreed to help with the sets. Consuela was going to work on makeup. Gigi had not volunteered for anything. When we asked her what she was going to do, she shrugged and didn't answer.

Miss Lovett said we could all audition for the different parts in the play. I was really interested in being Priscilla. She is the heroine. Both Captain Miles Standish and the handsome, young John Alden are in love with her. She is the most beautiful maiden in Plymouth, Massachusetts. That's where the Pilgrims used to live. I told my friends how much I would like to play that part. Everyone said I would be perfect . . . except Gigi. She said that it was a hard part to do, and maybe I wouldn't be able to play it. I really got annoyed and asked her what she meant.

"I just don't think you are right to play Priscilla. That's all," she said.

"What do you mean by right?" I asked. But Gigi only shrugged and didn't say another word. She was beginning to get on my nerves.

Auditions for the parts were going to start Tuesday. Lots of kids had volunteered to audition. Paquito said he would try out for the brave Captain Miles Standish. Consuela said she was too afraid to get up in front of everybody and make a fool of herself. Gigi didn't show any interest in the play and refused to even talk to us about it. Finally the day came for the girls to read for the part of Priscilla. I was so excited I could hardly wait. Miss Lovett had given us some lines to study. I had practiced real hard. She called out all the names of those who were going to read. I was surprised when I heard her call out "Georgina Mercado." I didn't even know Gigi wanted to try out for Priscilla. I looked at Gigi, but she ignored me. We began reading. It was my turn. I was very nervous and kept forgetting my lines. I had to look down at the script a whole lot. Several other girls were almost as nervous as I was. Then it was Gigi's turn. She recited the part almost by heart. She hardly looked at the script. I noticed that she was wearing one of her best dresses. She had never looked that good in school before. When she finished, everybody clapped. It was obvious that she was the best one. Miss Lovett made a fuss.

"You were just wonderful, Georgina," she said, "made for the part!" Boy, would I have liked another chance. I bet I could have done better than Gigi.

Why hadn't she told me she wanted the part? It's a free country, after all. She could read for the same part as me. I wasn't going to stop her! I was really angry at Gigi.

After school everyone was still making a fuss over her. Even Paquito had to open his stupid mouth.

"Oh, man, Gigi!" he said. "You were really good. I liked the part when John Alden asked you to marry Captain Miles Standish and you said, 'Why don't you speak for yourself, John?' You turned your head like this." Paquito imitated Gigi and closed his eyes. "That was really neat!" Consuela and the others laughed and agreed.

I decided I wasn't walking home with them.

"I have to meet my brothers down by the next street," I said. "I'm leaving. See you." They hardly noticed. Only Consuela said goodbye. The rest just kept on hanging all over Gigi. Big deal, I thought.

Of course walking by myself and watching out for the tough kids was not something I looked forward to. Just last Friday Hilda Gonzales had gotten beat up and had her entire allowance stolen. And at the beginning of the term Paquito had been walking home by himself and gotten mugged. A bunch of big bullies had taken his new schoolbag complete with pencil and pen case, then left him with a swollen lip. No, sir, none of us ever walked home from school alone if we could help it. We knew it wasn't a safe thing to do. Those mean kids never bothered us as long as we stuck together. Carefully I looked around to make sure none of the bullies were in sight. Then I put some speed under my feet, took my chances, and headed for home.

Just before all the casting was completed, Miss Lovett offered me a part as one of the Pilgrim women. All I had to do was stand in the background like a zombie. It wasn't even a speaking part.

"I don't get to say one word," I protested.

"Felicidad Maldonado, you are designing the stage sets and you're assistant stage manager. I think that's quite a bit. Besides, all the speaking parts are taken."

"I'm not interested, thank you," I answered.

"You know" — Miss Lovett shook her head — "you can't be the best in everything."

I turned and left. I didn't need to play any part at all. Who cared?

Gigi came over to me the next day with a great big smile all over her face. I just turned away and made believe she wasn't there.

"Felita, are you taking the part of the Pilgrim woman?" she asked me in her sweetest voice, just like nothing had happened.

"No," I said, still not looking at her. If she thought I was going to fall all over her like those dummies, she was wasting her time.

"Oh," was all she said, and walked away. Good, I thought. I don't need her one bit!

At home Mami noticed something was wrong.

"Felita, what's the matter? You aren't going out at all. And I haven't seen Gigi for quite a while. In fact I haven't seen any of your friends."

"Nothing is the matter, Mami. I just got lots of things to do."

"You're not upset because we couldn't give you a birthday party this year, are you?" Mami asked. "You know how hard the money situation has been for us."

My birthday had been at the beginning of November. We had celebrated with a small cake after dinner, but there had been no party.

"No. It's not that," I said and meant it. Even though I had been a little disappointed, I also knew Mami and Papi had done the best they could.

"We'll make it up to you next year, Felita, you'll see."

"I don't care, Mami. It's not important now."

"You didn't go having a fight with Gigi or something? Did you?"

"Now why would I have a fight with anybody!"

"Don't raise your voice, miss," Mami said. "Sorry I asked. But you just calm down."

The play was going to be performed on the day before Thanksgiving. I made the drawings for most of the scenery. I made a barn, a church, trees and grass, cows, and a horse. I helped the others make a real scarecrow. We used a broom and old clothes. Paquito didn't get the part of Captain Miles Standish, but he made a wonderful fence out of cardboard. It looked just like a real wooden fence. Consuela brought in her mother's old leftover makeup. She did a good job of making up everybody.

By the time we set up the stage, everything looked beautiful. Gigi had tried to talk to me a few times. But I just couldn't be nice back to her. She acted like nothing had happened, like I was supposed to forget she hadn't told me she was going to read for the part! I wasn't going to forget that just because she was now Miss Popularity. She could go and stay with all her newfound friends for all I cared!

The morning of the play, at breakfast, everybody noticed how excited I was.

"Felita," Papi exclaimed, "stop jumping around like a monkey and eat your breakfast."

"She's all excited about the school play today," Mami said.

"That's right. Are you playing a part in the play?" Papi asked.

"No," I replied.

"But she's done most of the sets. Drawing and designing. Isn't that right, Felita?"

"Mami, it was no big deal."

"That's nice," said Papi. "Tell us about it."

"What kind of sets did you do?" Johnny asked.

"I don't know. Look, I don't want to talk about it."

"Boy, are you touchy today," Tito said with a laugh.

"Leave me alone!" I snapped.

"Okay." Mami stood up. "Enough. Felita, are you finished?" I nodded. "Good. Go to school. When you come back, bring home a better mood. Whatever is bothering you, no need to take it out on us." Quickly I left the table.

"Rosa," I heard Papi say, "sometimes you are too hard on her."

"And sometimes you spoil her, Alberto!" Mami snapped. "I'm not raising fresh kids."

I was glad to get out of there. Who needs them, I thought.

The play was a tremendous hit. Everybody looked wonderful and played their parts really well. The stage was brilliant with the color I had used on my drawings. The background of the countryside, the barn, and just about everything stood out clearly. Ernesto Bratter, the stage manager, said I was a good assistant. I was glad to hear that, because a couple of times I'd had to control my temper on account of his ordering me around. But it had all worked out great.

No doubt about it. Gigi was perfect as Priscilla. Even though the kids clapped and cheered for the entire cast, Gigi

got more applause than anybody else. She just kept on taking a whole lot of bows.

Afterward Miss Lovett had a party for our class. We had lots of treats. There was even a record player and we all danced. We had a really good time.

Of course Priscilla, alias Gigi, was the big star. She just couldn't get enough attention. But not from me, that was for sure. After the party Gigi spoke to me.

"Your sets were really great. Everybody said the stage looked wonderful."

"Thanks." I looked away.

"Felita, are you mad at me?"

"Why should I be mad at you?"

"Well, I did get the leading part, but . . ."

"Big deal," I said. "I really don't care."

"You don't? But . . . I . . ."

"Look," I said, interrupting her, "I gotta go. I promised my mother I'd get home early. We have to go someplace."

I rushed all the way home. I didn't know why, but I was still furious at Gigi. What was worse was that I was unhappy about having those feelings. Gigi and I had been real close for as far back as I could remember. Not being able to share things with her really bothered me.

We had a great Thanksgiving. The dinner was just delicious. Abuelita[1] brought her flan. Tío[2] Jorge brought lots of ice cream. He always brings us kids a treat when he visits. Sometimes he even brings each one of us a small gift — a nature book or crayons for me and puzzles or sports magazines for my brothers. He's really very nice to us. One thing about him is that he's sort of quiet and doesn't talk much. Papi says that Tío Jorge has been like that as far back as he can remember.

Abuelita asked me if I wanted to go home with her that evening. Boy, was I happy to get away from Mami. I just couldn't face another day of her asking me questions about Gigi, my friends, and my whole life. It was getting to be too much!

It felt good to be with Abuelita in her apartment. Abuelita never questioned me about anything really personal unless I

---

[1]**Abuelita** (ä b$\overline{oo}$ ā **lē'**tə): Grandmother.

[2]**Tío** (**tē'**ō): Uncle.

wanted to talk about it. She just waited, and when she sensed that I was worried or something, then she would ask me. Not like Mami. I love Mami, but she's always trying to find out every little thing that happens to me. With my abuelita sometimes we just sit and stay quiet, not talk at all. That was nice too. We fixed the daybed for me. And then Tío Jorge, Abuelita, and I had more flan as usual.

"Would you like to go to the park with me this Sunday?" Tío Jorge asked me.

"Yes."

"We can go to the zoo and later we can visit the ducks and swans by the lake."

"Great!" I said.

Whenever Tío Jorge took me to the zoo, he would tell me stories about how he, Abuelita, and their brothers and sisters had lived and worked as youngsters taking care of farm animals. These were the only times I ever heard him talk a whole lot.

"It's not just playing, you know," he would say. "Taking care of animals is hard work. Back on our farm in Puerto Rico we worked hard, but we had fun too. Every one of us children had our very own favorite pets. I had a pet goat by the name of Pepe. He used to follow me everywhere." No matter how many times he told me the same stories, I always enjoyed hearing them again.

"Well." Tío Jorge got up. "It's a date then on Sunday, yes?"

"Yes, thank you, Tío Jorge."

"Good night," he said and went off to bed.

Abuelita and I sat quietly for a while, then Abuelita spoke.

"You are getting to be a big girl now, Felita. You just turned nine years old. My goodness!"

I loved her the best, more than anybody. I hadn't been to stay with her since the summer, and somehow this time things felt different. I noticed how tired Abuelita looked. She wasn't moving as fast as she used to. Also I didn't feel so little next to her anymore.

"Tell me, Felita, how have you been? It seems like a long time since we were together like this." She smiled her wonderful smile at me. Her dark, bright eyes looked deeply into mine. I felt her warmth and happiness.

"I'm okay, Abuelita."

"Tell me about your play at school. Rosa tells me you worked on the stage sets. Was the play a success?"

"It was. It was great. The stage looked beautiful. My drawings stood out really well. I never made such big drawings in my life. There was a farm in the country, a barn, and animals. I made it the way it used to be in the olden days of the Pilgrims. You know, how it was when they first came to America."

"I'm so proud of you. Tell me about the play. Did you act in it?"

"No." I paused. "I didn't want to."

"I see. Tell me a little about the story."

I told Abuelita all about it.

"Who played the parts? Any of your friends?"

"Some."

"Who?"

"Well, this boy Charlie Martinez played John Alden. Louie Collins played Captain Miles Standish. You don't know them. Mary Jackson played the part of the narrator. That's the person who tells the story. You really don't know any of them."

I was hoping she wouldn't ask, but she did.

"Who played the part of the girl both men love?"

"Oh, her? Gigi."

"Gigi Mercado, your best friend?" I nodded. "Was she good?"

"Yes, she was. Very good."

"You don't sound too happy about that."

"I don't care." I shrugged.

"But if she is your best friend, I should think you would care."

"I . . . I don't know if she is my friend anymore, Abuelita."

"Why do you say that?"

I couldn't answer. I just felt awful.

"Did she do something? Did you two argue?" I nodded. "Can I ask what happened?"

"Well, it's hard to explain. But what she did wasn't fair."

"Fair about what, Felita?"

I hadn't spoken about it before. Now with Abuelita it was easy to talk about it.

"Well, we all tried out for the different parts. Everybody knew what everybody was trying out for. But Gigi never told anybody she was going to try out for Priscilla. She kept it a great big secret. Even after I told her that I wanted to try for the part, she kept quiet about it. Do you know what she did say? She said I wasn't right for it . . . it was a hard part and all that bunch of baloney. She just wanted the part for herself, so she was mysterious about the whole thing. Like . . . it was . . . I don't know." I stopped for a moment, trying to figure this whole thing out. "After all, I am supposed to be her best friend . . . her very best friend. Why shouldn't she let me know that she wanted to be Priscilla? I wouldn't care. I let her know my plans. I didn't go sneaking around."

"Are you angry because Gigi got the part?"

It was hard for me to answer. I thought about it for a little while. "Abuelita, I don't think so. She was really good in the part."

"Were you as good when you tried out for Priscilla?"

"No." I looked at Abuelita. "I stunk." We both laughed.

"Then maybe you are not angry at Gigi at all."

"What do you mean?"

"Well, maybe you are a little bit . . . hurt?"

"Hurt?" I felt confused.

"Do you know what I think? I think you are hurt because your best friend didn't trust you. From what you tell me, you trusted her, but she didn't have faith in you. What do you think?"

"Yes." I nodded. "Abuelita, yes. I don't know why. Gigi and I always tell each other everything. Why did she act like that to me?"

"Have you asked her?"

"No."

"Why not? Aren't you two speaking to each other?"

"We're speaking. Gigi tried to be friendly a few times."

"Don't you want to stay her friend?"

"I do. Only she came over to me acting like . . . like nothing ever happened. And something did happen! What does she think? That she can go around being sneaky and I'm going to fall all over her? Just because she got the best part, she thinks she's special."

"And you think that's why she came over. Because she wants to be special?"

"I don't know."

"You should give her a chance. Perhaps Gigi acted in a strange way for a reason."

"She wasn't nice to me, Abuelita. She wasn't."

"I'm not saying she was. Or even that she was right. *Mira*, Felita, friendship is one of the best things in this whole world. It's one of the few things you can't go out and buy. It's like love. You can buy clothes, food, even luxuries, but there's no place I know of where you can buy a real friend. Do you?"

I shook my head. Abuelita smiled at me and waited. We were both silent for a long moment. I wondered if maybe I shouldn't have a talk with Gigi. After all, she had tried to talk to me first.

"Abuelita, do you think it's a good idea for me to . . . maybe talk to Gigi?"

"You know, that's a very good idea." Abuelita nodded.

"Well, she did try to talk to me a few times. Only there's just one thing. I won't know what to say to her. I mean, after what's happened and all."

"After so many years of being close, I am sure you could say 'Hello, Gigi. How are you?' That should be easy enough."

"I feel better already, Abuelita."

I kept thinking of what Abuelita had said, and on Monday I waited for Gigi after school. It was as if she knew I wanted to talk. She came over to me.

"Hello, Gigi," I said. "How are you?"

"Fine." Gigi smiled. "Wanna walk home together?"

"Let's take the long way so we can be by ourselves," I said.

We walked without saying anything for a couple of blocks. Finally I spoke.

"I wanted to tell you, Gigi, you were really great as Priscilla."

"Did you really like me? Oh, Felita, I'm so glad. I wanted you to like me, more than anybody else. Of course it was nothing compared to the sets you did. They were something special. Everybody liked them so much."

"You were right too," I said. "I wasn't very good for the part of Priscilla."

"Look." Gigi stopped walking and looked at me. "I'm sorry about . . . about the way I acted. Like, I didn't say anything to you or the others. But, well, I was scared you all would think I was silly or something. I mean, you wanted the part too. So, I figured, better not say nothing."

"I wouldn't have cared, Gigi. Honest."

"Felita . . . it's just that you are so good at a lot of things. Like, you draw just fantastic. You beat everybody at hopscotch and kick-the-can. You know about nature and animals, much more than the rest of us. Everything you do is always better than . . . what I do! I just wanted this part for me. I wanted to be better than you this time. For once I didn't wanna worry about you. Felita, I'm sorry."

I was shocked. I didn't know Gigi felt that way. I didn't feel better than anybody about anything I did. She looked so upset, like she was about to cry any minute. I could see she was miserable and I wanted to comfort her. I had never had this kind of feeling before in my whole life.

"Well, you didn't have to worry. 'Cause I stunk!" We both laughed with relief. "I think I was the worst one!"

"Oh, no, you weren't." Gigi laughed. "Jenny Fuentes was the most awful."

"Worse than me?"

"Do you know what she sounded like? She sounded like this. 'Wha . . . wha . . . why don't you . . . speeek for your . . . yourself *Johnnnn?*'" Gigi and I burst into laughter.

"And how about that dummy, Louie Collins? I didn't think he read better than Paquito."

"Right," Gigi agreed. "I don't know how he got through the play. He was shaking so much that I was scared the sets would fall right on his head."

It was so much fun, Gigi and I talking about the play and how we felt about everybody and everything. It was just like before, only better.

Author

Nicholasa Mohr is well known as an artist and an author of award-winning realistic books about city teenagers. You have just read part of her fourth book, *Felita,* which was chosen as a Notable Children's Trade Book in the Field of Social Studies in 1979. Ms. Mohr grew up in New York City, in a neighborhood much like Felita's.

An excerpt from

The Voyage of the *Dawn Treader*

by C. S. Lewis

Eustace Clarence Scrubb was a tiresome, whining child who got no pleasure from playing or reading. Indeed, his greatest pleasure came from pestering other people. His cousins, Lucy and Edmund, have come to spend the summer at Eustace's house, where the three of them might have had a fine time. However, Eustace spoils the fun by being so disagreeable.

One day while the three children are studying a painting of a sailing ship that hangs in Lucy's room, a strange thing happens. They are magically pulled into the painting where the waves, the wind, and the ship are very real. The ship belongs to King Caspian of Narnia, a kingdom Lucy and Edmund have visited before. Caspian and his sailors are sailing the Dawn Treader *in search of seven Narnian lords who have not returned from a journey. They are delighted to welcome their old friends, and Eustace, on the adventure; it is impossible for the children to return home anyway. Eustace becomes more disagreeable than ever, especially to Reepicheep, the noble talking mouse.*

After a violent storm, the adventurers dock at Dragon Island to rest. Eustace wanders off and loses his way in a fog. After stumbling down a mountain, he sees an old dragon die. On searching the dragon's cave, he finds gold, diamonds, and other treasures. Filled with greed, Eustace crams a jeweled bracelet on his arm and falls asleep on top of the treasure.

The Adventures of Eustace

Meanwhile Eustace slept and slept — and slept. What woke him was a pain in his arm. The moon was shining in at the mouth of the cave, and the bed of treasures seemed to have grown much more comfortable: in fact he could hardly feel it at all. He was puzzled by the pain in his arm at first, but presently it occurred to him that the bracelet which he had shoved up above his elbow had become strangely tight. His arm must have swollen while he was asleep (it was his left arm).

He moved his right arm in order to feel his left, but stopped before he had moved it an inch and bit his lip in terror. For just in front of him, and a little on his right, where the moonlight fell clear on the floor of the cave, he saw a hideous shape moving. He knew that shape: it was a dragon's claw. It had moved as he moved his hand and became still when he stopped moving his hand.

"Oh, what a fool I've been," thought Eustace. "Of course, the brute had a mate and it's lying beside me."

For several minutes he did not dare to move a muscle. He saw two thin columns of smoke going up before his eyes, black against the moonlight; just as there had been smoke coming from the other dragon's nose before it died. This was so alarming that he held his breath. The two columns of smoke vanished. When he could hold his breath no longer he let it out stealthily; instantly two jets of smoke appeared again. But even yet he had no idea of the truth.

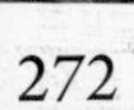

Presently he decided that he would edge very cautiously to his left and try to creep out of the cave. Perhaps the creature was asleep — and anyway it was his only chance. But of course before he edged to the left he looked to the left. Oh horror! there was a dragon's claw on that side too.

No one will blame Eustace if at this moment he shed tears. He was surprised at the size of his own tears as he saw them splashing on to the treasure in front of him. They also seemed strangely hot; steam went up from them.

But there was no good crying. He must try to crawl out from between the two dragons. He began extending his right arm. The dragon's fore-leg and claw on his right went through exactly the same motion. Then he thought he would try his left. The dragon limb on that side moved too.

Two dragons, one on each side, mimicking whatever he did! His nerve broke and he simply made a bolt for it.

There was such a clatter and rasping, and clinking of gold, and grinding of stones, as he rushed out of the cave that he thought they were both following him. He daren't look back. He rushed to the pool. The twisted shape of the dead dragon lying in the moonlight would have been enough to frighten anyone but now he hardly noticed it. His idea was to get into the water.

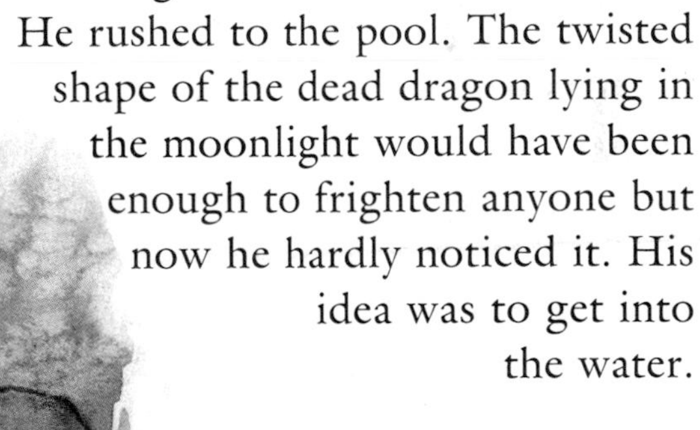

But just as he reached the edge of the pool two things happened. First of all it came over him like a thunderclap that he had been running on all fours — and why on earth had he been doing that? And secondly, as he bent towards the water, he thought for a second that yet another dragon was staring up at him out of the pool. But in an instant he realized the truth. That dragon face in the pool was his own reflection. There was no doubt of it. It moved as he moved: it opened and shut its mouth as he opened and shut his.

He had turned into a dragon while he was asleep. Sleeping on a dragon's hoard with greedy, dragonish thoughts in his heart, he had become a dragon himself.

That explained everything. There had been no two dragons beside him in the cave. The claws to right and left had been his own right and left claws. The two columns of smoke had been coming from his own nostrils. As for the pain in his left arm (or what had been his left arm) he could now see what had happened by squinting with his left eye. The bracelet which had fitted very nicely on the upper arm of a boy was far too small for the thick, stumpy foreleg of a dragon. It had sunk deeply into his scaly flesh and there was a throbbing bulge on each side of it. He tore at the place with his dragon's teeth but could not get it off.

In spite of the pain, his first feeling was one of relief. There was nothing to be afraid of anymore. He was a terror himself now and nothing in the world but a knight (and not all of those) would dare to attack him. He could get even with Caspian and Edmund now . . .

But the moment he thought this he realised that he didn't want to. He wanted to be friends. He wanted to get back among humans and talk and laugh and share things. He realised that he was a monster cut off from the whole human race. An appalling loneliness came over him. He began to see that the others had not really been friends at all. He began to wonder if he himself had been such a nice person as he had always supposed. He longed for their voices. He would have been grateful for a kind word even from Reepicheep.

When he thought of this, the poor dragon that had been Eustace lifted up its voice and wept. A powerful dragon crying its eyes out under the moon in a deserted valley is a sight and a sound hardly to be imagined.

At last he decided he would try to find his way back to the shore. He realised now that Caspian would never have sailed away and left him. And he felt sure that somehow or other he would be able to make people understand who he was.

He took a long drink and then (I know this sounds shocking, but it isn't if you think it over) he ate nearly all the dead dragon. He was half-way through it before he realised what he was doing; for, you see, though his mind was the mind of Eustace, his tastes and his digestion were dragonish. And there is nothing a dragon likes so well as fresh dragon. That is why you so seldom find more than one dragon in the same country.

Then he turned to climb out of the valley. He began the climb with a jump and as soon as he jumped he found that he was flying. He had quite forgotten about his wings and it was a great surprise to him — the first pleasant surprise he had had for a long time. He rose high into the air and saw innumerable mountain-tops spread out beneath him in the moonlight. He could see the bay like a silver slab and the *Dawn Treader* lying at anchor and camp fires twinkling in the woods beside the beach. From a great height he launched himself down towards them in a single glide.

Lucy was sleeping very sound for she had sat up till the return of the search party in hope of good news about Eustace. It had been led by Caspian and had come back late and weary. Their news was disquieting. They had found no trace of Eustace but had seen a dead dragon in a valley. They

tried to make the best of it and everyone assured everyone else that there were not likely to be more dragons about, and that one which was dead at about three o'clock that afternoon (which was when they had seen it) would hardly have been killing people a very few hours before.

"Unless it ate the little brat and died of him: he'd poison anything," said Rhince. But he said this under his breath and no one heard it.

But later in the night Lucy was waked, very softly, and found the whole company gathered close together and talking in whispers.

"What is it?" said Lucy.

"We must all show great constancy," Caspian was saying. "A dragon has just flown over the tree-tops and lighted on the beach. Yes, I am afraid it is between us and the ship. And arrows are no use against dragons. And they're not at all afraid of fire."

"With your Majesty's leave — " began Reepicheep.

"No, Reepicheep," said the King very firmly, "you are *not* going to attempt a single combat with it. And unless you promise to obey me in this matter I'll have you tied up. We must just keep close watch and, as soon as it is light, go down to the beach and give it battle. I will lead. King Edmund will be on my right and the Lord Drinian on my left. There are no other arrangements to be made. It will be light in a couple of hours. In an hour's time let a meal be served out and what is left of the wine, also. And let everything be done silently."

"Perhaps it will go away," said Lucy.

"It'll be worse if it does," said Edmund, "because then we shan't know where it is. If there's a wasp in the room I like to be able to see it."

The rest of the night was dreadful, and when the meal came, though they knew they ought to eat, many found that they had very poor appetites. And endless hours seemed to pass before the darkness thinned and birds began chirping here and there and the world got colder and wetter than it had been all night and Caspian said, "Now for it, friends."

They got up, all with swords drawn, and formed themselves into a solid mass with Lucy in the middle and Reepicheep on her shoulder. It was nicer than the waiting about and everyone felt fonder of everyone else than at ordinary times. A moment later they were marching. It grew lighter as they came to the edge of the wood. And there on the sand, like a giant lizard, or a flexible crocodile, or a serpent with legs, huge and horrible and humpy, lay the dragon.

But when it saw them, instead of rising up and blowing fire and smoke, the dragon retreated — you could almost say it waddled — back into the shallows of the bay.

"What's it wagging its head like that for?" said Edmund.

"And now it's nodding," said Caspian.

"And there's something coming from its eyes," said Drinian.

"Oh, can't you see," said Lucy. "It's crying. Those are tears."

"I shouldn't trust to that, Ma'am," said Drinian. "That's what crocodiles do, to put you off your guard."

"It wagged its head when you said that," remarked Edmund. "Just as if it meant *No.* Look, there it goes again."

"Do you think it understands what we're saying?" asked Lucy.

The dragon nodded its head violently.

Reepicheep slipped off Lucy's shoulder and stepped to the front.

"Dragon," came his shrill voice, "can you understand speech?"

The dragon nodded.

"Can you speak?"

It shook its head.

"Then," said Reepicheep, "it is idle to ask you your business. But if you will swear friendship with us raise your left foreleg above your head."

It did so, but clumsily because that leg was sore and swollen with the golden bracelet.

"Oh look," said Lucy, "there's something wrong with its leg. The poor thing — that's probably what it was crying about. Perhaps it came to us to be cured like in Androcles and the lion."

"Be careful, Lucy," said Caspian. "It's a very clever dragon but it may be a liar."

Lucy had, however, already run forward, followed by Reepicheep, as fast as his short legs could carry him, and then of course the boys and Drinian came, too.

"Show me your poor paw," said Lucy, "I might be able to cure it."

The dragon-that-had-been-Eustace held out its sore leg gladly enough, remembering how Lucy's cordial had cured him of sea-sickness before he became a dragon. But he was disappointed. The magic fluid reduced the swelling and eased the pain a little but it could not dissolve the gold.

Everyone had now crowded round to watch the operation, and Caspian suddenly exclaimed, "Look!" He was staring at the bracelet.

"Look at what?" said Edmund.

"Look at the device on the gold," said Caspian.

"A little hammer with a diamond above it like a star," said Drinian. "Why, I've seen that before."

"Seen it!" said Caspian. "Why, of course you have. It is the sign of a great Narnian house. This is the Lord Octesian's arm-ring."

"Villain," said Reepicheep to the dragon, "have you devoured a Narnian lord?" But the dragon shook his head violently.

"Or perhaps," said Lucy, "this *is* the Lord Octesian, turned into a dragon — under an enchantment, you know."

"It needn't be either," said Edmund. "All dragons collect gold. But I think it's a safe guess that Octesian got no further than this island."

"Are you the Lord Octesian?" said Lucy to the dragon, and then, when it sadly shook its head, "Are you someone enchanted — someone human, I mean?"

It nodded violently.

And then someone said — people disputed afterwards whether Lucy or Edmund said it first — "You're not — not Eustace by any chance?"

And Eustace nodded his terrible dragon head and thumped his tail in the sea and everyone skipped back (some of the sailors with ejaculations I will not put down in writing) to avoid the enormous and boiling tears which flowed from his eyes.

Lucy tried hard to console him and even screwed up her courage to kiss the scaly face, and nearly everyone said "Hard luck" and several assured Eustace that they would all stand by him and many said there was sure to be some way of disenchanting him and they'd have him as right as rain in a day or two. And of course they were all very anxious to hear his story, but he couldn't speak. More than once in the days that followed he attempted to write it for them on the sand. But this never succeeded. In the first place Eustace (never having read the right books) had no idea how to tell a story straight. And for another thing, the muscles and nerves of the dragon-claws that he had to use had never learned to write and were not built for writing anyway. As a result he never got nearly to the end before the tide came in and washed away all the writing except the bits he had already trodden on or accidentally swished out with his tail. And all that anyone had seen would be something like this — the dots are for the bits he had smudged out —

I WNET TO SLEE . . . RGOS AGRONS I MEAN DRANGONS CAVE CAUSE ITWAS DEAD AND AINIG SO HAR . . . WOKE UP AND COU . . . GET OFFF MI ARM OH BOTHER . . .

It was, however, clear to everyone that Eustace's character had been rather improved by becoming a dragon. He was anxious to help. He flew over the whole island and found that it was all mountainous and inhabited only by wild goats and droves of wild swine. Of these he brought back many carcasses for the revictualling of the ship. He was a very humane killer too, for he could dispatch a beast with one blow of his tail so that it didn't know (and presumably still doesn't know) it had been killed. He ate a few himself, of course, but always alone, for now that he was a dragon he liked his food raw but he could never bear to let the others see him at his messy meals. And one day, flying slowly and wearily but in great triumph, he bore back to camp a great tall pine tree which he had torn up by the roots in a distant valley and which could be made into a capital mast. And in the evening if it turned chilly, as it sometimes did after the heavy rains, he was a comfort to everyone, for the whole party would come and sit with their backs against his hot sides and get well warmed and dried; and one puff of his fiery breath would light the most obstinate fire. Sometimes he would take a select party for a fly on his back, so that they could see wheeling below them the green slopes, the rocky heights, the narrow pit-like valleys, and far out over the sea to the eastward a spot of darker blue on the blue horizon which might be land.

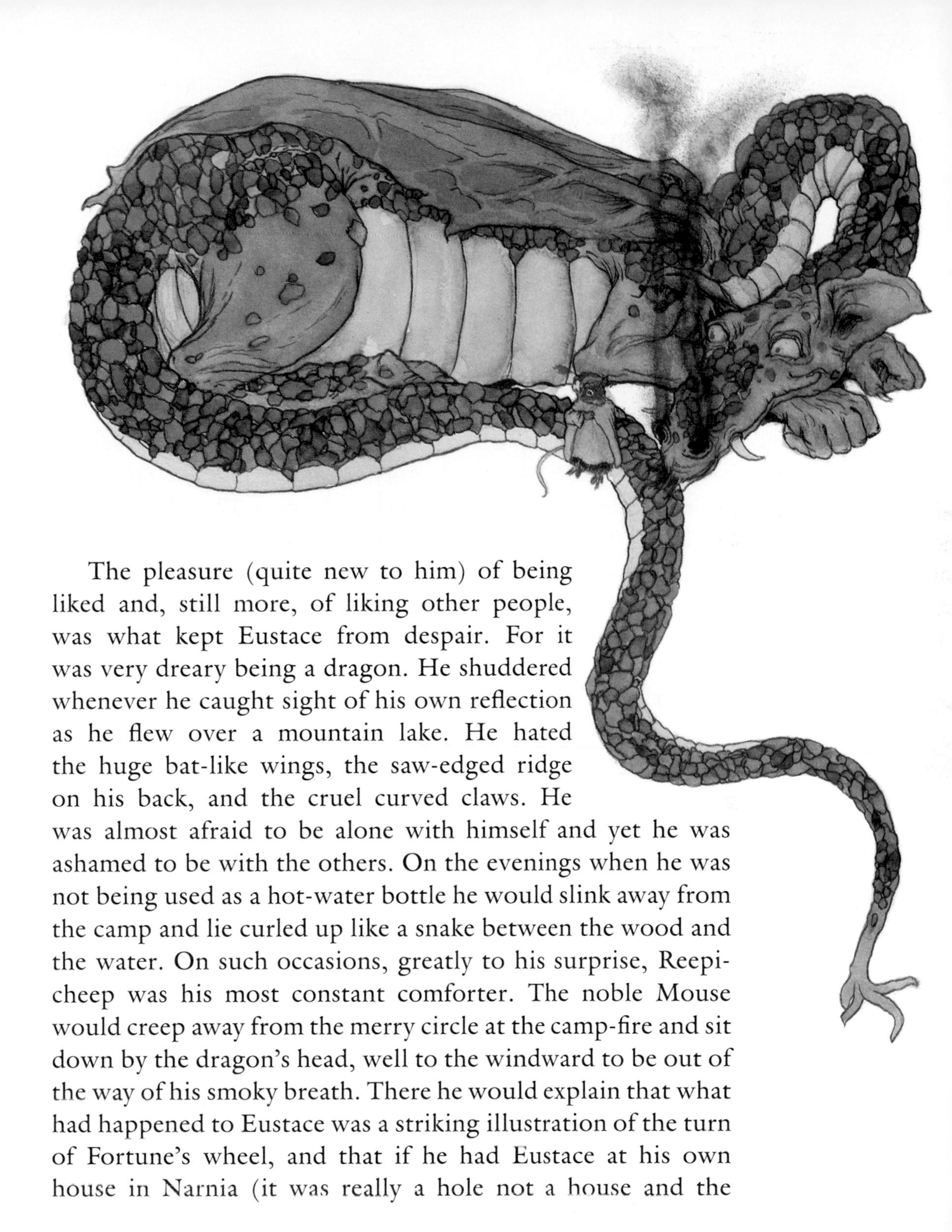

The pleasure (quite new to him) of being liked and, still more, of liking other people, was what kept Eustace from despair. For it was very dreary being a dragon. He shuddered whenever he caught sight of his own reflection as he flew over a mountain lake. He hated the huge bat-like wings, the saw-edged ridge on his back, and the cruel curved claws. He was almost afraid to be alone with himself and yet he was ashamed to be with the others. On the evenings when he was not being used as a hot-water bottle he would slink away from the camp and lie curled up like a snake between the wood and the water. On such occasions, greatly to his surprise, Reepicheep was his most constant comforter. The noble Mouse would creep away from the merry circle at the camp-fire and sit down by the dragon's head, well to the windward to be out of the way of his smoky breath. There he would explain that what had happened to Eustace was a striking illustration of the turn of Fortune's wheel, and that if he had Eustace at his own house in Narnia (it was really a hole not a house and the dragon's head, let alone his body, would not have fitted in) he could show him more than a hundred examples of emperors, kings, dukes, knights, poets, lovers, astronomers, philosophers, and magicans, who had fallen from prosperity into the most distressing circumstances, and of whom many had recovered and lived happily ever afterwards. It did not, perhaps, seem so very comforting at the time, but it was kindly meant and Eustace never forgot it.

Eustace eventually becomes a better person after having spent some time in the skin of a dragon. You can continue with the adventures of Eustace, Edmund, Lucy, Caspian, and the other characters on board the Dawn Treader *by reading* ***The Voyage of the* Dawn Treader** *by C. S. Lewis. This is the third book in the series,* THE CHRONICLES OF NARNIA.

Author

C. S. Lewis (Clive Staples Lewis), a distinguished scholar, literary critic, and writer, was born in 1898 in Belfast, Ireland. As a child, he read constantly and wrote and illustrated stories. In 1918 he entered Oxford University, in England, where he was a brilliant scholar and where J. R. R. Tolkien, another author of books for young people, was one of his best friends. After graduation, Lewis remained at Oxford teaching English literature for almost thirty years. To literature for children, he gave the seven-book series containing *the Lion, the Witch, and the Wardrobe, Prince Caspian, The Voyage of the* Dawn Treader, *The Silver Chair, The Horse and His Boy, The Magician's Nephew,* and *The Last Battle*. In 1956, Mr. Lewis received the Carnegie Medal, the British counterpart of the Newbery Medal, for *The Last Battle*.

Boarding House

by Ted Kooser

The blind man draws his curtains for the night
and goes to bed, leaving a burning light

above the bathroom mirror. Through the wall,
he hears the deaf man walking down the hall

in his squeaky shoes to see if there's a light
under the blind man's door, and all is right.

"Boarding House" from *A Local Habitation and a Name* by Ted Kooser. Copyright © 1974 by Ted Kooser. Reprinted by permission of Solo Press.

An excerpt from

The MacLeod Place

by William H. Armstrong

Tor MacLeod had spent most of his life on his grandparents' farm, where his grandfather Angus raised sheep. This year, for the first time, Tor had his own four sheep and was eagerly waiting for their lambs to be born.

Home from the High Meadow

As the days passed, Tor grew more and more impatient. His grandfather's Black-faced Highlands already had so many lambs that he had to count the marks scratched on the shed wall to total up the number. Almost every day as the sheep wandered in at grain time, several ewes would be hanging back so that newborn lambs could keep up.

When Tor thought of keeping his four prize Cheviots in the shed, his grandpa had said, "It's better for the lambs if they're born in some sunny spot by a stone wall; and the ewe will find the warmest place. This time of year it's much warmer outside when the sun is high than in the shed. The sun's bringing out more new green every day, and there's nothing like new grass to get plenty of milk ready for when your lambs do come. They're finding more to nibble too. They're not even in any hurry to get to the grain trough."

"But these are my own first lambs," Tor would interrupt. "Why do all yours have to be born first?"

"Any day now," Angus MacLeod would answer, putting his hand on the boy's shoulder as they leaned against the shed gate, "you'll have four, maybe six. Sometimes Cheviots have twins their first lambing. Cheviots are born small, but they're active and tough. They're on their feet and getting milk in half the time it takes most breeds."

Finally a day came that set Tor's heartbeat racing. When the flock came in long after sundown, he counted only three of his ewes among his grandfather's many. He climbed the shed gate and counted again. When he was sure one was missing, he found Angus in the barn and said, "One's lambed. She didn't come in."

Halfway across the night pasture, in search of the missing ewe, Angus MacLeod was falling behind the boy and dog. Maybe Tor wanted to handle this alone.

"You don't have to come with me," the boy called without looking back. He had already repeated the same thing several times since they had left the barn.

The man now realized that he was out of place. The joy of finding his first lamb was something a boy would rather not

share with anyone. Angus MacLeod understood. "Are you sure?" he called after the boy.

"I'm sure," the boy called without slackening his ever-quickening strides. The man watched until the boy had disappeared around the corner of the wall beyond the night pasture. He measured the amount of daylight left the boy, then made his way back past the barn to the kitchen.

"Should you have let him go alone?" Una MacLeod asked Angus when she had heard why Tor had not come in with him.

"He'll be all right," Angus replied. "I started with him, but by the time we were halfway across the night pasture, he and Shep were fifty yards in front. He had said about a half dozen times, 'You don't have to go with me.' It finally dawned on me that this was no ordinary venture. He was going to find his very own first lamb. When he's telling the story on the school bus tomorrow, he won't have to say 'me and Grandpa.' He'll say 'I' like a real shepherd."

Una MacLeod glanced at the wall rack by the kitchen door. "He never remembers to change his good Mackinaw and school boots. I hope he doesn't come home carrying a wet lamb in his arms with that good jacket."

"He'll be careful. Besides, they can't be too far. The Indian mound pasture and the high meadow have been closed off since last fall. When I was a boy, I used to find one up there occasionally. Pa said the sun was warmer there at the bottom of the cliffs than anywhere else on the mountain."

Tor saw his grandfather disappear behind the kitchen door far below. He circled the fields with confidence. He searched along the walls. He startled a fox sparrow from its busy scratching in winter's dead grass and leaves. He put up a covey of bobwhites that had already gone to roost in their tight circle on the ground. They rose with a great flutter in all directions. He sent Shep to search the swales and the far side of knolls. Intermittently he called, "Rachel, Rachel." His grandfather had told him that this was the Old Testament name for little ewe.

Now the bobwhites Tor had scattered began to call each other from all directions to reassemble for the night. It was their covey call, rather plaintive, with a touch of mysterious lure.

At last he was approaching the entrance to the Indian mound pasture and the high meadow. The strip of orange-red above the Alleghenies was narrowing fast and fading into a dark magenta. Shep had returned from searching the last swales which were fast filling with purple. Tor was beginning to worry. He had kept a pace which had made Shep trot at intervals when he returned from his knoll and swale assignments and moved beside the boy.

But now Tor ceased his calling and stood listening. No hurry or worry was great enough to keep him from standing still to hear the winsome, bewitching "Bobwhite, bobwhite, is your wheat ripe?" that came to him. It seemed to soften the land and brighten the western sky's fading glow. Somctimes after it had been repeated three times the caller would add, "More wet, more wet." This in summer would bring his grandfather up short, and he would say, "He's calling for rain."

When there were only two or three stragglers left answering each other with "Bobwhite, bobwhite," Tor walked on, but at a less hurried step.

By the time he reached the gate to the Indian mound pasture, all was quiet. He knew the birds were back on the ground in their compact little circle, wing to wing, tails in and heads out, so each could take off "like shot out of a cannon," as Grandpa said. "It takes a smart fox to get one."

Years of sliding to and fro, or the rattling of the wooden bolt by summer's breeze and winter's wind, had worn the edges from the bolt slot so that the gate had been opened either by the wind or some thoughtless hunter.

Tor had gone with his grandfather to look for lost heifers often enough to have learned to look for tracks. In the gateway he found them — one set of sheep tracks going into the Indian mound pasture and the high meadow. These were two separate fields, but they served as a single summer pasture for sheep and young cattle. So Tor knew the barway between them was always open. They covered a great expanse of acreage, running north all the way to the base of the cliffs of the Hanging Gardens. His grandfather always used a horse when checking the stock here in summer.

Tor knew it was the nature of all animals to give birth to their young in as much privacy as they could find. "They'll go as far as they can," his grandpa always said. "They'll go to the highest spot so they can keep an eye out for the approach of an enemy. This is a carry-over from the days when they were wild."

Tor found himself repeating his grandfather's words aloud. Shep thought he was talking to him. He wagged his tail and moved around to where he could look up into the boy's eyes as if to question, "What do you want me to do now?"

Tor looked back over the gentle slanted and rolling fields he had crossed. It had grown dark enough now so he could see the lighted windows of the kitchen far away. The evening star glimmered just above the mountains in the west.

He wished he had not come alone. If he had known the gate would be open, he would have ridden Little Sorrel, the horse his grandfather had named for Stonewall Jackson's famous war-horse. He tried to pick out the cliffs at the end of the upland. The distance and the dark cut them off; they were too far away.

He'd better go back and get his grandpa with a lantern, he thought. Maybe his ewe was still trying to have the lamb. She wouldn't be making a sound. He couldn't find her in the dark. The March wind was beginning to sweep the land. It was cold. Maybe the lamb would be chilled and die if he took time to go back for his grandfather. Sometimes ewes have trouble with their first lamb. Maybe his ewe was dead, and the lamb dead, still inside her.

If the lamb had been born and was all right, he could find them in the dark. The mother would bleat about every twenty minutes for the lamb to rise on its wobbly legs and get milk. He would listen in one spot and then move on to another and listen again.

If he went back, his grandmother would say, "You're chilled through and through, child. Eat your supper and do your schoolwork. Your grandfather will ride Little Sorrel up and look."

And worst of all, Grandpa might say, "You'll never find one ewe in that high meadow tonight. Sometimes it's hard enough to find a whole flock in the daytime. A lamb won't freeze outside tonight. What's happened has happened. We might as well wait 'til morning."

Tor rubbed his hand over the head of Shep for a long time. He patted him gently. Finally he spoke. "We'll go on, Shep." And boy and dog turned from looking back at the faraway glow of the kitchen window, a dim speck, the only light that showed on the whole horizon, and headed north into the backland.

He picked out the stars in the handle of the Big Dipper. The evening star had seemed near and flaming-warm. The stars in the handle of the Big Dipper now appeared far away and starkly cold.

The boy sent the dog in one direction and then another with the command, "Find the sheep, Shep."

As they approached the Indian mound, he kept the dog by his side. His grandfather had told him the mound was where the Monacan Indians had lived. They were a small branch of the Cherokee tribe, and this was the site of their "long house," where they held tribal council meetings. They had once lived farther south along Cedar Creek and the Lost River near Natural Bridge, which they called the Bridge of God. When they had been driven from the valley land, they had moved into the mountains. In time they had been driven westward across the mountains, finally ending up on far western desert land which no one else wanted.

Tor wondered how many chiefs were buried in the mound. He stopped and listened to the distant "Who, whoo, who-oo cooks for you" of a great horned owl. It sounded like the signal whoop of an Indian. It was answered by the mournful whistle of a screech owl, rising to a tremulous cry, then falling to a low plaintive wail. Grandpa called it the shivers owl. Said it ran shivers up and down your spine. Shep's tail tapping the ground sounded like a muffled drumbeat. Tor ran his hand over Shep's head. This only made the drumbeat louder.

Past the Indian mound, Tor quickened his pace. The call of the bobwhite had said stay and listen; but there was something in the night cry of the owls which said hurry.

Shep covered the directions where the boy pointed. Tor listened for an excited bark, which would tell him that his sheep was found, but each time Shep returned as quietly as he went. The light in the kitchen windows had fallen below Tor's view. He wished he would see a lantern crossing the fields below; that would help him keep his directions.

Back in the kitchen Una MacLeod was putting the boy's supper in the warming closet of the stove. Angus stood in the kitchen door listening.

"You must get the lantern and go and help him," Una MacLeod repeated with more determination than the time before. She had said it several times.

"I'll go," Angus replied. "But it's a great adventure for the boy. Pa used to send me out with a feed sack to carry the lambs home in. I forgot to tell Tor to take one. I'll give him a little more time. He knows sheep. If the lamb hadn't been born long, he'll wait to let it get first milk before he disturbs them. That's important. The moon'll be up soon and it's full, the planter's moon. Time to get the ground ready for planting as soon as it dries out."

Angus had lighted the fire in the fireplace to take the chill off. He closed the kitchen door and sat by the fire. Una noticed that he did not remove his boots. She was glad.

Tor missed the gap that led from the Indian mound pasture into the high meadow. He finally remembered that it was at the crown of a knoll, so he followed the stone wall uphill until he came to it. He had only missed it by a few yards. For an instant he was proud of himself. He would tell Grandpa that he was almost as good as him about finding his way over the land.

He stood at the gap and called, "Rachel, Rachel," in all directions. When he did it facing the Big Dipper, a faint echo came back to him. He knew that was the direction of the cliffs and the woodland. His voice had echoed off the cliffs. He repeated his grandpa's words to Shep, "They'll go as far as they can, hide in the brush or woods if they can."

The thought of going all the way to the cliffs and the woods sent more shivers up his spine than the screech owl had. He called Shep to his side.

A small arc of gold had appeared above the far mountains. In no time at all it was a half circle. Then it was a great bright disk, clearing the mountain, climbing up the sky. By its light Tor could see the stone walls that ran down the ridge. In the distance he could see the outline of the cliffs against the sky.

From somewhere on the mountain, a fox barked at the moon. Tor remembered that his grandpa said they'd never bark when they were hungry — but when they'd feasted on a rabbit or something, they'd sit on their haunches and bay at the moon just like a dog.

Tor suddenly realized that Shep had disappeared on his own. Was it the fox or had he scented the ewe? Tor wondered if the fox might not have feasted on his lamb. No, the mother would butt the daylights out of the fox. Tor whistled for his dog. A faint echo came back from the faraway cliffs. The echo sounded like somebody had whistled a soft tune.

Shep came bounding back from the direction of the woodland. With the moon up, Tor felt much braver. He heard the bark of the fox again, much closer. Shep stopped and pricked up his ears. "No, Shep," the boy said. Shep dropped back to walk with him.

Tor found himself veering toward the corner of the high meadow. He pointed for Shep to search in that direction. He would go to the top of the last rise and wait for Shep. The stone wall that bordered the high meadow ran just inside the woods. He would stay out in the moonlight and let Shep go into the dark under the hemlocks.

Once long ago, when he was only five or six, his grandpa had shown him one of the trees with great strips of its bark torn off. "A killer bear testing his strength," his grandfather had said. He had probably gotten a whiff of the sheep or cattle, his grandfather had explained, and that had whetted his appetite for the kill. So he tested his claws on the tree. But a bear could never catch sheep in the open. Only if he got the sheep in a corner and they were scared stiff with fright. Then he would maul them to death. Grandpa had found three of his Black-faced Highlands mangled and one half-eaten in the hemlock corner. "But that was before you were born," his grandfather had said.

Shep returned from searching and gave the boy the same disappointed look. Relieved, Tor now pointed in the direction of the hemlock corner, wondering if he'd feel any better about going in if Shep found her there.

There were still bears in the mountain, even if they hadn't killed any sheep for years. Tor had read in the paper about hunters shooting them, but not so much on his mountains as across the valley in the Alleghenies.

Shep had scarcely started toward the dark woods when Tor heard a sharp clipped bark. The dog was back in an instant, wagging his tail and barking. Tor quieted the dog and moved very cautiously in the direction Shep led. Misgivings replaced the instant excitement he had enjoyed at hearing Shep's bark. They were still in the open. She wouldn't have had her lamb here. Shep moved ahead quietly as Tor had ordered. Tor peered through the moonlight, pausing with every step to listen.

After not more than a dozen steps, it came to him — the rapid thump, thump, thump of a sheep stomping her foot. Tor picked up Shep's dark form in the moonlight. And there right in front of him was the ewe. Tor moved closer and saw a white ball directly under her. She stomped her foot at the dog and boy, but moved to one side, then turned and put her nose against the white ball and bleated. The white ball divided in half; each half bounced in a different direction.

Tor could scarcely believe his eyes or the action which followed. His ewe had twins. He had thought only in terms of one tiny new lamb, still wobbly on its rubbery legs.

In the barn lot his ewes were so tame he could rub his hand over the soft wool, scratch their heads, and they would follow him, asking for more. Now the ewe was wild, moving in a circle, trying to keep her lambs together and away from boy and dog. The lambs were several hours old and, as was characteristic of Cheviots, quite capable of trying to keep out of reach of the stranger who had just appeared. Shep moved in a wide arc outside the circle of ewe, lambs, and boy.

Tor tried to turn the ewe in the direction of home, but she would not lose sight of her lambs. She walked backward or circled or went from side to side. When the boy realized that they were getting nowhere, he caught the lambs and held them in his arms. Now the mother moved back and forth in front of him, never letting the lambs out of her sight. The lambs squirmed in his arms. When the ewe had run under his feet and he had tripped and nearly fallen on the lambs several times, he decided there had to be a better way.

He had seen his grandfather walking calmly, a grain sack over his shoulder with two woolly heads sticking out of slits he had made in the sack, and the ewe walking behind, bleating as she followed. "Why didn't we remember to bring a grain sack?" Tor spoke aloud to Shep, who was still staying well out of the way.

One lamb squirmed free and bounced off its mother's back to the ground as she darted in front of Tor. He was afraid to squeeze the other tight enough to hold it. So he put it gently on the ground.

He began to unbutton his Mackinaw. He would tie it into a bag and carry them that way. He felt in his pockets for string. He always had several pieces. But tonight, when he needed it for something far more important than tying rubber bands on a pronged stick to make a gravel shooter, he had none.

For the first time during the whole night he began to sniffle. He blew his nose, and an idea was born. Better than tying his Mackinaw into a bag, he would cut his handkerchief in half, tie the end of each sleeve, put a lamb in each, with its head sticking out, and carry them on his back. "The way Indians would carry papooses," he said to Shep. He cut the hem of the handkerchief with his knife and ripped it the rest of the way. He was already cold without his jacket, but that didn't matter.

It worked. With boy and lambs and jacket on the ground in a heap, the frantic mother dancing wildly, Tor stuffed one lamb in tailfirst, held his knee on it while he got the other in, hung them low over his back so the mother could see them, and started for home. The ewe followed on his heels, bleating with each step. Shep dropped behind to drive but found that unnecessary. His only problem was keeping up.

Halfway across the Indian mound pasture Tor saw the moving light of a lantern far below on the horizon. He was no longer cold. He heard no drumbeats as he passed the Indian mound. The moonlight on the fields and the bleating of his ewe brought the world alive and made it beautiful.

When man and boy came together, the man held the lantern high and studied the boy's precious burden. "How'd you ever think of that," he asked, "and how'd she ever get into the upper land?"

"The gate was open," the boy replied. And after a long pause he added, "On the way up I was thinking of Indians, so I thought of this."

"Want me to carry them the rest of the way?"

"No, they aren't a bit heavy."

The man thought of taking his jacket off to put around the boy. But then he thought better and didn't. Instead he blew out the lantern.

Over the fields drenched in moonlight, a man and a boy walked in silence. The thoughts of each too meaningful for words, one too wise, the other too happy.

Author

Ever since his school days in Virginia, where he grew up on a farm, William H. Armstrong has had the creative-writing urge. He has written award-winning books for young people, as well as educational textbooks for adults. For many years Mr. Armstrong has raised purebred Corriedale sheep near his hillside home, which he built with his own hands.

A Zillion Stars

by Yoshiko Uchida

When Mama first told me we were going to spend a weekend at the Harada farm in Livingston, I didn't want to go.

"Aren't they the ones with the two boys?"

Mama nodded. "That's right. Danny and Jimbo."

"How old are they?" I asked cautiously.

"Oh, Danny must be almost twelve now, and I guess little Jimbo is seven."

I groaned. Now I *knew* I didn't want to go. Danny would probably be mean and bossy, and Jimbo would be a pest.

But Papa had just saved up enough to buy a second hand Model T, and he'd already put up a sign in the window of our grocery store saying it'd be closed over the weekend.

"Maybe my tonsils will swell up again," I thought. "Then I'll have to go to bed with a temperature and not have to go." When I opened my mouth and looked at my tonsils, though, they were just sitting there, two small, pink, healthy-looking lumps, not a bit swollen like they'd been last Christmas when I didn't want them to be.

"You'll enjoy the farm, Rumi," Papa said to me. "They have acres of vineyards and a pair of mules, some chickens and a dog."

It was only the dog that interested me. I was dying to have a dog. But Mama said we couldn't have one while we lived in the small flat above Papa's store.

"Wait until we can move to a real house someday, Rumi," she said.

"I could be an old lady by then," I thought.

Well, anyway, we went to Livingston.

Papa was feeling so good, he was whistling and singing almost from the minute we left Oakland. He drove carefully while we were on the main highway. But when he turned off onto the narrow dirt road that led to the farm, he stepped on the gas and made the dust billow up behind us like a small tornado.

"Papa, aren't you going too fast?" Mama asked nervously.

But Papa only rolled up the window to keep out the dust and told her everything was under control.

I could see rows and rows of grapevines now, stretching out in neat, straight lines on either side of the road. And when I saw the water tower off to our right, Papa said we were almost there.

"There's the barn," he said, pointing to a sloping brown roof, and then I saw the Haradas' small white house sheltered near a cluster of trees.

"We're here!" Papa shouted, and he began to honk his horn.

That was when I smelled burning rubber.

"Papa, something's burning," I yelled at him.

Mama sniffed and said. "Rumi's right. I think the car's on fire."

"Nonsense," Papa scoffed, but he turned around just to make sure, and that was when he crashed into the dog house and came to a screeching stop only a few yards from the Haradas' house.

"Look out!" Mama screamed. But it was too late. The dog house was smashed and tipped over on its side.

The chickens fluttered and squawked all over the yard, and an old brown collie barked furiously at us. Danny and Jimbo were right behind him, charging toward us like a couple of wild boars. They were barefoot, brown as toasted almonds, and wearing faded wool swim trunks.

By the time we jumped out of the car, Mr. and Mrs. Harada had rushed from their house.

"Your wheels are on fire!" Mr. Harada shouted.

And he and Papa threw quick handfuls of dirt and sand at the flames that spurted from the rear wheels.

“I guess I had the brakes tightened too much,” Papa said sheepishly. “I don’t know too much about cars yet.”

The fire was out in a few minutes, but Jimbo kept throwing fistfuls of dirt at the smoldering tires and then at his big brother, until Danny wrestled him to the ground and made him say he was sorry. I didn’t wait around for Jimbo to start pelting me next. I just ran and caught up with Mama and Mrs. Harada who were walking toward the house. They were already talking as though they’d never stop.

Mama and Mrs. Harada sailed together from Japan on the same ship a long time ago when they both came to America to get married and were good friends ever since. They wrote long letters to each other, but this was the first time we’d ever come to visit them in Livingston.

Mrs. Harada kept telling me how nice it was to have a girl around the house for a change, and I helped her serve the ice cold lemonade and the pale yellow sponge cake that was still warm. I could tell Mrs. Harada had put her best cloth on the dining room table, because it looked just like the big white crocheted cloth Mama used when we had company.

I watched Danny and Jimbo from the corner of my eye while I ate my cake, and once I caught Danny eyeing me back. But the minute they’d swallowed the last of the lemonade, they went slamming out the back door, and their mother was so busy talking, she didn’t even notice.

I knew the grownups would be talking for hours about the farm and the grocery store and how it had been back in Japan. They were getting swallowed up in times and places I didn’t know about. So pretty soon, I just slipped out the back door too.

I looked at the small vegetable garden behind the house where Mrs. Harada was growing corn and beans and tomatoes, and then I walked toward the barn.

The barn was nice and cool, and it smelled of fresh hay and animals. I looked for the mules and found them outside standing in the hot sun, swishing flies with their tails. I lured them over to the fence with some weeds I pulled from the ground. But when they got close and sniffed them, they just bared their huge yellow teeth at me as though I'd been mean for having made them come to the fence for nothing.

I finally found Rick, the old collie, lying in the shade of the walnut tree, and he gave me a friendly wag of his tail even though it was my papa who'd smashed up his house. His nose felt cool and wet even in all that heat, and when I scratched his head, he thumped his tail again. I loved him so much that I just ached to have a dog of my own.

I walked out a little way after that, right up to the edge of the vineyards. They looked as though they went on forever, curving clear around the entire world, and I could feel the sun beating down on them and on my head like a silent drum.

There were no sounds of streetcars or rumbling delivery trucks. I felt as though somebody had put a huge glass bowl over my head that shut out all the sounds of the world, and suddenly I wanted to make some noise.

"Hey, Danny, Jimbo!" I shouted as loud as I could. "Where are you?"

I knew they wouldn't answer even if they could hear me. But I just wanted to hear my voice hollering out there in all that space, so I hollered again. But nobody answered.

The boys didn't turn up until it was almost time for supper, and Mr. Harada had already begun barbecuing chicken over hot charcoals. They came running down the dirt road grinning and covered with dirt and grime.

"Just look at yourselves," Mrs. Harada scolded, as she heaped fresh beans and corn and tomatoes from her garden into big serving bowls. And she sent them off to wash up at the pump outside, still talking to them after they'd gone.

"You could at least have invited Rumi to go swimming with you," she grumbled into the tomatoes.

But I really didn't care that much. I didn't know how to swim anyway.

We ate outside sitting on mats spread out beneath the trees, and when we'd finished, old Rick came to lie down beside me instead of by either of the boys. That made me feel good, but I guess it bothered Danny because after a while he slid over next to me and showed me how to pick fleas from Rick's back.

"You gotta be real quick," he explained "cuz those fleas can jump about three or four feet." He parted the long hair on Rick's back and looked carefully for the tiny black specks that burrowed in the dog's pink flesh.

When he caught one, he squeezed the flea between his two thumbnails, making a tiny popping sound. Then he showed me the smear of blood left on his nail saying, "That's most likely *my* blood." And he pointed to the ring of red welts around both his ankles. Just seeing them made me feel itchy over my entire body, but I kept looking until I finally caught a flea of my own.

We stayed outside until long after the sun went down, and Mr. Harada brought out a kerosene lamp that I think attracted every bug around for a hundred miles.

I was surprised when Mrs. Harada got up and said it was about time to begin the baths. I knew there was no bathroom in their house and wondered if we were all going to have to take turns standing under the cold water pump. But Mr. Harada brought out a square tin tub which he set over a small pit beyond the pump. He filled it up with water and then built a small fire beneath it. Then he strung up a rope between two trees and hung a couple of blankets across it.

After a while he called, "Well, the water should be just right now. Who takes the first bath?"

Mrs. Harada said it should be me. I was afraid I was going to get cooked alive in that hot tin tub, but she showed me the fire had been banked and brought me a bucket of cold water in case the bath water was too hot.

I washed and rinsed myself on the wood platform beside the tub and then climbed onto the wood float and felt it sink beneath my feet. There was a rush of warm water gurgling all around me, and I let myself sink down until I could feel the water tickle my chin.

I turned around so I could look out at the vineyards and the lemon wedge of a moon that sat in the star-filled sky. I held my breath and listened to the nighttime sounds of the crickets and all the other creatures that lived in the fields. They were all talking like crazy, and I could even hear some frogs having a friendly conversation somewhere out there.

I was beginning to like Livingston and could have sat there all night in watery splendor, but I had to get out when Mama came to tell me to hurry because the others were waiting.

The next morning, Mr. Harada let me pitch some hay down to the mules with an enormous pitchfork bigger than I was. He talked a lot more when we were alone, because when Mrs. Harada was around, she did most of the talking.

He told me all about how he grew his grapes; how they had to be irrigated and weeded and watched carefully until they were ready to be harvested and packed and shipped out all over California. And he told me how it had been in the early days when he was still a bachelor and first came to Livingston from Japan.

"Oh, what a barren desolate place it was then, Rumi," he said, growing serious. "It was the kind of land nobody else wanted because nothing would grow on it. Each time we planted our small seedlings, the wind would rip through the fields tearing them up by the roots or covering them with dust that smothered and killed them."

"Then why didn't you just leave?" I asked.

Mr. Harada looked at me as though he couldn't believe I could ask such a stupid question. "And give up?" he asked. "We were determined, Rumi. We would never give up. Every time those seedlings were torn from the ground, we all went out there in those hot, dry fields and planted new ones, again and again, year after year, until one day we finally conquered the wind and the dust and even the sun. And now look at what we have."

I could just feel how proud he was of his land, and I wanted to say something nice to him. But I didn't know what to say, so I just worked even harder at pitching the hay even though my arms ached so much I thought they'd just drop off.

We had a picnic by the Merced River with rice balls and left over chicken for lunch, and Papa tried to teach me how to swim. But I kept breathing water up my nose and sinking to the riverbed like a sack of sand.

"You ain't never gonna learn how to swim," Jimbo scoffed.

But Danny just said, "Aw leave her alone, Jimbo. She comes from Oakland where they don't have any rivers or irrigation ditches to swim in."

We didn't have wagon rides in the moonlight either, and Mr. Harada said he thought that might be a nice thing to do.

That night I couldn't wait for the mules to get hitched up to the wagon, and I was the first one to be hoisted up on the big flat wagon. There wasn't any hay to sit on, but Mrs. Harada spread out a couple of old blankets, and we went bouncing along over the bumpy dirt roads that cut through the dark vineyards.

After a while, Papa and Mr. Harada began to sing some old Japanese folk songs they knew, and when they stopped, I started singing "Old MacDonald Had a Farm," and Danny and Jimbo pitched right in with me.

We must have sung all five verses at least four times, until finally Mama said, "I think that's enough, Rumi."

Danny's father let him take the reins for a while then, and I almost fell off the wagon when Danny offered to let me hold them too.

"It don't matter much who's got the reins," he said, not wanting to give me too much credit, "the old mules know where to go."

It was true, they just plodded along, their heads bobbing up and down, as though it was the most natural thing in the world for them to be pulling us through the night time fields, instead of hauling crates of grapes to the packing shed. It made me feel proud just to hold the reins as though I were really driving them.

When Mr. Harada took the reins again to head for home, Danny and Jimbo and I went to the back of the wagon and sprawled out on our backs to look up at the sky. I never knew before that there were so many stars up there. Back home in Oakland, I couldn't even see the sky from my bedroom window.

Out there in the country, the stars were so bright and seemed so close, it was almost as if they were talking to us in clear shining voices, like crystal bells.

"Betcha there're a hundred million stars up there," Jimbo said suddenly.

"Naw, more like a hundred billion," Danny corrected.

But I said, "You're both wrong. There're at least a million, billion, *zillion* stars up there."

I was waiting for Danny to tell me I was crazy, but he surprised me again.

"Yup," he said in a faraway voice, "I just guess maybe there *are* a zillion stars up there all right."

It was funny how that trip to Livingston turned out to be just about the best vacation I ever had in my whole entire life.

Sometimes, even now, when I lie in bed and close my eyes, I can still see those zillion stars blinking across that dark night sky. And sometimes, I even think a little bit about Danny Harada and how he turned out not to be so bad after all.

Author

Yoshiko Uchida was born in California. Her parents had come there from Japan. In her story "A Zillion Stars," the author recalls a childhood trip with her family to visit friends in the California countryside. Besides short stories, Yoshiko Uchida has written more than twenty children's books, including collections of Japanese folktales and realistic stories about Japanese or Japanese-American children.

A Song of Greatness

A Chippewa Indian song transcribed by Mary Austin

When I hear the old men
Telling of heroes,
Telling of great deeds
Of ancient days,
When I hear them telling,
Then I think within me
I too am one of these.

When I hear the people
Praising great ones,
Then I know that I too
Shall be esteemed,
I too when my time comes
Shall do mightily.

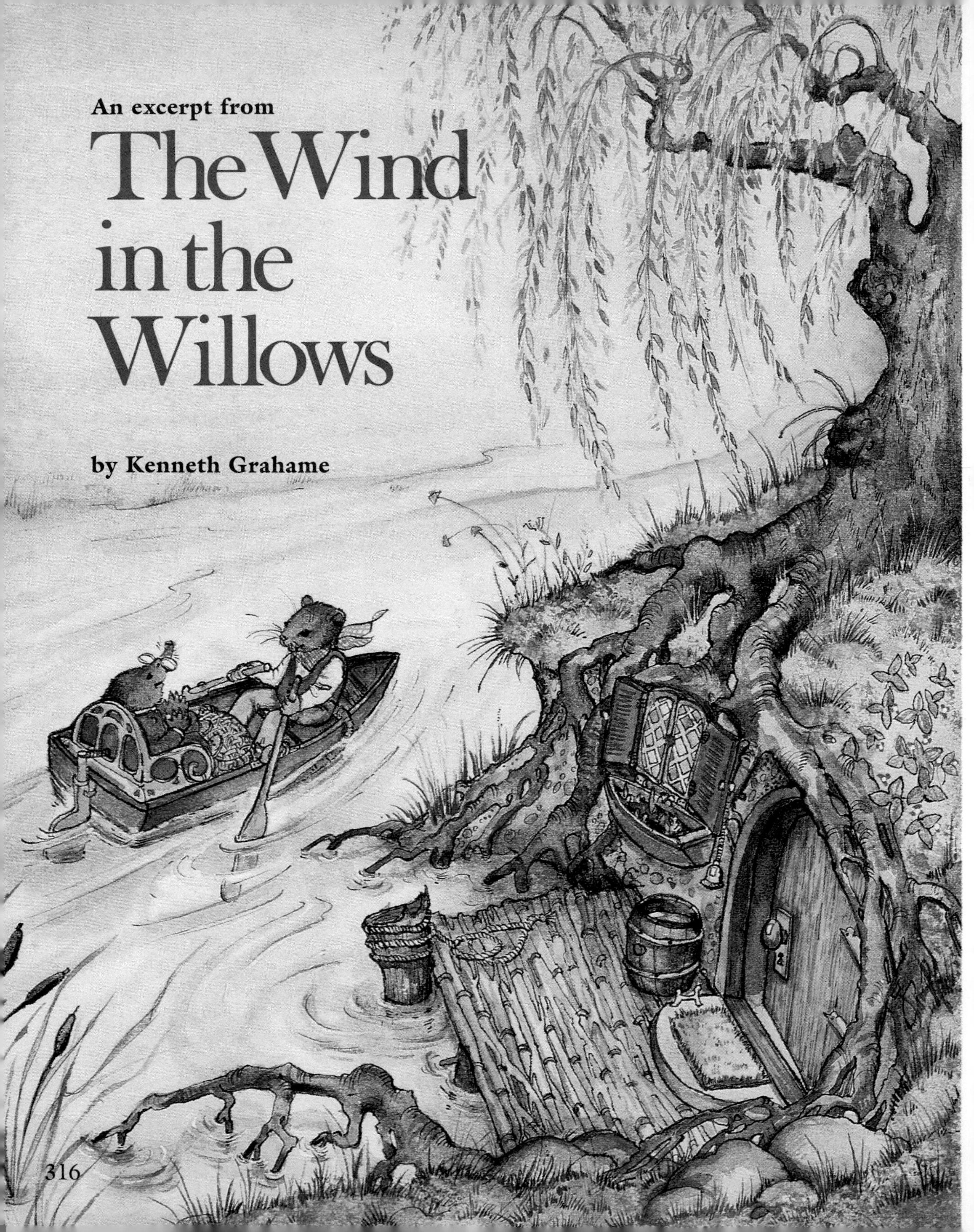

An excerpt from

The Wind in the Willows

by Kenneth Grahame

Not simply an "animal story," rather a story whose characters just happen to be animals, The Wind in the Willows *recounts the adventures of the Mole, the Water Rat, and the boastful and impetuous, but warm-hearted, Toad. In the excerpt that follows, the reader is transported to the English countryside where the three friends travel by caravan along the "open road."*

The Open Road

"RATTY," said the Mole suddenly, one bright summer morning, "if you please, I want to ask you a favour."

The Rat was sitting on the river bank, singing a little song. He had just composed it himself, so he was very taken up with it, and would not pay proper attention to Mole or anything else. Since early morning he had been swimming in the river in company with his friends the ducks. And when the ducks stood on their heads suddenly, as ducks will, he would dive down and tickle their necks just under where their chins would be if ducks had chins, till they were forced to come to the surface again in a hurry, spluttering and angry and shaking their feathers at him, for it is impossible to say quite *all* you feel when your head is under water. At last they implored him to go away and attend to his own affairs and leave them to mind theirs. So the Rat went away, and sat on the river bank in the sun, and made up a song about them, which he called

"DUCKS' DITTY"

All along the backwater,
Through the rushes tall,
Ducks are a-dabbling,
Up tails all!

Ducks' tails, drakes' tails,
Yellow feet a-quiver,
Yellow bills all out of sight
Busy in the river!

Slushy green undergrowth
Where the roach swim —
Here we keep our larder,
Cool and full and dim.

Every one for what he likes!
We like to be
Heads down, tails up,
Dabbling free!

High in the blue above
Swifts whirl and call —
We are down a-dabbling
Up tails all!

"I don't know that I think so *very* much of that little song, Rat," observed the Mole cautiously. He was no poet himself and didn't care who knew it; and he had a candid nature.

"Nor don't the ducks neither," replied the Rat cheerfully. "They say, '*Why* can't fellows be allowed to do what they like *when* they like and *as* they like, instead of other fellows sitting on banks and watching them all the time and making remarks and poetry and things about them? What *nonsense* it all is!' That's what the ducks say."

"So it is, so it is," said the Mole, with great heartiness.

"No, it isn't!" cried the Rat indignantly.

"Well then, it isn't, it isn't," replied the Mole soothingly. "But what I wanted to ask you was, won't you take me to call on Mr. Toad? I've heard so much about him, and I do so want to make his acquaintance."

"Why, certainly," said the good-natured Rat, jumping to his feet and dismissing poetry from his mind for the day. "Get the boat out, and we'll paddle up there at once. It's never the wrong time to call on Toad. Early or late he's always the same fellow. Always good-tempered, always glad to see you, always sorry when you go!"

"He must be a very nice animal," observed the Mole, as he got into the boat and took the sculls, while the Rat settled himself comfortably in the stern.

"He is indeed the best of animals," replied Rat. "So simple, so good-natured, and so affectionate. Perhaps he's not very clever — we can't all be geniuses; and it may be that he is both boastful and conceited. But he has got some great qualities, has Toady."

Rounding a bend in the river, they came in sight of a handsome, dignified old house of mellowed red brick, with well-kept lawns reaching down to the water's edge.

"There's Toad Hall," said the Rat; "and that creek on the left, where the notice-board says, 'Private. No landing allowed,' leads to his boathouse, where we'll leave the boat. The stables are over there to the right. That's the banqueting-hall you're looking at now — very old, that is. Toad is rather rich, you know, and this is really one of the nicest houses in these parts, though we never admit as much to Toad."

They glided up the creek, and the Mole shipped his sculls as they passed into the shadow of a large boathouse. Here they saw many handsome boats, slung from the cross-beams or hauled up on a slip, but none in the water; and the place had an unused and a deserted air.

The Rat looked around him. "I understand," said he. "Boating is played out. He's tired of it, and done with it. I wonder what new fad he has taken up now? Come along and let's look him up. We shall hear all about it quite soon enough."

They disembarked, and strolled across the gay flower-decked lawns in search of Toad, whom they presently happened upon resting in a wicker garden-chair, with a preoccupied expression of face, and a large map spread out on his knees.

"Hooray!" he cried, jumping up on seeing them, "this is splendid!" He shook the paws of both of them warmly, never waiting for an introduction to the Mole. "How *kind* of you!" he went on, dancing round them. "I was just going to send a boat down the river for you, Ratty, with strict orders that you were to be fetched up here at once, whatever you were doing. I want you badly — both of you. Now what will you take? Come inside and have something! You don't know how lucky it is, your turning up just now!"

"Let's sit quiet a bit, Toady!" said the Rat, throwing himself into an easy chair, while the Mole took another by the side of him and made some civil remark about Toad's "delightful residence."

"Finest house on the whole river," cried Toad boisterously. "Or anywhere else, for that matter," he could not help adding.

Here the Rat nudged the Mole. Unfortunately the Toad saw him do it, and turned very red. There was a moment's painful silence. Then Toad burst out laughing. "All right, Ratty," he said. "It's only my way, you know. And it's not

such a very bad house, is it? You know you rather like it yourself. Now, look here. Let's be sensible. You are the very animals I wanted. You've got to help me. It's most important!"

"It's about your rowing, I suppose," said the Rat, with an innocent air. "You're getting on fairly well, though you splash a good bit still. With a great deal of patience, and any quantity of coaching, you may ——"

"O, pooh! boating!" interrupted the Toad, in great disgust. "Silly boyish amusement. I've given that up *long* ago. Sheer waste of time, that's what it is. It makes me downright sorry to see you fellows, who ought to know better, spending all your energies in that aimless manner. No, I've discovered the real thing, the only genuine occupation for a lifetime. I propose to devote the remainder of mine to it, and can only regret the wasted years, that lie behind me, squandered in trivialities. Come with me, dear Ratty, and your amiable friend also, if he will be so very good, just as far as the stable-yard, and you shall see what you shall see!"

He led the way to the stable-yard accordingly, the Rat following with a most mistrustful expression; and there, drawn out of the coach-house into the open, they saw a gipsy caravan, shining with newness, painted a canary-yellow picked out with green, and red wheels.

"There you are!" cried the Toad, straddling and expanding himself. "There's real life for you, embodied in that little cart. The open road, the dusty highway, the heath, the common, the hedgerows, the rolling downs! Camps, villages, towns, cities! Here to-day, up and off to somewhere else to-morrow! Travel, change, interest, excitement! The whole world before you, and a horizon that's always changing! And mind, this is the very finest cart of its sort that was ever built, without any exception. Come inside and look at the arrangements. Planned 'em all myself, I did!"

The Mole was tremendously interested and excited, and followed him eagerly up the steps and into the interior of the caravan. The Rat only snorted and thrust his hands deep into his pockets, remaining where he was.

It was indeed very compact and comfortable. Little sleeping-bunks — a little table that folded up against the wall — a cooking-stove, lockers, bookshelves, a bird-cage with a bird in it; and pots, pans, jugs and kettles of every size and variety.

"All complete!" said the Toad triumphantly, pulling open a locker. "You see — biscuits, potted lobster, sardines — everything you can possibly want. Soda-water here — bacon there — letter-paper, jam, cards and dominoes — you'll find," he continued, as they descended the steps again, "you'll find that nothing whatever has been forgotten, when we make our start this afternoon."

"I beg your pardon," said the Rat slowly, as he chewed a straw, "but did I overhear you say something about '*we*,' and '*start*,' and '*this afternoon*'?"

"Now, you dear good old Ratty," said Toad imploringly, "don't begin talking in that stiff and sniffy sort of way, because you know you've *got* to come. I can't possibly manage without you, so please consider it settled, and don't argue — it's the one thing I can't stand. You surely don't mean to stick

TRAVEL
LOG

to your dull fusty old river all your life, and just live in a hole in a bank, and *boat*? I want to show you the world! I'm going to make an *animal* of you, my boy!"

"I don't care," said the Rat doggedly. "I'm not coming, and that's flat. And I *am* going to stick to my old river, *and* live in a hole, *and* boat, as I've always done. And what's more, Mole's going to stick to me and do as I do, aren't you, Mole?"

"Of course I am," said the Mole loyally. "I'll always stick to you, Rat, and what you say is to be — has got to be. All the same, it sounds as if it might have been — well, rather fun, you know!" he added wistfully. Poor Mole! The Life Adventurous was so new a thing to him, and so thrilling; and this fresh aspect of it was so tempting; and he had fallen in love at first sight with the canary-coloured cart and all its little fitments.

The Rat saw what was passing in his mind, and wavered. He hated disappointing people, and he was fond of the Mole, and would do almost anything to oblige him. Toad was watching both of them closely.

"Come along in and have some lunch," he said diplomatically, "and we'll talk it over. We needn't decide anything in a hurry. Of course, *I* don't really care. I only want to give pleasure to you fellows. 'Live for others!' That's my motto in life."

During luncheon — which was excellent, of course, as everything at Toad Hall always was — the Toad simply let himself go. Disregarding the Rat, he proceeded to play upon the inexperienced Mole as on a harp. Naturally a voluble animal, and always mastered by his imagination, he painted the prospects of the trip and the joys of the open life and the roadside in such glowing colours that the Mole could hardly sit in his chair for excitement. Somehow, it soon seemed taken for granted by all three of them that the trip was a settled thing; and the Rat, though still unconvinced in his mind, allowed his good-nature to override his personal objections. He could not bear to disappoint his two friends, who were already deep in schemes and anticipations, planning out each day's separate occupation for several weeks ahead.

When they were quite ready, the now triumphant Toad led his companions to the paddock and set them to capture the old grey horse, who, without having been consulted, and to his own extreme annoyance, had been told off by Toad for the dustiest job in this dusty expedition. He frankly preferred the paddock, and took a deal of catching. Meantime Toad packed the lockers still tighter with necessaries, and hung nose-bags, nets of onions, bundles of hay, and baskets from the bottom of the cart. At last the horse was caught and harnessed, and they set off, all talking at once, each animal either trudging by the side of the cart or sitting on the shaft, as the humour took him. It was a golden afternoon. The smell of the dust they kicked up was rich and satisfying; out of thick orchards on either side of the road, birds called and whistled to them cheerily; good-natured wayfarers, passing them, gave them "Good day," or stopped to say nice things about their beautiful cart; and rabbits, sitting at their front doors in the hedgerows, held up their fore paws, and said, "O my! O my! O my!"

Late in the evening, tired and happy and miles from home, they drew up on a remote common far from habitations, turned the horse loose to graze, and ate their simple supper sitting on the grass by the side of the cart. Toad talked big about all he was going to do in the days to come, while stars grew fuller and larger all around them, and a yellow moon, appearing suddenly and silently from nowhere in particular, came to keep them company and listen to their talk. At last they turned into their little bunks in the cart; and Toad, kicking out his legs, sleepily said, "Well, good night, you

fellows! This is the real life for a gentleman! Talk about your old river!"

"I *don't* talk about my river," replied the patient Rat. "You *know* I don't, Toad. But I *think* about it," he added pathetically, in a lower tone: "I think about it — all the time!"

The Mole reached out from under his blanket, felt for the Rat's paw in the darkness, and gave it a squeeze. "I'll do whatever you like, Ratty," he whispered. "Shall we run away to-morrow morning, quite early — *very* early — and go back to our dear old hole on the river?"

"No, no, we'll see it out," whispered back the Rat. "Thanks awfully, but I ought to stick by Toad till this trip is ended. It wouldn't be safe for him to be left to himself. It won't take very long. His fads never do. Good night!"

The end was indeed nearer than even the Rat suspected.

After so much open air and excitement the Toad slept very soundly, and no amount of shaking could rouse him out of bed next morning. So the Mole and Rat turned to, quietly and manfully, and while the Rat saw to the horse, and lit a fire, and cleaned last night's cups and platters, and got things ready for breakfast, the Mole trudged off to the nearest village, a long way off, for milk and eggs and various necessaries the Toad had, of course, forgotten to provide. The hard work had all been done, and the two animals were resting, thoroughly exhausted, by the time Toad appeared on the scene, fresh and gay, remarking what a pleasant easy life it was they were all leading now, after the cares and worries and fatigues of housekeeping at home.

They had a pleasant ramble that day over grassy downs and along narrow by-lanes, and camped, as before, on a common, only this time the two guests took care that Toad should do his fair share of work. In consequence, when the time came for starting next morning, Toad was by no means so rapturous about the simplicity of the primitive life, and indeed attempted to resume his place in his bunk, whence he was hauled by force. Their way lay, as before, across country by narrow lanes, and it was not till the afternoon that they came out on the high road, their first high road; and there disaster, fleet and unforeseen, sprang out on them — disaster momentous indeed to their expedition, but simply overwhelming in its effect on the after-career of Toad.

They were strolling along the high road easily, the Mole by the horse's head, talking to him, since the horse had complained that he was being frightfully left out of it, and nobody considered him in the least; the Toad and the Water Rat walking behind the cart talking together — at least Toad was talking, and Rat was saying at intervals, "Yes, precisely; and what did *you* say to *him*?" — and thinking all the time of something very different, when far behind them they heard a faint warning hum, like the drone of a distant bee. Glancing back, they saw a small cloud of dust, with a dark centre of energy, advancing on them at incredible speed, while from out the dust a faint "Toot-toot!" wailed like an uneasy animal in pain. Hardly regarding it, they turned to resume their conversation, when in an instant (as it seemed) the peaceful scene was changed, and with a blast of wind and a whirl of sound that made them jump for the nearest ditch, it was on them! The "toot-toot" rang with a brazen shout in their ears, they had a moment's glimpse of an interior of glittering plate-glass

and rich morocco, and the magnificent motor-car, immense, breath-snatching, passionate, with its pilot tense and hugging his wheel, possessed all earth and air for the fraction of a second, flung an enveloping cloud of dust that blinded and enwrapped them utterly, and then dwindled to a speck in the far distance, changed back into a droning bee once more.

The old grey horse, dreaming, as he plodded along, of his quiet paddock, in a new raw situation such as this simply abandoned himself to his natural emotions. Rearing, plunging, backing steadily, in spite of all the Mole's efforts at his head, and all the Mole's lively language directed at his better feelings, he drove the cart backwards towards the deep ditch at the side of the road. It wavered an instant — then there was a heart-rending crash — and the canary-coloured cart, their pride and their joy, lay on its side in the ditch, an irredeemable wreck.

The Rat danced up and down in the road, simply transported with passion. "You villains!" he shouted, shaking both fists. "You scoundrels, you highwaymen, you — you — roadhogs! — I'll have the law on you! I'll report you! I'll take you through all the Courts!" His home-sickness had quite slipped away from him, and for the moment he was the skipper of the canary-coloured vessel driven on a shoal by the reckless jockeying of rival mariners, and he was trying to recollect all the fine and biting things he used to say to masters of steam-launches when their wash, as they drove too near the bank, used to flood his parlour carpet at home.

Toad sat straight down in the middle of the dusty road, his legs stretched out before him, and stared fixedly in the direction of the disappearing motor-car. He breathed short, his face wore a placid, satisfied expression, and at intervals he faintly murmured "Toot-toot!"

The Mole was busy trying to quiet the horse, which he succeeded in doing after a time. Then he went to look at the

cart, on its side in the ditch. It was indeed a sorry sight. Panels and windows smashed, axles hopelessly bent, one wheel off, sardine-tins scattered over the wide world, and the bird in the bird-cage sobbing pitifully and calling to be let out.

The Rat came to help him, but their united efforts were not sufficient to right the cart. "Hi! Toad!" they cried. "Come and bear a hand, can't you!"

The Toad never answered a word, or budged from his seat in the road; so they went to see what was the matter with him. They found him in a sort of trance, a happy smile on his face, his eyes still fixed on the dusty wake of their destroyer. At intervals he was still heard to murmur "Toot-toot!"

The Rat shook him by the shoulder. "Are you coming to help us, Toad?" he demanded sternly.

"Glorious, stirring sight!" murmured Toad, never offering to move. "The poetry of motion! The *real* way to travel! The *only* way to travel! Here to-day — in next week to-morrow! Villages skipped, towns and cities jumped — always somebody else's horizon! O bliss! O toot-toot! O my! O my!"

"O *stop* it, Toad!" cried the Mole despairingly.

"And to think I never *knew*!" went on the Toad in a dreamy monotone. "All those wasted years that lie behind me, I never knew, never even *dreamt*! But *now* — but now that I know, now that I fully realize! O what a flowery track lies spread before me, henceforth! What dust-clouds shall spring up

behind me as I speed on my reckless way! What carts I shall fling carelessly into the ditch in the wake of my magnificent onset! Horrid little carts — common carts — canary-coloured carts!"

"What are we to do with him?" asked the Mole of the Water Rat.

"Nothing at all," replied the Rat firmly. "Because there is really nothing to be done. You see, I know him from old. He is now possessed. He has got a new craze, and it always takes him that way, in its first stage. He'll continue like that for days now, like an animal walking in a happy dream, quite useless for all practical purposes. Never mind him. Let's go and see what there is to be done about the cart."

A careful inspection showed them that, even if they succeeded in righting it by themselves, the cart would travel no longer. The axles were in a hopeless state, and the missing wheel was shattered into pieces.

The Rat knotted the horse's reins over his back and took him by the head, carrying the bird-cage and its hysterical occupant in the other hand. "Come on!" he said grimly to the Mole. "It's five or six miles to the nearest town, and we shall just have to walk it. The sooner we make a start the better."

"But what about Toad?" asked the Mole anxiously, as they set off together. "We can't leave him here, sitting in the middle of the road by himself, in the distracted state he's in! It's not safe. Supposing another Thing were to come along?"

"O, *bother* Toad," said the Rat savagely; "I've done with him!"

They had not proceeded very far on their way, however, when there was a pattering of feet behind them, and Toad caught them up and thrust a paw inside the elbow of each of them, still breathing short and staring into vacancy.

"Now, look here, Toad!" said the Rat sharply: "as soon as we get to the town, you'll have to go straight to the police-

station, and see if they know anything about that motor-car and who it belongs to, and lodge a complaint against it. And then you'll have to go to a blacksmith's or a wheelwright's and arrange for the cart to be fetched and mended and put to rights. It'll take time, but it's not quite a hopeless smash. Meanwhile, the Mole and I will go to an inn and find comfortable rooms where we can stay till the cart's ready, and till your nerves have recovered their shock."

"Police-station! Complaint!" murmured Toad dreamily. "Me *complain* of that beautiful, that heavenly vision that has been vouchsafed me! *Mend* the *cart*! I've done with carts for ever. I never want to see the cart, or to hear of it, again. O, Ratty! You can't think how obliged I am to you for consenting to come on this trip! I wouldn't have gone without you, and then I might never have seen that — that swan, that sunbeam, that thunderbolt! I might never have heard that entrancing sound, or smelt that bewitching smell! I owe it all to you, my best of friends!"

The Rat turned from him in despair. "You see what it is?" he said to the Mole, addressing him across Toad's head: "He's quite hopeless. I give it up — when we get to the town we'll go to the railway-station, and with luck we may pick up a train there that'll get us back to River Bank tonight. And if ever you catch me going a-pleasuring with this provoking animal again!" — He snorted, and during the rest of that weary trudge addressed his remarks exclusively to Mole.

On reaching the town they went straight to the station and deposited Toad in the second-class waiting-room, giving a porter twopence to keep a strict eye on him. They then left the horse at an inn stable, and gave what directions they could about the cart and its contents. Eventually, a slow train having landed them at a station not very far from Toad Hall, they escorted the spell-bound, sleep-walking Toad to his door, put him inside it, and instructed his housekeeper to feed him, undress him, and put him to bed. Then they got out their boat from the boat-house, sculled down the river home, and at a very late hour sat down to supper in their own cosy riverside parlour, to the Rat's great joy and contentment.

The following evening the Mole, who had risen late and taken things very easy all day, was sitting on the bank fishing, when the Rat, who had been looking up his friends and gossiping, came strolling along to find him. "Heard the news?" he said. "There's nothing else being talked about, all along the river bank. Toad went up to Town by an early train this morning. And he has ordered a large and very expensive motor-car."

Author

Kenneth Grahame was born in 1859 in Edinburgh, Scotland, and was raised in England near the Thames River. There he learned about the types of river animals that appear in his book *The Wind in the Willows,* part of which you have just read. This book grew out of stories that Mr. Grahame made up for his son Alastair. Throughout Alastair's childhood, Mr. Grahame also wrote letters to his son with further adventures of Toad and his friends. *The Wind in the Willows* has delighted readers of all ages ever since its publication in 1908. Like another of Mr. Grahame's books, *The Reluctant Dragon,* it was made into a popular movie by Walt Disney.

In addition to writing, Mr. Grahame worked for the Bank of England and was Secretary of the Bank at the time of his retirement in 1908. He died in 1932.

Houghton Mifflin Literature

In the selections you have just read from *Understanding Self and Others,* the question "Who am I?" is a voyage through stormy waters. It is a voyage which everyone must make. Understanding one's self and others is basic to what it means to be alive.

As you read *Abel's Island* by William Steig, you will be whisked off to a place where a pampered mouse named Abel, used to a life of ease, is forced to see himself clearly, for the first time.

5

Facing Challenges of Nature

Something Told the Wild Geese

by Rachel Field

Something told the wild geese
  It was time to go.
Though the fields lay golden
  Something whispered, — "Snow."
Leaves were green and stirring,
  Berries, luster-glossed,
But beneath warm feathers
  Something cautioned, — "Frost."
All the sagging orchards
  Steamed with amber spice,
But each wild breast stiffened
  At remembered ice.
Something told the wild geese
  It was time to fly, —
Summer sun was on their wings,
  Winter in their cry.

An excerpt from

The Hammerhead Light

by Colin Thiele

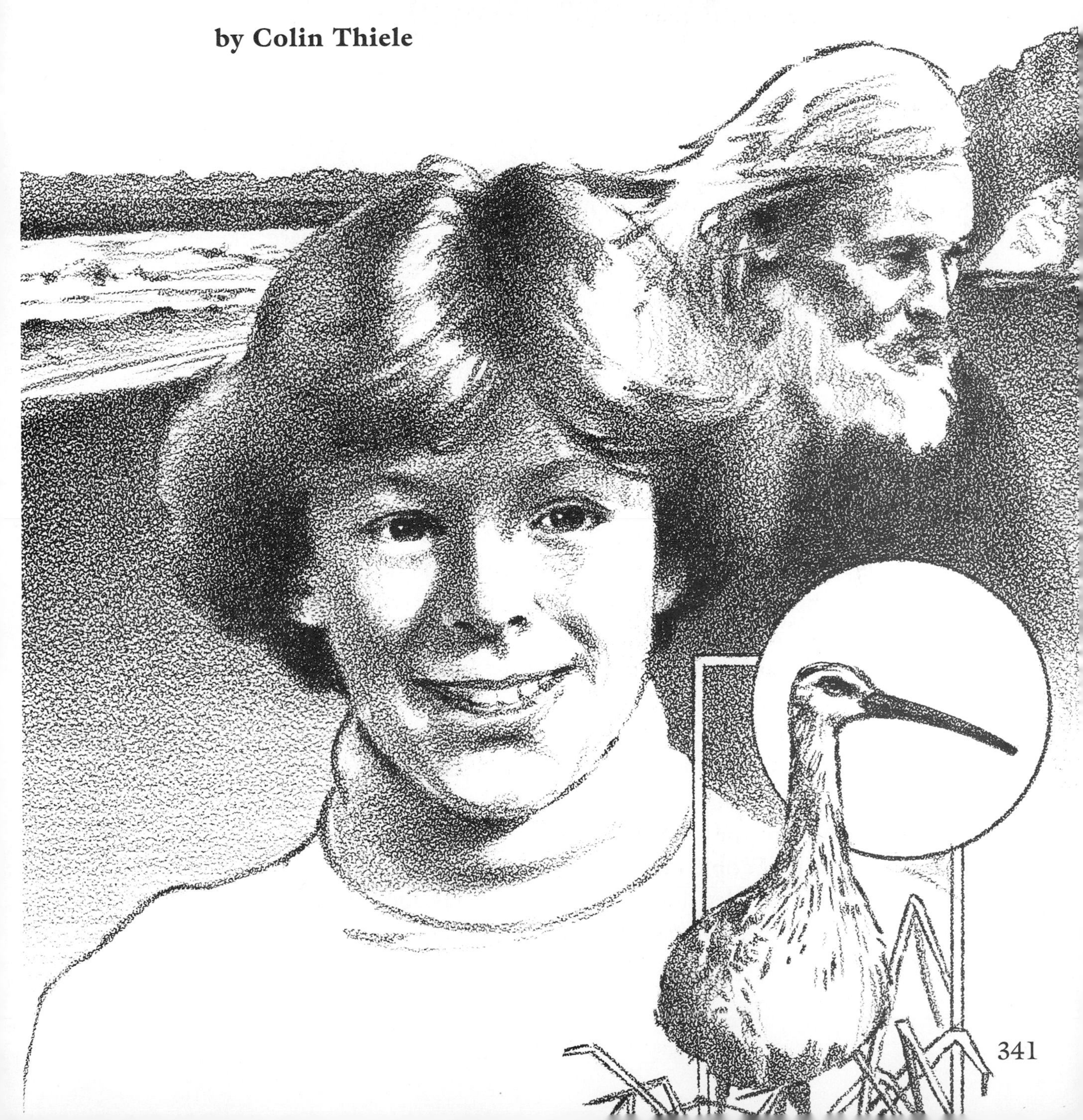

The Whimbrel

About a hundred people lived in the little town of Snapper Bay in southern Australia. Some of them were young, and some were old, and some were in-between.

Axel Jorgensen was seventy-two, with a mop of white hair and a cotton-wool beard, and legs that bowed outward like bananas. He looked something like Father Christmas.

Tessa Noble was twelve, with a mop of brown hair and tapioca-freckled cheeks, and legs that bowed inward at the knees like bent sticks. She lived in a white house in the main street of Snapper Bay. There was only one street in the whole town, so it had to be the main one anyway. She lived with her father and mother and her grown-up brother, Jody, and Jody's wife, Bridget.

Axel Jorgensen lived by himself in a wooden hut far around the curve of the bay, away from the town. It was the place where the sandy beach ended and the first rocks reared up near the start of the Hammerhead Handle. He was a fisherman and a forager, a boatman and a beachcomber, a talker and a teacher. He taught Tessa many things. When they walked along the coast together he taught her about seashells and albatrosses, and when they walked inland by the lakes and marshes he taught her about summer sedges, snails, and spoonbills in the wildlife sanctuary. She thought he was one of the Wise People of the World.

She had called him Uncle Axel for as long as she could remember, even though they were not related. He often came to have a meal in Tessa's house, and Tessa's father went fishing with him whenever he could. She spent as much time pottering about near his shack as she did in her own little street in Snapper Bay.

The shack was filled with things that Tessa's mother called junk. There were oars and rusty oarlocks, bits of rope, rudder pins and grappling hooks, boxes, chains, and old craypots that seemed ancient enough to have come out of Noah's Ark. For Axel had been a sailor as well as a beachcomber, a lighthouse keeper as well as a fisherman. He had known Tessa since the day she was born.

Axel loved all living things — even Rump, the young wombat, who caused him a lot of trouble. Rump had been run over by a car near the Murray River, and the driver had picked him up and left him with Axel, just like a patient in a hospital. When Rump had recovered he had stayed on, burrowing in the bank behind the hut or wandering down to the town to thin out someone's vegetable garden.

"It's that potbellied wombat again," people used to say when they found out. "Take him back to Axel."

And so Rump would soon be back digging in his bank again or snuffling in a corner of the hut or scrabbling under the floor. Once Axel had disappeared completely into a new wombat hole while he had been stirring the porridge at the stove. But he was never angry with Rump. He wouldn't even call him a pet. He was a mate, he said, a friend and a companion.

One morning when Tessa walked around the long curve of the beach to Axel's hut she found him busy and excited. He was working at the vise on his bench near the door of his shack.

"What are you doing?" she asked. "What's up?"

"You'll never guess, Tessa girl," he said. She knew that something had happened, because he never called her Tessa girl unless he was excited.

"What is it, then?"

"Look inside." He nodded his head at the shack. "But move slowly."

She was suspicious and walked very carefully. "Is it a snake?"

"Not a snake. Come and see."

At first she couldn't see anything at all in the shadow. She opened her eyes wide and then puckered them quickly to get a clearer view.

"I can't see a thing."

"Not very smart, are you?" He chuckled. "Wouldn't take you out to see things in the marshes."

"Is it a . . . Oh!" Suddenly she saw it. There was a little silence while she took a breath and looked at it. Axel went on working busily at the vise on his bench.

It was a bird with a long curved beak, lying on its side in a large wire cage, panting. It was streaked brown and buff over the wings and body, but its breast was white and its crown had long white stripes above the eyes. It was beautiful — lovely mottled feathers and bright frightened eyes, and a long slender downward-curving bill.

"What is it?" Tessas asked at last.

Axel straightened up and stopped his filing at the vise. "A whimbrel," he said.

"A whimbrel." Tessa tasted the name on her tongue. "I like that. It's a name with meanings in the sounds."

"Yes," Axel answered. "Speed and distance, and lonely faraway cries in the night."

Tessa paused and looked at it again. "Is it hurt?"

"Yes."

She sensed something in his voice. "Is it very bad?"

"Pretty bad."

"Wings?" she asked.

Axel took the thing he was making out of the vise, examined it, put it back, and turned toward her.

"He's lost a foot, Tessa. He can't stand up properly."

She was horrified. "A foot? How on earth could he have lost a foot?"

"Who knows?"

"A fish? Do you think maybe a barracuda bit it off?"

Axel shook his head. "It would have happened on the land — or in the air. He likes the inlets and the mud flats."

"A sharp piece of iron, then? Or a piece of wire — a power line he didn't see when he was flying fast?"

Axel's big mop of white hair trembled as he shook his head again. "No. A bullet, more likely."

Tessa was appalled. "Not a bullet!" she said quickly. "Nobody would shoot at a whimbrel!"

"No?" Axel rubbed angrily with a file. "Have you seen the way Tiny Herbert or Joe Zucci handle a rifle around here? Like maniacs!"

"But not at a whimbrel. Surely they wouldn't shoot at a whimbrel."

"They'd shoot at anything. At a stilt or a curlew or an ibis or a pelican, at a spoonbill or a snipe or a swallow or a swan, at a post or a tin or a light bulb or a tank. They ought to be locked up."

"That's awful." She was silent for a while. "What's going to happen to him?"

Old Axel looked up sharply. "What do you think? He can't live as he is, can he? He has to fly all the way to Siberia or Canada in a few weeks' time."

"But that's on the other side of the world!"

"Yes. Big enough trip to tackle with two legs."

She sat on an old box near the door and glanced back and forth from Axel to the whimbrel. "Can he land on one foot, and take off again?"

"Most birds can stand on one foot — if it's not too windy. But his other foot is hurt too — the claw."

"Can't he stand at all, then?"

"He can tumble about and hop and flap and flop. But how could he live like that? How could he get enough food? It would be better to put him away than to let him starve to death."

Her eyes opened wide. "Put him away?"

"Yes. Kill him kindly."

"No," she said quickly. "Oh no, you wouldn't do that." She paused for a second and looked at the old man shrewdly. "You couldn't do that, could you?"

He seemed to be so busy at his vise that at first she thought he hadn't heard her. But after a while he went on without looking up. "Sometimes things have to be done even when you don't want to do them. Even when it's very hard."

"I know you wouldn't do it," she said confidently, "even if you could." She stood up and went over to him. "What are you making?"

He unfastened something very small from the vise and held it up. It was a foot. A tiny wooden foot — for a whimbrel.

Tessa held the whimbrel while Axel tried to fit the artificial foot. It was not an easy thing to do, even though the little piece of wood was carefully made, with three carved toes, and a hollow stem to fit over the stump of the leg.

Fortunately the whimbrel didn't struggle. Axel showed Tessa how to hold it firmly and gently with the wings wrapped against its body. Although it was frightened it seemed to know that they were trying to help. Its dark eyes blinked and flashed, and when its head moved jerkily its long bill darted about like a probe. Tessa was spellbound.

"It must be four inches long," she said.

Axel didn't even look up. "Four!" he said. "More like sixteen; nice streamlined bird, the whimbrel."

"Not the bird. The bill."

"What about the bill?"

"It must be four inches long."

"The bill is, yes. Not the bird."

"No, the bill, the bill."

"Well, why didn't you say so in the first place?"

Tessa snorted. "Really, Uncle Axel!" She was about to say much more, but decided to hold her peace. She looked down at the whimbrel again, at the great curving beak, as black as ebony, at the white breast, the mottled back, and the light stripe running above the eyebrows and over the curve of his head.

"Oh, you're a beautiful fellow," she said. But the bird suddenly struggled and she had to tighten her grip.

"Hold still, Willie," said old Axel gently. "We've nearly finished."

"Is that his name — Willie?"

"Suits him, I reckon. Will-he walk? Or won't he?"

"*Will-he* walk! That's a dreadful joke, Uncle Axel."

"Well, we'll soon know."

"Finished?"

"Finished."

Axel put his pliers and other tools aside and straightened up. "Put him down in his pen."

The whimbrel fluttered for a minute, but he settled down quickly and began to pace up and down in the cage. At first he lifted his leg with a high awkward step like a man learning to walk on skis, but before long he grew used to it and stomped about happily. Tessa had her nose pressed against the wire. "It works, Uncle Axel," she said excitedly. "It actually works."

"Of course it works," he answered haughtily.

"D'you think he'll be able to fly now, and land without somersaulting?"

"Give him a day or two to get used to it," Axel said. "It's not every day that a bird has to learn to fly with a wooden leg."

It was wise to wait. Two days later the wooden leg was useless. After Willie had walked in his tray of water a few times the light wood grew soggy and began to break up.

"Fat lot of use that was, Willie," said Axel. "Wouldn't have lasted you to Mount Gambier, let alone to the other side of the world. We'll have to do better than that."

So he worked at his bench for another whole day and made a metal foot — of aluminum. It was beautifully shaped, but it was too hard to fit to Willie's leg.

"Won't work," Axel admitted at last. "Might hurt him; probably do more harm than good."

Tessa was downhearted. "Whatever are we going to do, then? He looks so helpless when you take his foot away from him."

"We'll win yet. I've still got bags of ideas."

This time he made a plastic foot, cutting the shape carefully to match the real one, and melting out a hollow stem with a red-hot skewer. It fitted beautifully. But Axel was still not satisfied. He experimented for another two days, making more and more little feet and varying the length and diameter of the hollow stem until he had one that was perfect. It fitted snugly over the whole of the stump of Willie's leg and extended a half inch or so beyond it so that the two legs — the real one and the artificial one — were of exactly the same length. Then Axel fastened a tiny clamp around the stump to be doubly sure.

"Now, Willie," he said, "you ought to be able to dance to music."

Willie walked as if he was marching in a brass band. He looked so pleased that Tessa thought his big bill would break out into a long downward-curving smile.

"He's all right this time," she said. "Now he really can look after himself."

Axel kept him for another week, checking the foot carefully every day. By now Willie was quite tame, standing quietly when they came near him and even eating out of their hands. Tessa could see that Axel was becoming so fond of him that soon he wouldn't be able to part with him.

"Are you going to keep Willie?" she asked slyly one day. "Or are you going to set him free?"

Axel looked at her quizzically.

Tessa was very uncomfortable. She knew she had been rude and she was certain that he knew it too.

"Come on then," he said suddenly, lifting Willie out of his cage. "It's time you tested your new foot out in the wide world."

They carried the whimbrel inland over the dunes behind the shack until they came to the open flats beyond Snapper Bay. Then they stopped and both of them looked at Willie for the last time. His dark eyes were flashing and blinking. Tessa felt very sad, as if she was about to say farewell to a special friend forever.

"Good-bye, Willie," she whispered. "Look after yourself."

"Off you go," said Axel. "You'll be all right now."

He put Willie down on the firm clay near the edge of the mud flats. Willie stood for a second or two as if he was amazed at the sight of everything around him. Then he ran forward for a few steps and rose easily into the air. They both stood watching, holding their hands up to shade their eyes.

"Just look at him fly," Tessa said, "so fast and free."

"Beautiful," said Axel, watching intently. "Beautiful fellow."

They both remained with their hands to their eyes until the whimbrel curved downward at last toward the skyline by the marshes and they lost sight of him. Though the world was full of birds it was suddenly empty.

"Back home, Tessa," said Axel gently. He saw her eyes misting over and her lip trembling. "No need to be sad for Willie," he said quietly. "He's happy back with the other whimbrels — with all his friends. It wouldn't be right to keep him in a cage, especially when they all fly to the other side of the world. Think how lonely he would be then. You wouldn't like that."

She shook her head. "No, I wouldn't like that."

"And think what a hero he'll be. He'll be able to talk about his wooden leg for the rest of his life."

"His plastic leg."

"Just like old Mrs. Elliot with her operation."

Tessa smiled. "He will be sort of special, won't he?"

"Super special," said Axel. "There won't be another whimbrel like him in the whole world."

Author

A native Australian, Colin Thiele has been a teacher, a school principal, and a lecturer, as well as a well-known author. Besides children's books, his writings include poetry, short stories, articles, educational books, and radio plays. His work has won many awards and has been translated into several languages. The excerpt you have just read is from his children's book *The Hammerhead Light.*

Pearson, A Harbor Seal Pup

by Susan Meyers

The pup was an orphan. He was found one morning in April, alone and half-starved, on a deserted beach in northern California. Like all young harbor seals, he had soft, gray-spotted fur and big, dark eyes. He moved by inching along the sand on his belly, and he made a plaintive *krooh, krooh* sound like the mooing of a hungry calf.

No one knew what had happened to his mother. The woman who found him watched and waited to see if the mother seal would return. But she didn't. Perhaps she was dead. She may have been killed by a shark or a hunter. Without someone to feed and protect him, the pup would die.

So the woman made a phone call. She called the California Marine Mammal Center. And that afternoon, the seal's new life began.

The Marine Mammal Center is located on the coast of the Pacific Ocean, just outside the city of San Francisco. It is a combination hospital, orphanage, and shelter for sick and abandoned seals and sea lions. Most of the people who work there are volunteers who have a special interest in marine mammals. They give the animals brought to the Center the medical attention they need. They feed and care for them until they are healthy enough to be returned to the sea.

On the afternoon in April when the orphaned pup arrived, nine elephant seals and three harbor seal pups were already at the Center. Holly Garner, the acting curator, greeted the new seal. She stroked his sleek body and let him sniff her hand with his whiskered nose.

The pup was thin, but his eyes were bright and alert. He was no more than two weeks old. In his short life, all he had known was the sea and the sand and the comfort of his mother's body. Now, human hands were holding him. But he showed no fear. He looked around curiously. He listened alertly to the strange sounds and breathed in the strange smells.

"Let's call him Pearson," Holly said. It was a good-luck name — the name of a volunteer who had worked at the Center the summer before and had had great success with harbor seal pups.

Holly hoped that this pup would be a good-luck seal. She wrote the name on a chart and then began to examine the new patient.

Caring for marine mammals — especially young ones — is not an easy task. Whales, dolphins, walruses, seals, sea lions, and sea otters are all marine mammals. Millions of years ago, their ancestors lived on land. Now, although they live in the sea, these animals breathe air, are warm-blooded, and nurse their young with milk from their bodies, just as land-living mammals do. Because they live in the oceans, however, marine mammals are difficult to study. Many things about the way they behave and the way their bodies work are not known.

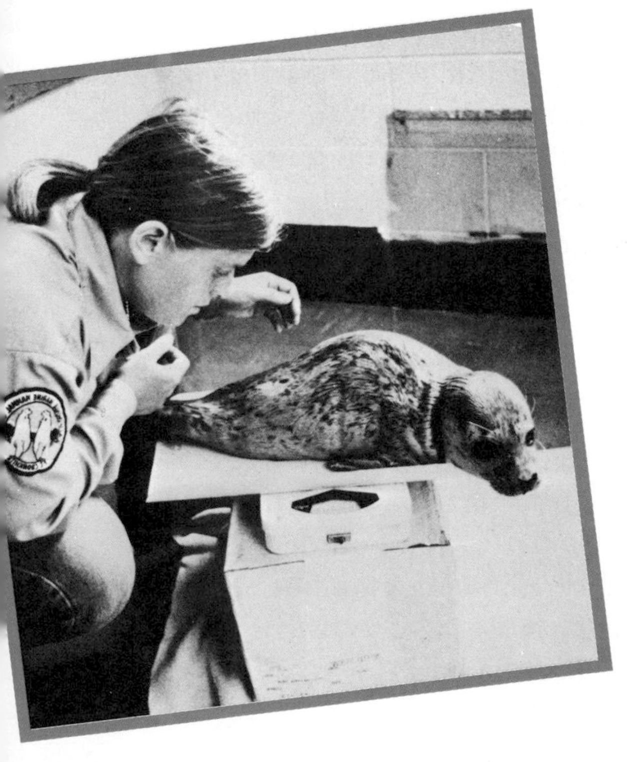

The people at the Marine Mammal Center had found that harbor seal pups which were brought to them were especially difficult to raise. They were often in poor health. Usually they were very young and seriously underweight. This made them delicate and vulnerable to disease.

Holly was glad, then, when she put Pearson on a scale and found that he weighed 21 pounds and 2 ounces — less than a pup his age should have weighed, but still enough to give him a good start.

His temperature was normal. His eyes were watering. This was a good sign, too; for unlike land-living mammals, seals have no internal tear ducts. When they are in good health, tears flow continuously down their cheeks. The area beneath their eyes is always wet.

Holly opened the pup's mouth and saw that his gums were pink and healthy looking. This meant that he was not in shock or bleeding internally. Sharp little canine teeth protruded through the gums. Harbor seals are born with these teeth already in place, for they nurse only a short time and then must be able to catch fish on their own.

But that lay in the future for Pearson. Right now, he used his teeth for another purpose. As Holly took her hand away from his mouth, he reached out and nipped the sleeve of her shirt.

Holly laughed. Pearson had spunk. There was no doubt about that. He was also, as far as she could tell, in good health. She wrote the findings of her examination on his chart, and slipped it into a file folder. Then she picked him up and put him into an indoor pen with the other harbor seal pups.

Pearson scooted around the cool, cement floor of the pen. He rolled onto a blanket. He touched noses with the other pups. Then he looked up at Holly. "Krooh," he cried. It sounded almost like a question.

"Don't worry, little fellow, you're going to be okay," Holly said, as if in answer.

She hoped that she was right.

Normally, harbor seals are hardy animals. They are found in oceans and bays of the Northern Hemisphere all around the world. In the United States, they live along both the Atlantic and Pacific coasts, and are often seen swimming in harbors close to towns and cities.

Unlike marine mammals such as whales and dolphins, harbor seals do not spend all their time in the water. They hunt fish and shellfish for food, but when they are tired, they come out of the sea to rest on rocks and quiet beaches.

Their pups may be born anywhere—on a beach, in a marsh, or even in the water. The baby seal can swim—though not expertly—from the moment it takes its first breath. But in the early weeks of life, the mother seal helps it. She cradles the pup in her front flippers. She holds it close to her when she dives. When the pup is tired, she lets it ride on her back.

The pup drinks milk from its mother. This milk is about ten times richer than cow's milk. It helps the pup to grow quickly and to develop a thick layer of fat, or blubber, which protects it from the cold.

At the Marine Mammal Center, the harbor seal pups are fed a formula made from cream, butter, cod-liver oil, pureed fish, and vitamins. The formula is fed to the pups through a tube which is inserted down their throats and into their stomachs.

The first time that Pearson was fed this way, he didn't like it at all.

One volunteer had to hold him still, while another opened his mouth. Quickly and expertly, she slipped the rubber tube over his tongue and down his throat. Pearson gagged and tried to wriggle free, but the volunteer held him firmly. Slowly, the formula was poured into a funnel and down the tube.

In the past, the people who worked at the Center had tried feeding the pups from ordinary baby bottles. But this had been a failure. They couldn't seem to grasp the nipple of a baby bottle properly, and in the attempt, the rubber was quickly torn to shreds.

The only way to get the formula the pups needed into their stomachs was to feed it to them by tube.

Eventually, most of the pups got used to the tube. They didn't gag and struggle when it was inserted. In fact, some even learned to swallow the end of the tube themselves, knowing that the satisfying feeling of a full stomach would quickly follow.

When the tube was removed from Pearson's throat, he lay still with his eyes closed. It had probably been days since he had eaten. Perhaps he needed time to get used to the feeling of a full stomach again. The volunteer stroked him gently. She knew that he was now on his way to gaining back the weight he had lost while lying alone and helpless on the beach. For the first time since he had been found and brought to the Center, Pearson had a chance. With luck, he might one day grow to be a strong and healthy adult seal.

The harbor seal pups were favorites with everyone who worked at the Center, and Pearson quickly became especially popular.

He was full of energy and high spirits, and was more active than any of the other pups. When he was inside, he liked to grab the blankets spread on the floor of the pen, and drag them about with his teeth. If the gate was left open, he was always ready to slip out and have a look around.

On his diet of rich formula, Pearson began to gain weight. Moving him from the inside pen, where the pups spent the night, to the outside pen and wading pool, where they spent the day, was a job. He was hard to hold. He had to be wrapped in a blanket so that if he wriggled, he would not slip and fall to the ground.

When Pearson had been at the Center for a week, Holly decided it was time to introduce him to fish.

In the sea, a harbor seal pup learns to catch and eat fish by watching its mother. By the time it is weaned, at the age of four or five weeks, it is able to feed on its own.

Without a mother, and living temporarily in captivity, Pearson had to be taught what a fish was and how to swallow it. Eventually, he would have to learn to catch one himself.

Holly started his training with a small herring — an oily fish which is a favorite with seals. Gently, she opened his mouth and slipped the fish in, headfirst. Harbor seals have sharp teeth for catching fish, but no teeth for grinding and chewing. They swallow their food whole.

But Pearson didn't seem to understand what he was supposed to do. He bit down on the fish and then spit it out. Holly tried again. This time, Pearson got the idea. He swallowed the herring in one gulp and looked eagerly for more.

Within a week, he was being hand-fed a pound of fish a day in addition to his formula. This new diet made him friskier than ever. He chased the other pups in the outside pen. He plunged into the small wading pool and rolled in the shallow water, splashing both seals and people.

Visitors who came to the Center were eager to see the pups. Holly worried about this, for she knew that, like all young animals, the pups needed plenty of rest. There was also a possibility that a visitor might be a carrier of germs which could make a young seal sick.

One of the problems with the orphaned pups brought to the Center was that they frequently had little resistance to illness. Most young mammals gain immunity, or protection from disease, from their mother's milk. But if a pup lost its mother before it had nursed long enough, it did not have this immunity. It could easily become sick.

In addition, some of the pups had probably been born prematurely, before they had a chance to develop fully in their mothers' bodies. Others had internal birth defects. Their lungs, livers, or kidneys did not function properly. Pups like these had very likely been abandoned on purpose. The mother seals had probably sensed that something was wrong and had simply left them to die.

The people at the Marine Mammal Center did not want any of the pups to die, but sometimes there was nothing they could do to save them. One morning, the smallest harbor seal pup was found dead in the inside pen. Within a week, the other two pups who had been at the Center when Pearson arrived also sickened and died.

Everyone felt sad. They knew that in the sea, animals often die young. Among harbor seals, perhaps as many as half the pups born never reach adulthood. But still, when it happened at the Center, it was hard to take. The volunteers wondered if the right things had been done. Had they fed the pups properly? Had they watched them carefully enough? Would the pups have lived if they had tried harder?

Now Pearson was the only pup left, and suddenly he seemed more special than ever. The volunteers couldn't help regarding him anxiously. He looked healthy, but they knew that looks were no guarantee. They made up their minds to do everything within their power to keep him strong and healthy. He had had good luck so far. His human friends were determined to make it continue.

Alone in his pen, Pearson slipped into the water of the little wading pool and rolled about. But there were no other pups to splash and chase.

From time to time he cried, but mostly he was silent. Harbor seal pups make their distinctive mooing sound only when they are very young. It is a signal to the mother seal. It helps her locate her pup on the beach or in the sea. After the age of four or five weeks, when the pup no longer needs its mother, it becomes silent.

Holly felt sorry for Pearson. She decided to move him to another pen. There he would be near a pair of young elephant seals. And he would have a larger pool. It was time for some real swimming.

At first, Pearson wasn't sure what to do in his new tank. It was much bigger and deeper than the old wading pool. But soon he felt at home. As the elephant seals next door watched, he swam eagerly back and forth. Down to the bottom he dove, then up again.

He practiced swimming on his back and on his stomach. He inspected the hose that brought fresh water into the tank. He turned in circles and chased his tail.

At mealtime, he was still swimming. Holly had to tempt him out of the pool by showing him the rubber tube that meant food. Pearson no longer had any trouble with tube feeding. Now he grabbed the end of the tube, pulled himself out of the tank, and swallowed the tube hungrily. When his feeding was over, he dozed contentedly in the late afternoon sun.

It was already May. As the warm spring days passed, Pearson grew steadily stronger. Soon he weighed 40 pounds — nearly 20 pounds more than he had weighed when he was brought to the Center.

And he had become an expert swimmer.

Like all seals, Pearson had a body which was streamlined and well-suited to life in the water. When swimming, he usually kept his front flippers pressed close to his sides. He used his rear flippers as a fish uses its tail, to propel himself quickly and gracefully forward.

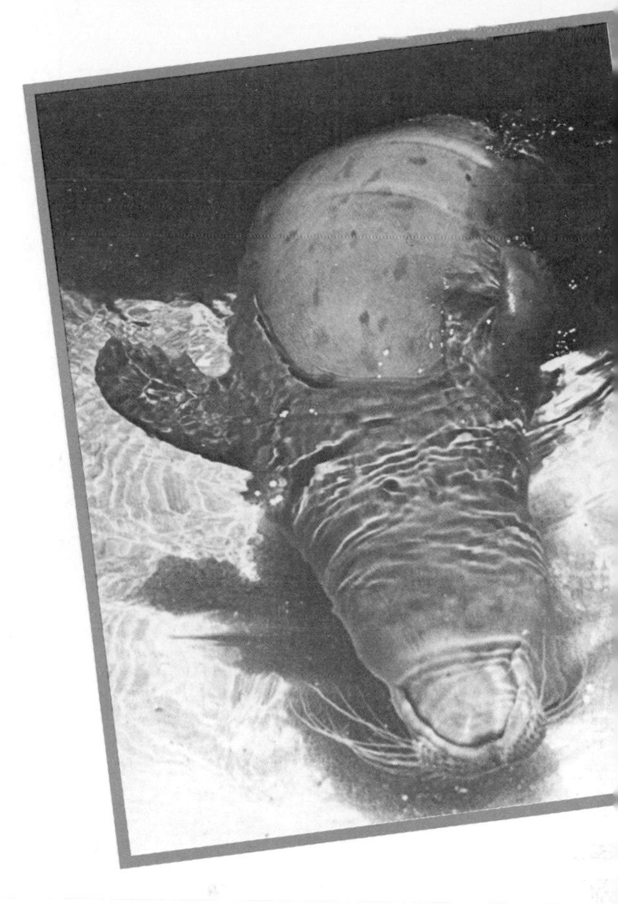

He could stay underwater for five minutes or more. Adult harbor seals can remain submerged for more than twenty minutes. During this time, the seal keeps its nostrils tightly closed. Its heartbeat slows. The veins in its flippers and skin contract. Its blood — which carries oxygen — is pumped primarily to the liver, lungs, kidneys, and brain. This oxygen-rich blood keeps these vital organs healthy. They are not damaged, even though the seal is not breathing.

While underwater, the seal uses its keen senses to hunt for fish and to remain alert to enemies. Its eyesight and hearing are excellent. In addition, it has a special kind of sensory ability. It can detect objects underwater by a method known as echo location.

To echo locate, a seal makes clicking sounds deep in its throat. The sound waves travel through the water. When they hit an object — such as a fish — they bounce, or echo, back. The returning waves hit the seal's whiskers. These whiskers are extremely sensitive. They are connected to the seal's brain by a network of nerves. In dark waters, the seal can tell, simply by the sensations in its whiskers, exactly what an object is and where it is located.

A seal does not need to be taught to echo locate, any more than it needs to be taught to see or to hear. But it does need to learn how to catch fish once it has found them.

Pearson's hunting lessons began one morning in June.

For the past weeks, Holly and the rest of the staff had been watching the young seal closely. They had kept track of his weight and had carefully observed his appearance and behavior. As the days passed, everyone had begun to feel reassured. Pearson showed no signs of illness. His body was sleek and fat. He had developed the thick layer of blubber seals need to keep warm in the sea. He no longer needed to be fed formula or to be brought inside for the night. There seemed to be no doubt about it. Pearson was going to live.

But keeping an animal alive was only part of the struggle. Once that goal had been reached, the next job — preparing the animal for return to the sea — had to be tackled.

In the sea, Pearson's mother would have taught him all he needed to know to survive as a seal. At the Center, that job had to be taken over by his human keepers. Lessons in catching fish were the first step.

One morning, a volunteer brought Pearson's breakfast into his pen. But, instead of feeding it to him by hand, as she usually did, she selected a tasty-looking herring and held it in the water in his tank. She wiggled it, making it look as if it were alive.

Pearson was curious. He swam toward the fish. He was hungry. Quickly he grabbed the herring. But instead of swallowing it at once — as he would have to do when chasing a group of fast-moving fish in the sea — he spit it out. He didn't know how to eat in this strange new way.

It took more than a week before Pearson finally learned to grab a fish in the water and swallow it at once. In another week, he was able to retrieve fish which were tossed into his tank. This made feeding time much easier. It also paved the way for the next step in Pearson's training program — learning to live without human companionship.

Harbor seals are naturally friendly and intelligent animals. In captivity, they respond affectionately to human attention. They like to be talked to and stroked. They come to know their names and to recognize the people who care for them.

The danger at the Center is that a pup like Pearson will become too attached to human beings. If he is to survive in the sea, he has to learn to live on his own. He cannot look to people for help.

Though it was hard, the volunteers gradually stopped spending so much time with Pearson. They fed him, but they did not pause to stroke his smooth gray fur, or to talk to him soothingly.

At first, Pearson seemed to miss his human companions. He watched for them. He scooted eagerly to the gate when they came to clean his pen or to bring him his dinner.

But gradually, he became more and more absorbed in his own affairs. He rested his head against the rim of the tank. He swam in circles, rippling the water with his flippers.

He slept in the warm summer sun.

He also listened to sounds. The cry of a bird or the bark of a dog in the distance would make him lift up his head and open his earholes wide.

As the summer went on, Pearson's mind and body slowly changed. He no longer looked like a baby. He weighed more than 50 pounds. His shape was longer and sleeker. His head was slimmer. His coat was a darker shade of gray.

He was no longer very interested in his human keepers. Sometimes he growled when the person cleaning his pen came too near. One day when Holly tried to pick him up to weigh him, he gave her a bad nip on the chin.

These changes in personality were hard to take. But at the same time, the people who worked at the Center knew that they were necessary. They were succeeding in their task of making Pearson independent. Though he had lived almost his entire life in captivity, he was definitely not a pet. Now that his babyhood was over, his natural instincts as a wild animal were beginning to assert themselves. It would soon be time to send him home to the sea.

The release of an animal from the Marine Mammal Center is an important event. It has to be well planned.The time and the place must be chosen with care. And the animal must be ready, both physically and mentally.

Pearson was in excellent condition, and by late July he weighed more than 60 pounds. Though this was much less than the 300 to 500 pounds he would weigh when fully grown, it was still enough to protect him for the present. He was too big to be easy prey for the sharks and killer whales which hunted smaller seal pups. In addition, if he had difficulty finding food during his first days in the sea, his weight would sustain him until he became a skilled hunter.

But Holly wished that he were more familiar with his own kind.

Harbor seals are naturally sociable animals. When on land, they gather together in groups. Besides providing companionship, these groups give the seals a degree of safety which they would not have on their own. Within a group, danger is likely to be sensed more quickly. One seal can give warning, and all the seals can escape.

There was no doubt that Pearson would be safer if he could join a group of harbor seals. And it might be easier for him to do this if he had some companions of his own kind at the Center. But Holly could see no way of providing any.

Then one morning, two young harbor seals which had been found stranded on a beach were brought to the Center. They were somewhat smaller than Pearson and had respiratory infections. They would probably have died if they had not been rescued and treated with antibiotics. Within a few days, they began to recover. And very soon, Pearson had the company he needed.

Holly and the rest of the staff and volunteers had mixed feelings as they began to think about Pearson's release. On the one hand, they were proud of the work they had done in raising the young seal to be strong, healthy, and independent. But on the other hand, they would miss him.

It had become a habit, when arriving at work, to ask, "How's Pearson this morning?" Everyone liked to see him

swimming round and round in his pool or basking in the warm sunshine. When he was gone, the Center wouldn't seem the same.

It wasn't easy, either, to decide where to let Pearson go. It would be simple to carry him down to the beach near the Center, but that was far from where he had been discovered as a young pup. Finally, a marshy area known as Mowry Slough was chosen. It was a two-hour drive from the Marine Mammal Center, but it was close to where Pearson had been found.

What was more, the Slough — which adjoins the San Francisco Bay — is part of a federal wildlife refuge. Visitors are not allowed to enter without special permission. Sharks are rarely seen in its waters. A group of harbor seals was already living there. Perhaps the very group to which Pearson's mother had belonged.

All in all, it was as safe and welcoming a place as could be found for Pearson to start his new life.

The day of the release — August 18 — dawned cool and foggy. Pearson was alone in his tank. The other seals had been moved to another pen. They were not yet ready to be returned to the sea, and Holly wanted them out of the way as final arrangements for the release were made.

During the past week, Pearson had been fed an extra rich diet, including several buckets of live anchovies. Although live fish were too expensive to be fed to the seals on a regular basis, Holly wanted to be sure that he could cope with the kind of food he would have to eat in the sea. Fortunately, the anchovies were no problem for Pearson. Though he had never seen live food, he was able to catch and eat the swiftly moving fish with ease.

During the past week, Pearson had also begun to spend almost all his waking hours circling round and round his tank. A volunteer counted and found that he swam 600 circles in one hour.

Perhaps he was responding, in the only way he could, to some inner urge to travel. Or he may have been simply exercising. Whatever the explanation, there was no doubt that Pearson's activity was completely absorbing.

He hardly noticed when Holly entered the pen. And it was only when she reached into the tank and grabbed him by the rear flippers that he stopped swimming. He squirmed in protest as she hauled him out. And he puffed angrily as she attached a metal tag through the thin flesh of his rear flipper.

Holly and the volunteer holding Pearson down were sorry to have to hurt him, but the tag was very important. It had a number on it which would identify him if he were ever found on a beach. A tag was the only way the Center had of keeping track of an animal after it was released.

Next, Pearson was weighed one last time. Sixty-five pounds, the dial on the scale read. Holly and the volunteer holding him staggered under the load.

The rescue truck holding a metal carrying case had been backed up to the gate of the pen.

Holly grabbed Pearson by the tail. Then, with an effort, she swung him up and into the case. Quickly, the door was shut.

Pearson didn't know what was happening. He scratched frantically at the metal case. He pulled himself up by his front flippers and peered out the barred window.

Holly wished she could explain what was taking place. But she knew that Pearson wouldn't be able to understand. All she could say was: "Don't worry, fellow. It's going to be all right. You'll be swimming again soon. I promise."

The sun came out as the rescue truck traveled over the highway. When it arrived at the entrance to the wildlife refuge, reporters from a local newspaper and television station were waiting. People were interested in the work that was being done at the Marine Mammal Center. There had already been several news stories about Pearson. Now the camera and reporters wanted one last picture and one last word of farewell.

The woman who had found Pearson when he was a tiny pup was also there. She and a friend were studying the harbor seals living at Mowry Slough. They had brought sleeping bags so that they could spend the night in the marsh, watching Pearson and the other seals after the release.

An agent of the Fish and Wildlife Service, which manages the refuge, joined the group as they started over the bumpy dirt road which led to the Slough.

The marshes were filled with birds. Great flocks of avocets and phalaropes took to the sky as the truck moved slowly along the road.

At last it stopped. The case was lifted off. In the distance was an inlet of water. A group of harbor seals could be seen dozing on the far bank. But in between the road and the water lay the muddy marshland of Mowry Slough. The heavy case, with Pearson inside, would have to be carried through the marsh to the water's edge.

The moment Holly and the volunteers stepped into the tall grass, they knew that this was not going to be an easy release. Thick black mud sucked at their boots. Pearson shifted from side to side within the crate.

The mud became deeper and deeper. Finally, Holly decided that the weight of the case, together with Pearson, was just too much. A large piece of wet canvas had been put inside the case to keep Pearson cool during the journey. Now the door to the case was opened, and Pearson was quickly wrapped in the canvas. He would be carried the rest of the way in this makeshift sling.

The seals on the far bank of the inlet had taken to the water. Their round gray heads dotted the surface. They watched curiously as the strange procession made its way slowly toward them.

Suddenly Holly stumbled. In a second, she was floundering thigh-deep in mud. The canvas dropped. And all at once, Pearson was free. Everyone was confused. Some tried to help Holly. Others looked for Pearson. He seemed to have disappeared.

Then out of the reeds at the water's edge, his sleek gray form emerged.

"There he goes!" someone shouted.

Pearson was in the water. He was swimming. He was free. The heads of the harbor seals in the water bobbed down and then up again, watching.

Holly struggled for a footing on the slippery tufts of grass. She hadn't even seen Pearson slip away. Now all that could be glimpsed of him was a round gray head moving through the water.

For a moment, everyone fell silent. The months of patient care and tireless watching and waiting were over. Pearson was on his own.

There seemed to be only one thing to say. And Holly said it. "Good luck, Pearson," she shouted, as the sleek gray head suddenly disappeared beneath the water. "Good luck!"

Author

As a child, living in the country with many different pets, Susan Meyers wanted to become a veterinarian or a zoo keeper. However, her father's script writing and her mother's storytelling influenced her final career choice. Susan Meyers is now a full-time writer — a job she finds "deeply satisfying."

Sea-Fever

by John Masefield

I must go down to the seas again, to the lonely sea and the sky,
And all I ask is a tall ship and a star to steer her by,
And the wheel's kick and the wind's song and the white sail's shaking,
And a grey mist on the sea's face and a grey dawn breaking.

I must go down to the seas again, for the call of the running tide
Is a wild call and a clear call that may not be denied;
And all I ask is a windy day and the white clouds flying,
And the flung spray and the blown spume and the sea gulls crying.

Shackleton's Epic Voyage

by Michael Brown

"Stand by to abandon ship!"

The command rang out over the Antarctic seas, and it meant the end of all Ernest Shackleton's plans. He was the leader of an expedition that had set out to cross the unknown continent of Antarctica. It was a journey no one before him had ever attempted.

For months his ship, the *Endurance,* had been trapped in ice. It drifted helplessly in the Weddell Sea, over four hundred miles east of the Antarctic mainland and twelve hundred miles south of the southernmost tip of South America. The pressure on the hull of the *Endurance* was extreme, and the ship's timbers groaned under the strain.

Now Shackleton's first goal was to lead his men to safety. They would try to cross the polar sea on foot and head for the nearest tiny island, 250 miles to the west.

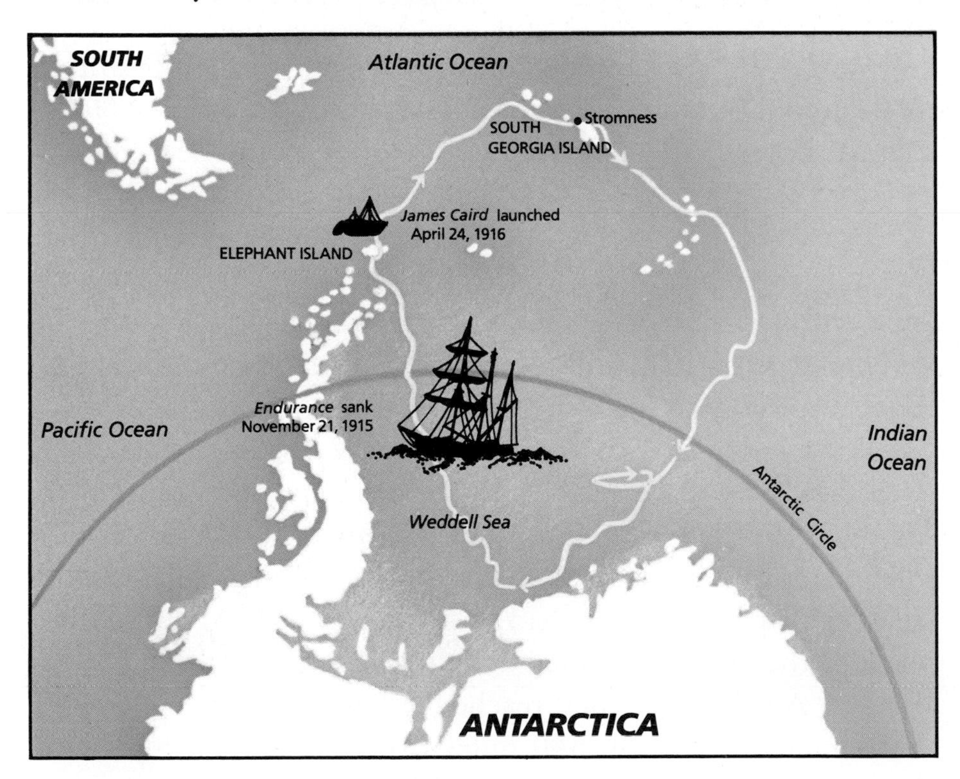

Slowly the men climbed overboard with the ship's stores. Shackleton, a gaunt, bearded figure, gave the order, "Hoist out the boats!" There were three, and they would be needed if the ice thawed.

Two days later, on October 30, 1915, the *Endurance* broke up and sank beneath the ice. In the bitter cold, the chances of survival seemed small. But spurred on by Shackleton the twenty-seven men set off, dragging their stores and the ship's boats on sledges across the uneven ice.

For five months the crew of the *Endurance* pushed their way slowly northwest across the frozen seas. Sometimes they dragged the sledges painfully behind them. Sometimes they drifted on large ice floes that slowly split into smaller and smaller pieces until they had to be abandoned. At times they took to the boats and sailed or rowed through melting ice. At last, in April 1916, they reached Elephant Island — a tiny, barren, rocky outcrop 540 miles from the nearest inhabited land, Port Stanley in the Falkland Islands.

By now the situation was grim. Food and other supplies were low. Still worse, five months of constant cold and hardship had weakened all of the men. They were in poor condition to face the coming winter.

Seeing this, Shackleton knew that he and his crew could not last much longer. He decided on a desperate attempt to find help before winter set in. He turned to the men. "We will make our camp here. Six of us will take the *James Caird* and try to reach Stromness. It's our only chance." Stromness was a whaling base on the island of South Georgia, eight hundred miles northeast of Elephant Island. To reach it they would have to cross some of the stormiest seas in the world.

The *James Caird* was the biggest of the ship's boats. Even so, it looked pitifully small to face the great gray seas of the southern ocean. Shackleton had the keel strengthened and added makeshift decking to give more shelter.

By April 24 all was ready, and the *James Caird* was launched from the beach. Some of the crew were soaked to the

skin as they worked. This could be deadly in the bitter cold and wind, so they changed clothes with those who were to stay behind. Shackleton shook hands with the men he was leaving, and then, amidst cheers, the *James Caird* set sail.

The little knot of men left behind was dwarfed by the high peaks of Elephant Island and was soon lost from sight.

The *James Caird* was alone on the vast heaving seas. With one arm gripping the mast, Shackleton guided the boat through the ice floes that threatened to hole the sides. At last they were in clear water, and with a fair wind, set their course for South Georgia.

Now began a fierce ordeal for the crew of the *James Caird.* The boat was small and crowded. It was almost impossible for the men to find space among the stores and the rocks carried for ballast. All cooking had to be done over a single primus stove that needed three men to handle it. One held a lamp; the other two lifted the cooking pot off whenever the violent pitching of the boat threatened to upset it. A fine spray of water constantly soaked its way through the flimsy decking.

There were storms and seas so big that in the trough of a wave the boat sometimes seemed surrounded by mountains of water. The waves towering above cut off the wind, so that the sails flapped uselessly.

Four days passed. A gale sprang up that threatened to swamp the *James Caird* and hurl its crew into the icy seas. "Lower the sails," shouted Shackleton, above the roar of the wind. "We'll heave to under bare poles and lie to the sea anchor." The sea anchor was a triangular canvas bag at the end of a long line, which held the bow of the boat into the wind. If the seas hit them sideways on, they would capsize.

No man aboard had faced such waves before. Sometimes looking out abeam they could see a great tunnel formed as the crest of a towering wave hung toppling over its base, then broke. Time after time it seemed they *must* be overwhelmed, but they survived.

The spray shot at them like burning arrows. It froze thick on the canvas decks and the bare masts and would soon make the boat top-heavy. Shackleton saw the danger. "We must get the ice off, or we'll capsize," he warned.

Some of the men struggled onto the heaving deck and chipped ice away with axes to free the boat of the deadly weight. Others hurled things overboard — spare oars and sleeping bags — anything they could do without that would lighten the load.

At last on the morning of the seventh day, the wind dropped. The sea calmed, the skies cleared, and for the first time the sun shone. Thankfully, the men dragged out sleeping bags and sodden clothes and hung them in the rigging to dry. Cape pigeons flew overhead, and porpoises played in the sea alongside. Shackleton and his men lay on deck soaking up the warmth. Hope surged in them; life was not so miserable after all.

For three days they sailed steadily on, and then a gale hit them like a blast from a great gun. Sun, pigeons, and porpoises disappeared. Snow squalls and huge waves hid everything from sight. At midnight, Shackleton was at the helm when he thought he saw a break in the sky. "Is the weather clearing?" he wondered. Then, to his horror, he realized that he was looking at the foam-capped top of the most gigantic wave he had ever seen!

"Hold on! It's got us!" he shouted from the helm. The breaking wave seized the boat and flung it forward, out of control, with the sea surging and foaming around it. Water poured in. "Bail for your lives!" cried Shackleton.

The men bailed frantically. At last they had flung enough water over the side to be safe, but conditions aboard were now much worse. Everything was drenched; there was not a dry

place in the boat. For three hours they struggled to light the stove and boil up some milk to warm themselves against the biting cold.

The next day the weather was better, but now there was a new danger. The water supply was running out. Unless the *James Caird* reached South Georgia soon, its crew would die of thirst.

Shackleton and his men were weary and downhearted. Tortured by thirst, they sailed listlessly on, believing that the end was near, yet hoping to sight land. Then on the morning of the fourteenth day, they saw two shags perched on a mass of seaweed. These birds never flew far from shore. Surely, surely land was near.

At noon, through a break in the clouds, Shackleton glimpsed the dark cliffs of South Georgia. It was a glad moment.

He steered the boat inshore, looking for a landing place, but everywhere rocky reefs or sheer cliffs barred the way. Night was closing in, and there was no hope of getting ashore until the next morning. It was a bitter disappointment to spend another night at sea.

But that same night another storm blew up. As hours passed, it swelled in strength until the wind was hurricane force. Nothing could be seen through the driving spray. The *James Caird,* tough as it was, strained to the utmost, so that its seams cracked open and water poured in. To add to this nightmare, the wind swung round and drove the boat slowly backwards, towards the dangerous coast they had seen the day before.

When all seemed lost, a miracle happened. The wind dropped and shifted to blow them offshore. They were saved from the reefs! But not from the torment of thirst. Shackleton knew they must land soon and find water.

After one more night at sea, the boat neared the shore again. They could see a wide bay. The wind was rising, and Shackleton decided he must run for that bay and take his chance. But as the *James Caird* neared the entrance, the crew saw that the way was blocked once more by a line of rocks like broken teeth. The sea thundered over them, sending up fountains of white spume.

The men braced themselves. They were sure that the *James Caird* would be dashed against the rocks.

Suddenly Shackleton shouted to the helmsman. He had seen a narrow gap. The next wave carried them forward and through this opening, so narrow that they could almost touch

the rocks on either side. Then, at last, they were safe in calm water. In the gathering darkness they beached the boat, and Shackleton leaped ashore. At his feet ran a stream of fresh water, and in a minute he and his crew were on their knees slaking their thirst. The worst was over.

Now Shackleton and his men began to explore the cove where they had landed. They found a small cave in which they lit a fire, and for the first time in two weeks, they spent a night ashore. But a long and dangerous journey was still ahead.

The whaling station at Stromness lay beyond high mountains, which had never yet been scaled. Shackleton set off with the two strongest members of his party, leaving the others with enough food for a few days.

The mountains rose four thousand feet, and the three men were often forced to turn back. They had no tent and kept going through the night, resting now and then, but not for long. They were exhausted but knew that if they stopped they would freeze to death.

Early the next morning they heard a strange sound. It was shrill and high pitched, eerie, spine tingling.

But it did not, after all, signal their death. It was a man-made sound — a steam whistle calling the people of the Stromness whaling station to work.

Shackleton and his men topped a final ridge. Below them were huts and distant figures.

In astonished silence, the workers watched as Shackleton and his men staggered towards them, like creatures from some earlier savage time. Two little boys took one look and ran, terrified by the sight of the ravaged, bearded faces and tattered clothes.

But the epic journey was over. Rescue of the entire crew was now certain. By his courage, Captain Shackleton had led his men through the perils of ice, thirst, wind, and storm. They had challenged the sea and won.

Author

Ever since his childhood, which he spent near the ocean in England, Michael Brown has loved the sea and sailing. The basis for his book *Shackleton's Epic Voyage,* which you have just read, was Ernest Shackleton's own short account of his adventure. Mr. Brown retold it and expanded it into a book.

Antarctica

Surrounding the South Pole is the continent of Antarctica, the coldest place on Earth. Even in summer, which occurs in December, January, and February, the average temperature is below freezing. However, in summer there are long periods of daylight. The photo above, left, was taken in December at 10:00 P.M.

Antarctica is covered with a solid ice cap that in some places is a mile thick. Huge sheets of ice called glaciers (above, right, top) creep slowly down the mountains to the sea. When chunks of ice break off from glaciers, they form icebergs, such as the one shown drifting in Hope Bay (above, right, bottom).

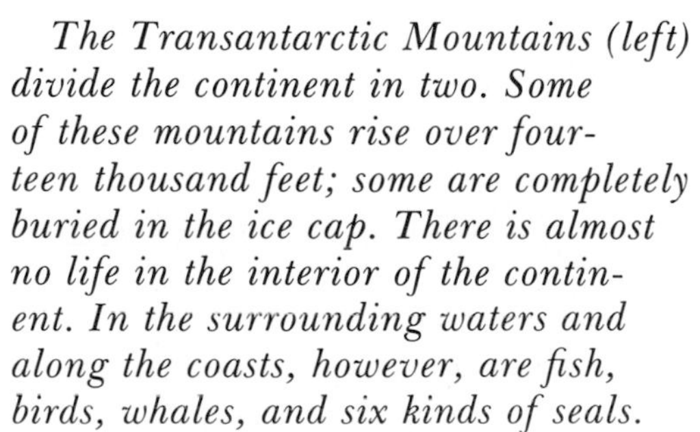

The Transantarctic Mountains (left) divide the continent in two. Some of these mountains rise over fourteen thousand feet; some are completely buried in the ice cap. There is almost no life in the interior of the continent. In the surrounding waters and along the coasts, however, are fish, birds, whales, and six kinds of seals.

The leopard seal (above, top) has strong jaws and sharp teeth. It sometimes preys on penguins and other seals. A more peaceful creature is the Weddell seal (above, bottom, left). The most common Antarctic seal is the crabeater (above, bottom, right). It does not eat crabs at all, but small sea animals called krill.

The birds that make Antarctica their home depend on the sea for food. Even those that fly, such as the blue-eyed shags (above, top) and the southern giant fulmar (above, bottom), rarely venture far inland.

The most familiar Antarctic birds are penguins, which don't fly at all. A colony of king penguins (center) on South Georgia Island give a friendly greeting to a visitor. Although only ten days old, these chinstrap penguin chicks (far right, top) are eager for food. A thick layer of fat protects penguins' bodies from the harsh climate. These gentoo penguins (far right, bottom) are weathering a fierce storm quite comfortably.

Ernest Shackleton and other explorers of his day sought to cross the Antarctic continent and to reach the South Pole. The Antarctic explorers of today are scientists. They staff about forty research bases, such as the Amundsen-Scott South Pole Station (above) located at the geographic South Pole. The twelve flags represent twelve nations, including the United States, that have signed a treaty to protect Antarctica.

Supplies are brought to the coast of Antarctica in ships called icebreakers. From there they are brought by plane to the research stations. Ski-equipped planes, like the one in the picture above, stop only long enough for

supplies to be quickly unloaded. Pilots do not turn off the engines, since they might not start again in the cold air and thin atmosphere.

Antarctica is a good place for scientists to study, because it is "unspoiled" by the effects of civilization. Until fairly recent times, no people had ever lived there.

Scientific research is carried on above and below the surface of Antarctica, as well as on it. Above, right, top: a weather balloon is launched at the South Pole Station. Above, right, bottom: a diver is lowered through the ice of McMurdo Sound to collect samples of tiny plants that live on the underside of the ice.

One Day in the Desert

by Jean Craighead George

Injured mountain lion approaching ki.

At daybreak on July 10th a mountain lion limped toward a Papago Indian hut, a small structure of grass and sticks on the bank of a dry river in the Sonoran Desert of Arizona. Behind it rose Mount Scorpion, a dark-red mountain. In all directions from the mountain stretched the gray-green desert. It was dry, hot and still.

The cactus wrens began to sing. The Gila woodpeckers squawked to each other across the hot air, arguing over their property lines. The kit foxes who had been hunting all night retreated into underground dens. The bats flew into caves on the mountain and hung upside down for the day.

The lion was hungry and desperately thirsty. A poacher's bullet had torn into the flesh of his paw, and for two weeks he had lain in his den halfway up the mountain nursing his feverish wound. As the sun arose this day, he got to his feet. He must eat and drink.

The desert stretched below him. He paused and looked down upon the dry river called an arroyo. It was empty of water, but could be a raging torrent in the rainy season after a storm. He twisted his ears forward. A Papago Indian girl, Bird Wing, and her mother were walking along the bank of the dry river. They entered the hut.

The lion smelled their scent on the air and limped toward them. He was afraid of people, but this morning he was desperate.

Six feet in length, he stood almost three feet tall. His fur was reddish brown above and white beneath. A black mustache marked his face. The backs of his ears and the tip of his tail were also black.

He growled as he came down the mountain, which was a huge clinker thrown up from the basement of the earth by an ancient volcano. Near its summit were pools where beaver and fish lived in the desert and which the mountain lion normally visited to hunt and drink. But today he went down, for it took less energy than going up.

The rising sun burned down from space, heating the rocks and soils until they were hot even through the well-padded feet of the lion. He stood in the shade of a rock at 8 A.M. when the temperature reached 80° Fahrenheit.

This day would be memorable. Bird Wing, her mother, the lion and many of the animals below Mount Scorpion would be affected by July 10th. Some would survive and some would not, for the desert is ruthless.

The Sonoran Desert is one of four deserts marked by distinctive plants that make up the great North American Desert, which extends from central Mexico to almost the Canadian border. The North American Desert covers more than 500,000 square miles.

All of the four deserts have one thing in common — little rain. Less than 10 inches a year fall on the greater parts of these deserts. The temperatures, however, vary from below freezing to the low 120s F.

Each one is slightly different. The Great Basin Desert of Oregon, California, Idaho, Nevada, Utah and Wyoming — the most northern and the coldest — is largely covered with sagebrush, a plant that has adapted to the dry cold.

The Mojave Desert of California is the smallest and driest, with less than 4 inches of rain a year. The teddy-bear cactus called cholla (choy-ya), a cactus so spiny it seems to have fur, dominates this desert.

The third, the Chihuahuan (chee-wa-wan) Desert, lies largely in Mexico. Only 10 percent of it is in the United States, in New Mexico, Arizona and Texas. On this desert the yuccas and agaves, or century plants, have adapted and grow abundantly, lending a special look to the land.

The fourth and most magnificent is the Sonoran Desert of Mexico and Arizona. Unlike the other deserts, it has two rainy seasons — showers in March and deluges in July and August. The rains nourish magnificent plants that support a great variety of creatures. The outstanding plant in this desert is the giant saguaro cactus, a tall plant that resembles a telephone pole with upturned arms. All the cacti — the saguaro, barrel, teddy bear and prickly pear — are unique to North America. They have evolved nowhere else in the world.

The North American Desert is dry because it is robbed of rain by the Pacific coast mountains. The clouds coming in from the ocean strike the high cold peaks and dump most of their moisture on the western side of the mountains. Practically no rain reaches the eastern side, which is in what is called the "rain shadow" by scientists.

All deserts are lands of extremes: too hot, too dry, too wet. Yet they abound with living things that have adjusted to these excesses. To fight dryness, plants store water in their tissues or drop their leaves to prevent evaporation from their broad surfaces. They also grow spines, which do not use much water and which cast shadows on the plant to protect it from the blazing sun. They thicken stems and leaves to hold water.

The animals adapt by seeking out cool microclimates, small shelters out of the terrible heat. The microclimates are burrows in the ground where it is cool, crevices and caves in rocks, or the shade. Because of the dryness, the thin desert air does not hold heat. Shady spots can be 20° F. cooler than out in the sun.

A few animals adapt to the harsh conditions by manufacturing water from the starch in the seeds they eat. The perky kangaroo rat is one of these. Others move in the cool of the night.

The coyote hunts in the dark, as do the deer, ringtailed "cat" (cacomistle), desert fox, raccoon and lion. The honeypot ant, on the other hand, has such a tough outer skeleton that it can walk in extremely hot sunshine.

On July 10th the wounded mountain lion was forced to hunt in the heat of the day. He could not wait for darkness. He made his way slowly down the trail toward the Papago Indian hut.

By 9 A.M. he was above the dwelling on a mountain ledge. The temperature climbed another degree. He sought the shade of a giant saguaro cactus and lay down to rest.

The scent of lion reached the nose of a coyote who was cooling off under the dark embankment of the dry river not far from the Papago Indian hut. He lifted his head, flicked his ears nervously and got to his feet. He ran swiftly into his burrow beneath the roots of the ancient saguaro cactus that grew beside the hut.

Coyote under saguaro cactus.

The huge cactus was over 100 years old, stood 75 feet tall and weighed more than 6 tons. The last of its watermelon-red fruits were ripe and on the ground. Bird Wing and her mother were going to gather them and boil them in the water they had carried in buckets from the village. The fruit makes a sweet, nourishing syrup.

At 11 A.M. they stretched out on their mats in the hut. It was much too hot to work. The temperature had reached 112° F.

The old cactus was drying up in the heat. It drew on the last of the water in the reservoir inside its trunk and shrank ever so slightly, for it could expand and contract like an accordion.

The mountain lion's tongue was swollen from lack of moisture. He got to his feet again.

A roadrunner, a ground-dwelling bird with a spiny crest and a long neck and legs, saw the lion pass his shady spot in the grass. He sped down the mountain, over the riverbank and into the dry riverbed. He stopped under the embankment where the coyote had been. There he lifted his feathers to keep cool. Bird feathers are perhaps the best protection from both heat and cold, for they form dead air space, and dead air is one of the best insulations.

The roadrunner passed a family of seven peccaries, piglike animals with coarse coats, tusks and almost no tails. They stay alive in the dry desert by eating the water-storing prickly pear cactus, spines and all. They were now lying in the cool of the paloverde trees that grow in thickets. Like the pencil-straight ocotillo and almost all the desert leafy plants, the paloverdes drop their leaves when the desert is extremely hot and dry. On July 10th they began falling faster and faster.

The scent of the lion reached the old boar. He lifted his head and watched the great beast. The lion turned away from the peccary family and limped toward the Indian hut. All the pigs, big and little, watched him.

Roadrunner passing family of peccaries.

A warm moist wind that had been moving northwest across the Gulf of Mexico for a day and a night met a cold wind blowing east from the Pacific coast mountains. The hot and cold air collided not far from the Mexico-Arizona border and exploded into a chain of white clouds. The meeting formed a stiff wind. It picked up the desert dust and carried it toward Mount Scorpion.

As the lion limped across the embankment under which the roadrunner was hiding, the air around him began to fill with dust.

Near the coyote den dwelled a tarantula, a spider almost as big as a man's fist and covered with furlike hairs. She looked like a long-legged bear, and she was sitting near the top of her burrow, a shaft she had dug straight down into the ground. The hot desert air forced her to let go with all eight of her legs. She dropped to the bottom of her shaft, where the air was cooler. The spider survives the heat by digging underground and by hunting at night. The moist crickets and other insects she eats quench her thirst.

A headstand beetle felt the heat of the day and became uncomfortable. He stopped hunting in the grass and scurried into the entrance of the tarantula hole. He was not afraid of the spider, with her poison fangs that kill prey, but he was wary of her. Hearing the spider coming up her shaft to see who was there, the headstand beetle got ready to fend her off. He stood on his head, aimed his rear end and mixed chemicals in his abdomen. The tarantula rushed at him and lifted her fangs. The headstand beetle shot a blistering-hot stream of a quinonoid chemical at the spider. She writhed and dropped to the bottom of her den. The headstand beetle hid under a grass plant by the tarantula's door.

The temperature rose several more degrees.

At 12:30 P.M. a desert tortoise, who was protected from the heat by two unusually thick shells of bone, went on eating the fruit of a prickly pear cactus. He was never thirsty. The moisture from the plants he ate was stored in his enormous bladder, a reservoir of pure water that desert tortoises have devised over the ages to adapt themselves to the dry heat. The water cools the reptiles on the hottest days and refreshes them on the driest.

The temperature reached 117° F. At last the tortoise felt warm. He turned around and pushed up on his toes. On his short legs he walked to his burrow under the paloverde bushes where the peccaries hunched, their eyes focused on the lion.

Inside his burrow the tortoise came upon a cottontail rabbit who had taken refuge there out of the hot sun. The tortoise could not go on. The heat poured in, and to lower the temperature he plugged up the entrance with his back feet. On the ceiling above his head clung a spiny-tailed lizard and a Texas banded gecko, reptiles who usually like the heat. At 12:30 P.M. on July 10th they sought the protection of the tortoise's burrow.

The temperature rose one more degree. A cactus wren who had sung at dawn slipped into her nest in a teddy-bear cactus at the edge of the paloverde thicket. She opened her beak to release heat.

The peccaries heard soft sounds like rain falling. Hundreds of small lizards who usually hunted the leaves of the paloverde, even on the hottest days, could no longer endure the high temperature. They were dropping to the ground and seeking shelter under sticks and stones.

A kangaroo rat was in her labyrinth under the leafless, pencillike ocotillo plants. She awakened when the temperature reached 119° F. Her bedroom near the surface of the desert floor had become uncomfortably hot. Her body was drying out. She scurried along a tunnel, turned a corner and ran down a slope toward a room under the giant saguaro cactus. She paused at her pantry to eat seeds of the mesquite tree before retiring to the cool, deep chamber. While she slept, her internal system converted the starch of the seeds into water and revived her dry body.

The lion walked into the paloverde bushes. The peccaries squealed in fright and trotted out into the terrible sunshine. In a cloud of dust they sped into the dry riverbed and frightened the roadrunner. He ran out from under the overhang and flew into the saguaro forest on the far side of the dry river. The pigs hid under the embankment where the roadrunner had been.

The injured lion could not chase the peccaries. He lifted his head, smelled the sweet piglets and climbed up the Indian trail till he was at the hut. Bird Wing and her mother were sleeping. He stared at them and crouched. Slinking low, he moved to a bucket, drank long and gratefully, then lay down in the doorway of the hut.

The temperature climbed one more degree. The birds stopped singing. Even the cicadas, who love hot weather and drum louder and faster in the heat, could no longer endure the fiery temperature. They stopped making sounds with their feet and wings and sat still. The Gila woodpecker flew into his hole in the giant saguaro. Below him, in one of his old nests, sat the sparrow-sized elf owl. He opened his beak and lifted his feathers.

Bird Wing was awakened by thirst. She tipped one of the water buckets and drank deeply. The desert was so quiet she became alarmed.

Clouds were racing toward Mount Scorpion. They were black and purple. Constant flashes of lightning illuminated them from within. She crept to the back of the hut and lay down beside her mother. She closed her eyes.

At 1:20 P.M. the temperature reached 121° F.

This hour on July 10th was the hottest hour on record at the bottom of Mount Scorpion.

Kangaroo rat in tunnel.

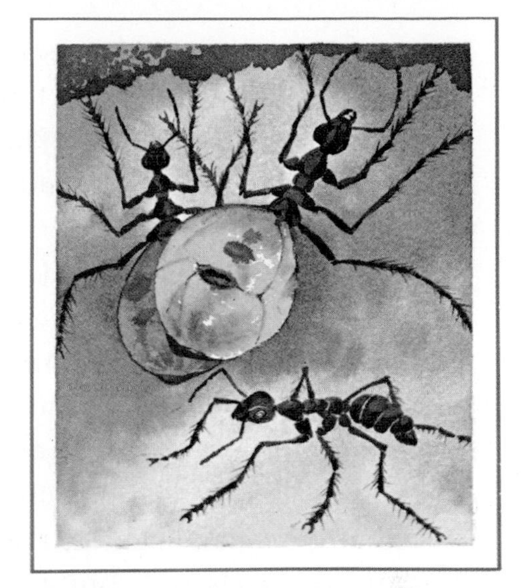

Honeypot ants clinging to cave ceiling.

Even the well-insulated honeypot ants could not tolerate the temperature. They ran toward the entrance of their labyrinth near a pack rat nest by the hut. Some managed to get underground in the caverns where sister ants hung from the ceilings. Forager honeypot ants store the sweets from plants they have gathered in the bellies of hanging ants, some of which become as round as balloons and as big as marbles. The last two foraging ants ran across the hot soil to get home. They shriveled and died in seconds.

The peccaries under the embankment dug into the earth to find coolness.

The clouds covered the sun.

Instantly, the temperature dropped four degrees.

The tortoise shoveled more dirt into the mouth of his burrow.

The thunder boomed like Indian drums.

The kangaroo rat felt the earth tremble. She ran to her door, smelled rain on the air and scurried to a U-shaped tunnel. She went down it and up to a room at the top. There she tucked her nose into her groin to sleep.

The temperature dropped five more degrees. A rattlesnake came out of the pack rat's nest and slid back to his hunting spot at the rear of the hut. The cicadas sang again. The cactus wren looked out of the entrance of her ball nest in the teddy-bear cactus.

A thunderclap exploded sharply. Bird Wing awoke. She saw the lion stretched in the doorway. She took her mother's arm and shook her gently until she awoke. Signaling her to be quiet, she pointed to the mountain lion. Bird Wing's mother parted the grass at the rear of the hut and, after pushing Bird Wing out, backed out herself.

The rattlesnake buzzed a warning.

The sky darkened. Lightning danced from saguaro cactus to saguaro cactus. Bird Wing's mother looked at the clouds and the dry arroyo.

"We must get out of here," she said. "Follow me up the mountain." They scrambled over the rocks on hands and feet without looking back.

Huge raindrops splattered onto the dust. Bird Wing and her mother reached an overhanging rock on the mountain. Lightning flashed around them like white horsewhips.

The thunder cracked and boomed. Then water gushed out of the sky. The rain fell in such torrents that Bird Wing and her mother could not see the dry river, the hut or the old saguaro. They sat quietly, waiting and listening.

A flash of lightning shot out of a cloud and hit the old saguaro cactus. It smoked, split and fell to the ground. The elf owl flew into the downpour. His wings and body became so wet, he soared down to the grass beneath the paloverde bushes. The woodpecker stayed where he was, bracing himself with his stiff tail.

The crash of the saguaro terrified the coyote. He darted out of his den under the tree and back to the dry riverbed. The peccaries dug deeper into the embankment. The roadrunner

Bird Wing and her mother sheltered from storm.

took to his feet and ran up the slope beyond the giant saguaro forest.

The rain became torrents, the torrents became waterfalls and the waterfalls cascaded out of the sky until all the moisture was wrung from the clouds. They drizzled and stopped giving rain. The storm clouds rumbled up the canyon above the dry riverbed.

The sun came out. Bird Wing and her mother did not move. They listened. The desert rocks dripped and the cacti crackled softly as they swelled with water. Cactus roots lie close to the surface, spreading out from the plants in all directions to absorb every possible drop of water. The roots send the water up into the trunks and barrels and pads to be stored.

A drumroll sounded up Scorpion Pass.

The peccaries heard it and darted out from under the embankment. They struggled up the bank and raced into the saguaro forest.

The lion got to his feet. He limped through the door.

The coyote rushed out of the dry riverbed. The wet elf owl hooked his beak around a twig of a paloverde and pulled himself upward toward higher limbs.

Water came bubbling and singing down the arroyo. It filled the riverbed from bank to bank, then rose like a great cement wall, a flash flood that filled the canyon. It swept over the embankment, over the hut, over the old saguaro cactus. It rose higher, thundered into the paloverdes and roared over the rocks at the foot of the mountain. It boomed into the valley, spread out and disappeared into the dry earth.

The coyote was washed out from under the embankment. He tumbled head over heels, swam to the surface and climbed onto an uprooted mass of prickly pears. On this he sailed into the valley and was dropped safely onto the outwash plain when the water went into the ground. Stunned, he shook himself and looked around. Before him the half-drowned pack rat struggled. Recovering his wits, the coyote pounced upon him.

The lion was lifted up by the flood and thrown against a clump of ocotillo. He clung to it for a moment, then, too weak to struggle, slipped beneath the water.

The flash flood that had trickled, then roared, trickled and then was gone. The banks of the arroyo dripped. Bird Wing and her mother walked to the spot where their hut had been. There was no sign of house, pack rat nest, saguaro, or lion.

"But for the lion, we would be dead," said Bird Wing. "We must thank him." She faced the mountain and closed her eyes for a moment. Her mother picked up an ocotillo stick and turned it over in her hand.

Mountain lion caught in flood.

"We will rebuild our house up the mountain above the flood line," she said. Bird Wing nodded vigorously and gathered sticks, too.

The kangaroo rat sat in her room above the U trap that had stopped the water from reaching her. She waited until the floodwaters seeped into the ground. Then she began to repair her labyrinth.

The peccaries came out of the saguaro forest and rooted for insects among the billions of seeds that had been dumped on the land by the flood. The land was greening, the sky was blue. The roadrunner came back to the saguaro forest, ran down a young snake and ate it. The cactus wren and owl did not call. The rattlesnake did not rattle. They had not survived the wrath of the desert on this day, July 10th.

Bird Wing walked to the arroyo edge. The earth trembled at her feet. She looked down. Plugs of sand popped out of the wet bank like corks. In each hole sat a grinning spadefoot toad, creatures who must grow up in the water. Then what were they doing in the desert? Waiting for just this moment.

They hopped into the brilliant sunshine and leaped into the puddles in the arroyo. Quickly they mated, quickly they laid eggs and quickly they ate and dug backward into the sand with the spades on their feet. Far underground their skins secreted a sticky gelatin that would prevent them from drying up. In this manner they survived in the hot waterless desert.

The warm sunlight of late afternoon heated the water in the puddles, speeding up the development of the toad eggs. They must hatch into pollywogs and change into toads before the blazing heat dried up the puddles.

At 7:33 P.M. soft blue and purple light swept over the beautiful desert. In the puddles pollywogs swam.

Author

Jean Craighead George comes from a family of naturalists and has built her own life around observing nature and writing about it. Her outstanding nature books for young people have received acclaim and won many different awards. Among her more than thirty books is *All Upon a Sidewalk,* which was named an Outstanding Science Trade Book for Children.

Houghton Mifflin Literature

In the selections you have just read from *Facing Challenges of Nature,* nature challenged many different creatures, including humans. For an orphaned harbor seal pup struggling to live, or for Antarctic explorers fighting the bitter cold and treacherous seas, survival meant overcoming the perils of nature.

Next you will read *The Terrible Wave* by Marden Dahlstedt. In this story, nature's challenge arrives with power and suddenness. A flood forces a group of people to muster every ounce of their courage and quick-thinking to turn a tragedy into a triumph.

6

Appearances Can Be Deceiving

The Boy Who Drew People Upside Down

by Jean Friedman

Marc Chagall
The Market Place, 1917
Oil on Canvas, 66 × 97.3 cm.
Metropolitan Museum of Art, New York
Bequest of Scofield Thayer, 1982

A young boy trudged through the falling snow to the old wooden synagogue, where all the boys of the town gathered to study. It was early morning in the small town of Vitebsk[1] in Russia.

As he walked through the narrow streets, he looked at the way the snow had turned the dirty cobblestones white and covered the wooden houses and sheds and fences of the town. The houses seemed wide-awake and watchful — as though they too could observe the townspeople hurrying back and forth and hear the cackling of the roosters that were being sold in the marketplace.

He wished he had time to sit down and sketch the scene, but it was late. Besides, drawing had already gotten him into trouble.

Last night he had sat in his room for hours watching the snowflakes whirl around the gas lamps in the street, causing strange halos to form around the glowing lights. He had looked at the people hurrying to their houses, dark against the snow and hunched from the cold. He loved to see their strange shapes and especially those of the carts drawn by the horses or mules. As he watched, he drew pictures, using paper from his schoolbook and some old paper bags his mother had given him.

Then his mother had knocked on his door. "Marc, it's almost dinner time. What are you doing?" He had shown the pictures to his mother. She had sighed, "Yes, my son, I see. More pictures."

She had turned the pictures over and had seen his homework, half completed, on the other side. "You know that paper is expensive, and I have no more to give you. You will have to take these to school with you tomorrow."

She had handed the pictures back to him and looked at him again. "Your duty is to learn the law and the history of our people. You are our eldest son and you have responsibilities."

---

[1]**Vitebsk** (**vē′** tĕpsk′)

As Marc approached the synagogue, his heart thumped louder and faster. His teacher, the rabbi, was a serious scholar and made no allowance for frivolity or inattention. What was he going to think of the drawings? Marc hesitated at the heavy, wooden door, then opened it and went in.

The other students were already seated at the long tables and benches, their books opened, ready for work. They tittered as he walked by, but they kept their faces hidden behind their books. No one wanted to risk a reprimand from the rabbi.

The rabbi looked up from his text and nodded in Marc's direction. "Marc, what will I do with you? You are late and even when you are here you are not *really* here. You are far away in some other world — dreaming." The rabbi paused. "Did you do your homework assignment?"

"I read the chapter," Marc answered quietly.

"Did you answer the questions?" asked the rabbi. Marc looked at his wet shoes and mumbled something.

"Speak up," instructed the rabbi.

"I ran out of paper," Marc said.

The rabbi sighed. "Ah, you've been drawing again. Bring up these drawings that are so much more important than your lessons. Let me see them."

Marc fumbled in his notebook and handed the papers to the rabbi, who was now standing over him in his long black robe.

"Well," the rabbi said after examining the drawings, "I think we had better talk about this after class."

The rest of the day passed slowly for Marc. Finally in the late afternoon, when all the other boys had left, the rabbi walked across the room to Marc's bench and sat down beside him. He pulled out Marc's pictures and studied them again. "These are fine drawings, Marc, but why do you have these

Marc Chagall
I and the Village, 1911
Oil on Canvas, 192.1 × 151.4 cm.
Collection, The Museum of Modern Art, New York
Mrs. Simon Guggenheim Fund

people flying over the town, and why does this house have an eye in it?"

"The people are flying because they are happy. It is the way they feel," answered Marc. "Sometimes I draw people upside down or sideways. It just depends on what I see. This house has an eye because, even though it is silent, it sees everything that goes on."

"Ah," said the rabbi, "you have quite an imagination. We must talk more about your drawings. But you must also do your lessons. I will give you extra paper — but only on the condition that you use it for your written work."

As Marc walked home, he thought about what the rabbi had said. Why was his teacher helping him? And did this mean that the rabbi thought drawing could be as important as studying? Marc wondered what his parents would think.

When he reached home, his mother met him at the door. On her head was a brightly colored kerchief, and she looked beautiful. "Come in quickly, Marc, before your father returns from evening prayer and finds you are late for the Sabbath."

She helped Marc pull off his coat and hung it on a chair near the wood-burning stove. Dinner was almost ready. The freshly baked challah was cooling on the sidetable, and the delicious smell of chicken soup with matzo balls filled the whole house. Marc watched as his mother prepared to light the candles. He loved Friday night when everything was made so bright and clean. It was the one time during the week that the white tablecloth was used, when candles were lit, and a special meal was prepared.

As his mother lit the candles and blessed them, Marc thought of how alive the flames looked. They seemed to be reaching up toward the moon — like people with outstretched arms.

When Marc's father came home, the eight children gathered around the table, and after everyone was seated, Marc's

Marc Chagall
Vitebsk Seen from Mount Zadunov, 1917
Oil on Canvas, 24⅜ × 32⅛ in.
Private Collection

father said the blessing over the wine. Then he took a loaf of challah, broke off a piece, and handed the rest to Marc's mother. When she had taken a piece and everyone else had had a share, another blessing was said, and the bread was eaten. Then Marc's mother ladled steaming soup into each bowl. Chicken would come later, with hot potato pancakes and shredded carrots sweetened with honey. Everyone seemed happy.

"Son, what happened at school today?" Marc's father asked suddenly. "I met the rabbi on my way back from the herring depot, and he said he wanted to stop by here later to discuss your work."

"My work?" Marc repeated. He looked at his father. "The rabbi saw some of my drawings and said he would give me extra paper for my lessons. That way I will have more paper for drawing." Marc tried to sound casual, but he stuttered over the last word.

"Marc, dear," his mother's voice was gentle, "don't you realize that the rabbi cannot afford to buy you supplies? I am sorry we cannot give you as much paper as you want, but he doesn't have the money, either." Her voice was sad.

Marc's father interrupted. "We will wait until the rabbi comes before we discuss this further."

Marc didn't enjoy the rest of his supper. He wondered what he had done that would make the rabbi want to stop by the house on Sabbath eve to discuss his work with his father.

But when the rabbi finally came, he didn't look angry at all. He smiled at Marc and murmured a Sabbath greeting to the family. Then he addressed Marc's mother and father.

"May we talk privately? With Marc, of course."

The rest of the family left the room, and the four of them sat down around the table.

"I will come straight to the point," the rabbi said. "Marc's work could be better, but I didn't come to discuss his schoolwork. He will never be a scholar."

When Marc saw the disappointment on his father's face, he felt like running out of the room.

"This does not surprise me," Marc's father answered. "In spite of what my wife and I tell him, our son spends most of his time dreaming and painting."

"That is why I asked to come by tonight," the rabbi said, looking at Marc's parents. "I believe that Marc has a special talent, something rare and unusual. He has the gift of making dreams come alive. He doesn't just draw objects, he draws the souls of things." The rabbi paused. "Marc must learn the importance of our ancient laws and traditions, but once he has, he too will be a kind of teacher."

Marc's father was looking intently at the rabbi now, waiting for his next words. His mother lowered her head, but Marc could see that she was smiling to herself.

"I have given a great deal of thought to this matter," said the rabbi, "and I would like to make a suggestion. As soon as Marc completes his studies, he should be apprenticed to the town painter and portrait artist, Juda Pen. There he can begin to learn the craft of painting and will be able to use his talent for earning a living. Meanwhile, I would encourage him in his artwork."

Marc was astounded. Did he hear the rabbi correctly? There was a look of surprise — and pride — on his father's face, as though he too were only beginning to realize what the rabbi was saying.

For the next hour Marc's father asked the rabbi about his son's studies and possible living arrangements; the rabbi said he would act as a go-between if Marc and his parents were agreeable. Marc could scarcely breathe a response; he was overcome with happiness.

Finally the rabbi stood up. “It is late and time that I left. You will have much to talk about.” At the door he turned to Marc and smiled. His eyes twinkled as he shook hands with Marc’s father. “This dreamer of yours,” he said, “who can say how far he will go?”

Marc turned to his father as the door closed. “Papa,” Marc asked, looking into his father’s eyes, “do you think I will be able to earn a living with my drawings and paintings?”

Marc’s father placed his hand gently on Marc’s shoulder. It was a moment both would remember.

“Marc, my son, you have a gift, and you must use it. Love it, work hard at it, and leave the rest to God.”

Marc did finish school and went on to study painting in Paris. He never lost his lyrical, even mystical, vision of things around him. His paintings are filled with the images of his childhood in the small Russian town of Vitebsk. Marc Chagall became one of the great painters of this century.

Author

Jean Friedman has had a lifelong interest in art. Painting has helped her to express her own imagination. When she was at Hunter College in New York, she studied Marc Chagall’s life and his painting. In the story you have just read, she has tried to make his art and his background come alive.

An excerpt from

Marc Chagall

by Ernest Raboff

Self-portrait with Seven Fingers, 1912

In the story you have just read, the rabbi said of young Marc Chagall, "He has the gift of making dreams come alive. He doesn't just draw objects, he draws the souls of things."

Look at these two famous paintings by Marc Chagall. Try to see how he used his gift to paint memories of his childhood.

The explanations with the paintings were written by an artist named Ernest Raboff. They tell what he sees and feels when he looks at the paintings. Look for the colors and objects that Raboff points out in each painting. Do you agree with his explanations? What else do you see in the paintings?

"Peasant Life" is the story of a small village, told for us in paint by a great storyteller. Chagall shows the pleasant everyday life of the village's rural people.

Notice the farmer's well-fed horse. This is the peasant's most important fellow worker and his loved companion.

The cottage, with its windows and shutters, the gas lantern, and the tree form the setting for this picture story. The horse and cart are ready to take the village family, with their many farm products, to market. The dancing couple completes Chagall's colorful picture of peasant life.

The "Green Violinist" is one of Chagall's painted memories of his uncle, who played the violin, and of his birthplace in Vitebsk, a town in Russia.

The fiddler, the violin, the violet clothes, and the soaring dancer create a sense of music through the artist's use of color. The green face and hand make the old tune seem as new as a fresh green spring. While the dark violet colors may reflect the sadness of the long, hard Russian winter, we are warmed by the glow from the orange violin.

An excerpt from

Fog Magic

by Julia Sauer

The Spell of the Fog

From the time she was a baby in her cradle, Greta had loved the fog.

Every soul in the little fishing village at the foot of the mountain had learned to accept the fog. It was part of their life. They knew that for weeks on end they must live within its circle. But they made no pretense of liking it. Those who tilled their little plots of land hated it when it kept their hay from drying. The men who fished dreaded it for it either kept them on shore altogether and cut down their meager earnings, or it made their hours on the sea more dangerous than ever. Only the lobster poachers who robbed honest men's lobster pots, or set their own out of season, liked it — the lobster poachers and small Greta. And with Greta it was more than liking. On days when the gray clouds of fog rolled in from the sea and spread over the village, she would watch it drift past the windows with a look on her small face that almost frightened her mother.

"Goodness, child," Gertrude Addington would say to the mite in the high chair, "you look as if you were seeing things — and pleasant things at that! I believe you like this beastly fog! Don't you know your father is out there, like as not running on a reef this very minute? And my clean clothes mildewing for want of a bit of proper sun to dry them by?"

But then Greta would gurgle so happily and throw wide her arms with such eagerness to grasp and hold this queer gray smoke that Gertrude's irritability would vanish like the fog itself when the sun comes suddenly through.

As soon as Greta could walk, Gertrude found that she might as well put her housework aside on foggy days and give herself to minding her child. The first thin wraiths of fog in the high pasture were enough to set her small daughter's eyes sparkling. By the time it hid the big rock at the top of the pasture, Greta would be working her way cautiously to the door; and when it drew close enough to blur their own out-buildings, she would be scampering down the pasture lane as fast as her uncertain little feet could carry her.

"I'm at my wits' end minding the child on foggy days," she said to old Kil. He had stopped on his way home from the smokehouse to leave a finnan haddie and he smiled down now at the bedraggled small girl whom Gertrude had just retrieved from beyond the garden. The old man laughed at her.

"Some are moonstruck, they say, and some are sunstruck," he said. "Maybe this one is fogstruck. Don't worry about her, Gertrude. It's good for a young one to want to know the world she lives in in all kinds of weather." He ran his big hand lightly over Greta's damp curls. "I can't see it does this little mess o' seaweed any harm to be well wetted down. But you might try mooring her to the apple tree and save yourself the minding of her."

So the small girl came to be moored at the end of the clothesline like an idle dory on every day when the gray wisps of fog came drifting in.

Greta was ten when she began to sense that she was looking for something within the fog. Until then it had only given her a happy feeling — just as the first snowflakes delighted some of the other girls and boys, or the first fall winds that set the birch leaves blowing. But from the day when she had gone alone to find old Rosie, the cow, nothing had been quite the same.

The village of Little Valley lay on the narrow neck of land between two great arms of the sea. Like a lazy giant, North Mountain lay sprawled the full length of the peninsula until, at the very end, it sat up in a startled precipice at the sight of the open sea. Years before, a number of villages had dotted the shore on either side. Now, only a few were left and those were dwindling in size as the men despaired of making a living by fishing. At the foot of the mountain and following the line of its base ran the highway. Here the Royal Mail, the grocery truck, the butcher, and the tourists who had lost their way made their daily or weekly or chance trip down the neck to the sea and back again. But there was another road — a road less direct — filled with convenient curves — the old Post Road. This was the road the first settlers had built in the wilderness. They had come by sea, many of them, and made their little clearings near the shore. Gradually they had extended their clearings inland and in time, and with tremendous effort, they had threaded their holdings together on a narrow uncertain road through the spruce forest. With the new highway, generations later, had come new houses, away from the shore and more sheltered. Only cellar holes remained to mark the earlier homes.

This old Post Road was a joy to Greta. A part of it ran through her father's land. Even though it had fallen so low as to serve as a mere lane to the pastures, there was something grand and romantic about it still. Years of spring freshets had washed away the dirt. The stones were bare that had formed its foundation. To follow it was like walking in the bed of a dry mountain stream. Greta knew every stone, every curve of it for miles, up over the high pastures and then down again toward the sea. This was the road her ancestors had traveled. Surely, she thought, it must lead somewhere worth going.

And then there was the day when old Rosie was particularly stubborn.

"Greta! Greta!" her mother called her from play. "Rosie isn't at the bars with the other cows. Your father's had a hard day getting in the hay. You'd best go and look for her before he does. You'll probably meet her on the way. You'll not need to go far."

Greta started willingly enough. She had heard the foghorn blowing at Tollerton, down in the Passage, and she knew there was fog on the way.

"Want me to go along?" one of the boys asked.

"You better not, Hazen. I may be late." She thanked him hastily and hurried away. To be caught in the fog and with the best excuse in the world was something too precious to share.

She found Rosie far off the Old Road and down at the cove. Rosie looked anything but guilty. Greta laughed.

"You darling," she said to her. "I think you stayed down here on purpose so I could drive you home in the fog. But that's not fair, you know, because Father would have had to come if Mother hadn't noticed."

She hurried Rosie across the stones of the shore and up through the thick spruce trees to the clearing beyond. The fog was closing in rapidly. You didn't notice it in the woods, but out in the open it was already thick. Even Rosie began to look soft and furry and indistinct, like an imaginary cow that you tried to see in the clouds.

It was just as they turned out of the path to the cove and into the Old Road that Greta happened to look off to the south.

"Rosie, wait," she called sharply.

She caught her breath and stared. If only stupid old Rosie could see it too. Surely there was the outline of a building. It was blurred and indistinct, but those straight upright lines, that steep angle — no spruces could look *that* way. Greta's heart almost stopped beating, but she had no silly feeling of fear. Fog had always seemed to her like the magic spell in the old fairy tales — a spell that caught you up and kept you as safe, once you were inside it, as you would have been within a soap bubble. But this was stranger than anything she had ever seen before. Here was a house — a house where no house stood! Indistinct though it was, she could follow every line of it. A high sharp roof, a peaked gable, a little lean-to at the side. It was all there. Just such a house as those she saw every day in the village.

"So this," she said to herself, "*this* is what can happen to you in a fog. I always knew that there must be something hidden."

It was the most exciting thing that had ever happened to her in her whole life. Rosie, far ahead, was mooing at the pasture bars, and Greta tore herself away to follow. Once inside the barn, she wished that she had stayed and gone closer.

She stood in the barn doorway looking out across the yard. The fog was dense and gray. It blanketed the yard and made the house across the intervening feet as dim as that other one had been. Behind her in the quiet sweet-smelling barn her father sat milking.

"Father," Greta spoke softly.

"Yes? What is it, Greta?" The milk streamed rhythmically into the pail.

"Father, down where the path to Little Cove turns off the Old Road, is there — is there any old house off in the spruces to the south?"

Her father never stirred on the milking stool, but he dropped his hands quietly on his knees. The barn was very still for a moment.

"There's an old cellar hole off there, Greta," he said at last. "There's been no house upon it in my day." His voice was as calm and slow as ever. And then he added something very strange. "Every cellar hole should have a house," he said quietly.

"Yes, Father," Greta answered. It was almost as if he'd told her that *she* should build a house and she had almost promised.

Rosie stirred restlessly. Father cleared his throat and went on milking.

"You'd best go in and help your mother with the tea," he said. "She'll be fussing. She doesn't know you're back."

Greta stepped out of the warm fragrant barn into the cool fog. It had always seemed to be whispering a secret to her. Now, at last, the words of the secret were coming more clearly.

Greta did not know what Walter Addington and his wife talked about that night. She went up to bed at her usual bedtime. Her little room with its steep sloping ceiling and its single window faced out toward the high pasture and the Old Road. Tonight you couldn't even see as far as the crooked apple tree by the well. She undressed and slipped into bed. The hushed voices in the room below and the distant rhythmic blowing of the foghorn in the Passage gave her the same warm, safe feeling they had always given her as she drifted off to sleep.

Whatever it was that was said that night, Gertrude was persuaded to let her child wander as she willed in the fog. Father had somehow worked the miracle. Sometimes Gertrude would look so perplexed, so distressed when Greta had finished her stint of housework and was free to go that the girl would come running back to throw her arms around her mother's neck.

"Why, Mother," she would say, "can't you see the fog is lovely? And I know every stone in the Old Road. I *can't* get lost. Please, *please* don't hate to let me go."

"Go on, child, go if you must." Gertrude would even laugh a little at her own vague fears. "It's just that you're so different from what *I* used to be at your age. We always hated this miserable wet fog. We'd scurry for home at the first sign of it." It was always the same. They never could understand each other about the fog.

One Saturday morning Greta opened her eyes to see a gray blanket filling the window space. A thick fog, and on a Saturday too, when there was no school! It was the first really foggy day since the night she had seen the strange house back in the spruces — the first chance she had had to see if she had imagined it all. She hurried through her Saturday work. She thought of every little thing her mother could possibly want done — the usual Saturday errands, the washing up. Her own little room was as tidy as a ship's cabin, her Sunday gloves were washed and hung on the bars over the stove to dry. The collar was pressed on her best dress. Gertrude eyed her sharply.

"I know why you're so light on your feet this morning," she said shortly. "You're wanting to go off again."

Greta laughed. Not even her mother's crossness could spoil this day.

"I may go, mayn't I, Mother?" she coaxed. "It's only eleven o'clock, and if I take a sandwich and start now, I can be way over the high pasture before noontime. *Please,* Mother. I may even find some early berries. At least I'll take a pail."

Gertrude had been churning. She was pressing the little pats of butter with an acorn stamp. She laid the stamp down and looked at Greta without a word.

"Mother," the girl said slowly. "Please try just once more to understand."

Gertrude's "Well?" wasn't encouraging and Greta began hesitantly.

"You — you know the way a spider web looks on foggy days. Strings and strings of the tiniest pearls, all in a lovely pattern. Well, everything else is different too when — when once you're inside," she finished stumblingly.

"Inside?" asked Gertrude sharply. "Inside *what,* I'd like to know?"

"Oh, just inside the fog," Greta told her. It was no use. She could never get it into words. No one else could see how the fog always seemed to her like a magic wall. You stepped through and walked until your own familiar house was gone. And then, sometime, something strange and wonderful would happen. She was sure of it.

She made her sandwich quickly, and pulled on her old coat and beret.

"Leave the bread tins and the dinner dishes for me, Mother. I'll wash them when I get back," she said as she opened the door.

"Don't be late," was her mother's answer. Then, a little more pleasantly, "I'll save a plate of chowder for your tea. You'll like as not be chilled through."

Greta gave her a loving little squeeze as she slipped out. The day had begun well, and the best part of it lay hidden ahead of her.

"Please let there be a house today on the old cellar hole," Greta kept saying to herself as she hurried along the Old Road. But how *could* there be? You could see things, perhaps, in the twilight that were never there at noon. That was it, of course. It was evening when she had gone after Rosie. Nothing like that could happen in the daytime. "*Maybe* there will be!" "There *can't* be." "*Maybe* there will be." "There *can't* be." Back and forth, back and forth the two thoughts went ticking in her mind. Her heart was beginning to thump in time to them.

"I'd better stop and get my breath at the sailors' graves," she thought. It was a spot where Father often stopped for a moment. Greta had never asked him why. On clear days the village looked its prettiest from there. But Greta thought it was Father's way of paying respect to the shipwrecked sailors who had been washed ashore in the cove years and years ago. Just where the fences met at the corner of the Ezra Knoll, they had buried them. There was nothing to show who they were or where they'd come from — nothing, now, to mark the graves except Father's care that that corner of the hay field was never mowed. Greta leaned on the fence and looked down at the unmowed corner.

"I hope they didn't come from a West Indies port," she thought. "They'd hate even to be buried here if they loved steady sunshine."

When she came to the path to Little Cove, Greta drew a long breath and looked over toward the clump of spruces. What she saw set her heart thumping. It was there! Again through the gray mist she could trace the darker outline of a house! For a moment she was tempted to push closer — to explore. Something held her back — and she was always glad that it had. Because the dim shadow of a house there at the fork became, through all the strange months that followed, a sort of magic beacon. When she could see it, she went on. When it wasn't there, she learned to turn back. It was always to be trusted. Disobey its message and there was a long walk, but nothing more. Only when its presence pointed the way was it wise to go full speed ahead.

To avoid temptation, Greta turned quickly into the right-hand fork that led to the high pasture. She didn't look back until she came to the burned patch where the berries grew. There, standing in the middle of the road, just where she had stopped a moment before, was the blurred figure of a bent old man. Where had he come from and who was he? No one she knew; she was sure of that, somehow. As she looked down at him, his hand shot up in the friendly gesture that old people in the village always used. Greta took off her beret and waved to him. He seemed satisfied. He moved toward the house and out of sight.

As she climbed on Greta realized suddenly that the words "Old Man Himion" were going over and over in her mind. "Where on earth did I ever hear of 'Old Man Himion'?" she asked herself. "Why, of course. It was Old Man Himion who had found the shipwrecked sailors in the cove!" She had heard that name from her grandfather. "And that must be Old Man Himion's house!" she thought. "The very house he had left when he had gone down to the cove on that morning after the big tempest so many years ago."

"I think I've seen Old Man Himion. And I think I know his house. And this fog is really truly magic," she sang as she started across the open pasture. The berries were thick and she stopped to pick for a while. Her pail was a good third full when she reached the other side of the open space.

The higher she climbed, the thicker the fog grew. Hurriedly, in great clouds it rolled over the top of the mountain. Then, its hurry spent, it spread out leisurely over the slopes below. Greta had to watch the ground closely to find her way. The rough foundation stones of the Old Road were the only guide. At the upper edge of the pasture, the road plunged into the thick spruce woods that covered the top. The trees seemed to hold the gray curtain back. Here the road was like a narrow dim tunnel; gray blanket above, wet green side walls, no sound but the sound of fog dripping from the spruces.

It was so very quiet in the spruces that Greta found herself picking her way cautiously as if she were afraid to turn a stone or make the slightest noise. Once she stopped to listen to the stillness. It was then that she heard the sound of trotting horses! Not the slow plod of oxen that she was used to, not the whir or rattle of a car on the highway, but the sharp rhythmic beat of horses' feet. They were coming toward her! And coming the way she had come! Occasionally she could hear a grating sound as the metal rim of a wheel glanced off a stone. She stepped to the side of the road. Who could possibly be driving on the Old Road? And where had such horses come from? Surely there were none in the village or in the town thirty miles away capable of holding that steady pace up the mountain. Greta was too excited to be frightened. She could only peer down along the dim road she had come and wait. Louder and louder came the clipped "trot, trot!" Around the bend in the road below they came into sight — two smartly groomed horses and a surrey driven by a woman dressed in gorgeous plum-colored silk. She was like a picture out of a book. Greta stared in amazement as the carriage came nearer. She hardly realized that the driver had noticed her when the horses were pulled up sharply and expertly swung to the right to cramp the wheels of the surrey.

"Come, come, child!" said a sharp, impatient voice. "Don't stand there dreaming in the fog. Climb in if you're going over the mountain." Greta climbed in. As she settled into the seat beside the driver, there was a billowing surge and rustle of taffeta, a flick of the whip and the horses were off.

Greta clung to the side of the surrey and stole a glance at her companion. Stiff and straight and elegant she sat, her eyes on the winding road. But at each motion of her arms as she drove there was a swish of costly silk. Greta was conscious of it above the sound of the horses. Who had talked of silk so rich and elegant that it sounded this way? She tried to remember. Oh, now she knew. It was Earl Frosst — the one the children called "The Early Frost." He had been telling old stories in the kitchen one night when she was doing her homework. His grandmother had been born on the other side of the mountain in the village of Blue Cove. It had been a rich village once and its women had dressed as few women in that part of the province had dressed. Early had said, "When Blue Cove women came over the mountain, it sounded like a three-master coming up into the wind!" Well, surely this purple taffeta would sound like the sails of a three-master. Greta let a little chuckle escape her. The woman looked down at her sharply.

"Few travel the road to Blue Cove afoot," she said. "Why are *you* going?"

"I like to walk in the fog," Greta told her.

"*Walk* in it, yes. But God help the men in boats on a day like this."

"But, but — as long as they can hear Tollerton blowing, they know where they are." Greta tried to defend the fog.

"Tollerton? Tollerton?" the woman looked puzzled.

"Yes, Tollerton — the foghorn in the Passage, I mean," Greta said.

"Well, it's time they had a foghorn in the Passage — with that treacherous current pulling between the Neck and the Islands. But you're talking nonsense, child. I never heard tell of one."

Greta caught her breath sharply and listened. They were on the side of the mountain toward the open sea, and the wind was blowing out of the southwest. Tollerton should have sounded more distinctly here than at home. But *there was no sound of it.* She had passed beyond the reach of Tollerton's warning voice.

The woman was silent. Her driving took all her attention as the road wound down from the level plateau. Greta was too

excited to speak. She knew somehow with certainty that when the road swung down toward the sea she would not find the familiar empty beach. She would find instead the once prosperous village of Blue Cove.

Two giant boulders stood where the old Post Road left the plateau and began to wind down toward the sea. The road had insisted on squeezing between them when it might just as easily have gone around. Greta had often traced the scorings on their inner surfaces, the straight lines that marked the years of travel. The rocks loomed ahead in the fog. It was exciting to think of dashing between them behind these brisk horses. She gripped the side of the surrey and leaned forward. The woman beside her gave a short laugh and reached for the whip.

"Never fear, child. We'll make it," she said. "They're the sentinels that guard Blue Cove. None passes but has a right there." She paused. "But *they* pass safely," she added.

"Have *I* a right there, do you think?" Somehow the question had to be asked. The woman turned to look down squarely into the girl's face.

"You've no cause to worry. You've the look of one that was always welcome there," she said curtly. Then the horses took all her attention. The boulders were upon them, dark shadows in the mist. The horses lunged through, then settled quietly again to a steadier pace.

Greta knew what this part of the mountain was like in clear weather. To the south of the road there was still unbroken forest — scarred here and there with burned patches, but otherwise dark, mysterious, treacherous, with unexpected chasms. Along the edge of the road to the north a high protective hedge of spruce and alder had been left, cut here and there with entrances. Beyond the hedge lay a clearing that sloped gently toward the sea. And dotting this clearing were cellar holes. Smooth little depressions they were; covered with the quick-springing growth of the pasture. It looked almost as if the homes of the departed inhabitants had sunk quietly into the earth.

Greta had often played in these cellar holes. It was fun to imagine where each house had stood, where the doorways had been, where the single street had led. Sometimes the shape of the depressions gave a clue; often a flat stone marked a doorstep. Once she had dug up a tiny spoon in a cellar hole. A salt spoon it was, with a strange name engraved on the handle. Her father said it was the name of a packet that had gone down off the Islands, years and years ago. The little salt spoon was one of her most treasured possessions, kept carefully hidden under the handkerchiefs in her dresser drawer.

Suddenly the woman pulled the team to a stop. They were opposite one of the entrances to the clearing. "You'd best get out here," she said abruptly.

Greta climbed quickly over the wheel. In front of her an archway, hung with its curtain of fog, opened into the clearing. But did it lead into the familiar pasture? Or did it lead to something very different? For the first time in all her wandering in the fog she hesitated. She turned back toward the surrey for reassurance. The woman was smiling at her now, kindly, all her grimness gone.

"Go on," she said gently. "In the second house you'll find Retha Morrill. You two will pull well together."

She touched the horses with her whip. Greta watched the surrey disappear into the thicker mists below. Then, with a pounding heart, she stepped through the arch of spruces.

Her feet crunched on gravel. She was walking on a neat path. At her right loomed a big barn. Beyond she traced the outlines of a house — small, neat, gray-shingled — and another, and another. A smell of wood smoke was in the air. Something brushed against her ankle. She looked down. A gray cat, the largest she had ever seen, was looking at her pleasantly.

"You beauty," Greta said to her and stooped to stroke the long hair. But it was one thing to greet a guest and quite another to be touched. Without loss of dignity, without haste, the gray cat was simply beyond reach. But she was leading the way, her plume of a tail erect. Where the second neat path turned off toward a house the cat looked back to be sure that Greta was following. Suddenly a door banged. Around the side of the house and down the path a little girl came running. She stopped when she saw Greta and gathered the cat into her arms. The two girls stood looking at each other.

"I'm Retha Morrill," said the Blue Cove child slowly, "and I think that Princess must have brought you." She smiled and took Greta's hand. "I'm glad you've come. Let's — let's go in to Mother."

Greta could think of nothing to say. She could only smile back and follow. But she knew, and Retha knew, that as the woman had said, they would pull well together. At the doorway Retha dropped Princess on the wide stone before the steps.

"Please wait here," she said. "I'll find Mother."

Greta nodded. She still wasn't sure of her voice. She watched Princess curl into a graceful heap on the stone — gray stone, gray fur, gray mist, gray shingles, all softly blending and blurring before her eyes. She knew that stone well. It had strange markings on it. She had often traced them with her finger where it lay in the empty pasture beside her favorite cellar hole.

There was a brisk step inside the house and a tall woman stood in the doorway. "Come in, child, come in," she began. Then she stopped and looked long at her visitor. And Greta looked up at her. She had never seen such blue eyes in all her life before — nor such *seeing* eyes. They were eyes that would always see through and beyond — even through the close mist of the fog itself. The woman put out her hand and drew Greta inside before she spoke again. Her voice was a little unsteady but very gentle.

"You are from over the mountain," she said. "I can tell. And I'd know it even if this were the sunniest day in the year."

Greta didn't quite know what the words meant but she knew somehow in her heart that she and this strange woman would understand each other without words. In just the flash of a moment they had traveled the longest road in the world — the road that leads from eye to eye.

"I am Laura Morrill," Retha's mother continued quietly. "Retha shouldn't have left you standing outside — not such a welcome guest. Now turn toward the light and let me look at you. Humph! Yes. You *must* be an Addington. Would your name be Greta, now? Yes?" She laughed. "So I guessed it right the very first time! Well, you have the Addington look and the Addington eyes, and there's always a Greta among the Addingtons! Yes, and there's always a child among the Addingtons that loves the fog it was born to. You're that child, I take it, in your generation." Her laughing face grew sober and she gave Greta a long, steady look. Then she smiled again quickly and smoothed back Greta's hair with a quick stroke of her hand.

"It's the things you were born to that give you satisfaction in this world, Greta. Leastwise, that's what I think. And maybe the fog's one of them. Not happiness, mind! Satisfaction isn't always happiness by a long sight; then again, it isn't sorrow either. But the rocks and the spruces and the fogs of your own land are things that nourish you. You can always have them, no matter what else you find or what else you lose. Now run along and let Retha show you the village. You two must get acquainted."

"May I leave my pail here?" Greta asked her. "I picked quite a few berries for Mother, coming over."

"Of course you may," Laura Morrill told her. "But that

reminds me! You must be hungry. We're through our dinner long since but I'll get you something. I dare say you left home early."

"I brought a sandwich to eat on the way," Greta told her. "Only there hasn't been time."

"Sit right down and eat it here, then. Retha, you fetch a glass of milk, and I'll get you a piece of strawberry pie. Retha went berrying early this morning too, and I made my first wild strawberry pie of the season."

After Greta had eaten she and Retha went out to explore the village. Its single street followed the curve of the shore line. There were houses on only one side, with patches of gardens behind white fences. Across the road in a narrow stretch of meadow, cows were grazing. Thick spruces hedged the meadow in at the lower side where there was a sharp drop, almost a precipice, to the shore. But the street was high enough so that Greta knew on a clear day you could look from the houses straight out to the open sea.

It was pleasant walking slowly up the street with Retha, but Greta couldn't find anything to say. To ask questions might break the spell. She might find herself back again in the empty clearing. And Retha knew that it would be impolite to question a stranger. They reached the end of the street before either spoke.

"There's our school, and there's our church," Retha said. She pointed out the little white building across the end of the street next to the neat church with its steeple.

"The shore curves in here, and there's another bay down there where you can find all sorts of things to play with. Our church is nice. Sometime maybe you'll be here on a Sunday so you can see it inside. There isn't any burying ground," she added. "It's all rock here and we can't have our own. When folks die they have to go over the mountain to be buried. Now let's go back to the Post Road and I'll show you the shore and the wharf and the fish houses and the stores."

In one of the dooryards two very small children were playing. As they came near Greta saw that there was a man seated on the ground, his back against the fence. One child tripped and sat down heavily, jolting out an indignant wail. The man reached out a long arm. He set the small thing on its feet again as you would set a ninepin, and gave it a comforting pat. The wail died suddenly, and the man slumped back. Greta laughed.

"He must like children," she said, "or they must like him. Why, he didn't even have to speak to that one."

"Sss-h," Retha warned her. "He *can't* speak, but we — we don't quite know — for sure — whether he can hear."

Whether he heard or only felt their approaching footsteps, the man turned suddenly and looked up at them between the pickets. A lean, dark, strange, and foreign face. The eyes were piercing, searching. Greta found she was standing quite still, giving this strange man a chance to look at her. Retha didn't seem to think it unusual. She was smiling at him and saying slowly,

"Anthony, this is my friend Greta Addington. She's from over the mountain." Then she pulled Greta gently away. The man turned to watch until they faded into the fog.

"But, Retha, you said he couldn't *hear,* and then you *spoke* to him. And he looks almost — almost savage. And still he was minding those babies."

"I said we don't *know* whether he hears or not. Or whether he could speak if he wanted to. But he's not savage. He only looks that way when he sees a stranger. I guess it's because he's always trying to find someone — someone he knows, I mean. But, Greta, did you see his — his legs?"

"I didn't see anything but his eyes. And anyhow, he was

almost hidden in that clump of monkshood. What about his legs?"

"He — he hasn't any," Retha said quietly.

"Hasn't any *legs?*" Greta could only stare in horror.

"They are gone just above his knees, so all he can do is crawl, and mind babies. But no matter how fierce he looks, *they* understand him. And he's always gentle."

"But what happened?"

Retha hesitated a moment. "We don't talk about him much. I'd like to ask Mother first if I should tell you. Let's go down to the wharf now." And Greta had to be content.

When they reached the Post Road, Retha pointed toward the shore. "See! The fog's lifting a little. You can see the end of the wharf from here and you couldn't see anything an hour ago. Come on."

Greta stood still. She couldn't explain it even to herself, but suddenly she knew how Cinderella felt when the first stroke of midnight began to sound.

"I think there isn't time to go down today, Retha," she said. "But I'd like to go next time I come. I must go home now. It'll be late when I get over the mountain."

"Your berries! You left your pail at our house," Retha reminded her.

They ran back to the house. In the doorway Mrs. Morrill stood holding the pail.

"The fog's lifting," she said quietly and held out the pail. "I put a piece of strawberry pie on top of your berries, but I don't think it'll crush them any. And come again, child. We'd like to see you often; that is, if your mother doesn't worry. You're like a visitor from another world." Then she added as an afterthought, "Coming as you do from over the mountain."

Greta thanked her and took the pail. Retha went as far as the Post Road with her. They said goodbye hurriedly. Greta left without daring to turn back and wave.

It was almost clear when she reached home, but late. Her mother greeted her with relief. Father had finished milking and sat reading the paper. Greta's conscience hurt her. She hadn't once thought of the mail, and someone else had gone to the post office. She held out the pail to her mother.

"There's a surprise in it, Mother," she said. Gertrude opened the pail.

"I *am* surprised," she said. "I never dreamed you'd find so many. It's early yet for strawberries."

Greta stood very still. Then she stepped over and looked into the pail. There were the berries she had picked. *But there was nothing else in the pail!*

Suddenly she wanted to cry, but her father was looking at her over the top of his paper. He was smiling at her just with his eyes, but he looked as if he understood.

"Fog thick at Blue Cove today?" he asked.

"Heavens, child, you have been way over there?" asked her mother.

How did Father know she had been to Blue Cove? Greta no longer wanted to cry. She could look back at Father and almost smile.

"Yes, Father," she said. "It was very thick today."

"I thought so," he answered and went back to his paper.

Author

Julia L. Sauer was born in Rochester, New York, and has lived there most of her life. She decided to become an author after she became the Children's Librarian at the Rochester Public Library. Because of her fondness for Nova Scotia she used that setting for her first book, *Fog Magic*. *Fog Magic* and a later book of the author's, *The Light at Tern Rock,* were both selected as Newbery Honor Books.

A larger-than-life look at one of the four thousand varieties of ladybeetles. This one was photographed on Prince Edward Island, Canada.

Lovable Ladybug

from the book *Never Pet a Porcupine*

by George Laycock

It seems strange for people to like a bug, but never step on a ladybug! It has friends everywhere.

The love between people and ladybugs, which are really not bugs but beetles, is not like young love in the springtime. It is a more practical type of love. People love ladybeetles because they eat aphids. Aphids attack rose bushes and alfalfa plants. So if you have ladybeetles for neighbors, things can't be all bad.

Who can forget, for example, the fame ladybeetles earned some eighty years ago in the citrus groves of California? About that time a parasite called the "cottony-cushion scale" slipped into the country from Australia as a stowaway. The cottony-cushion scale had an insatiable appetite for citrus leaves. Grapefruit, lemons and oranges were more than breakfast food to it. It ate them hour after hour, until the entire California citrus industry was faced with destruction. Grove owners applying to banks for loans soon found that their bankers searched the trees for cottony-cushion scale. If they found the pest, they refused to risk their money. And all the while, the cottony-cushion scale, unchecked by any of its natural enemies found in its native Australia, multiplied happily and marched forward through the citrus groves.

Word of the farmer's plight reached Washington. The U.S. Department of Agriculture promptly dispatched research specialists to Australia to seek out the natural enemy of the scale. What they found and brought back was a species of ladybeetle that specialized in eating cottony-cushion scale.

Above: A hungry seven-spot ladybeetle larva eating an aphid. The ladybeetle larvae leave little food for the adults, who must then migrate to find food.

Middle: An adult spotted ladybeetle feeding on marigold pollen, since the larvae have eaten all the aphids. Far right: A swarm of ladybeetles wintering in the mountains.

The little beetles, released in California, had the scale under control within two years, and the state's great citrus industry was saved. The cost had been less than $5,000. No wonder people love the ladybeetle!

Those orange or red ladybeetles with the black spots are members of a large clan. Around the world, there are some 4,000 species of them. And one of them, in a normal lifetime, can consume 7,000 aphids.

This fact has so impressed gardeners and farmers that for decades there has been a strong market for ladybeetles. One typical California bug merchant collects ladybeetles while they are hibernating. Next he puts them into cold storage. Later he measures them by the gallon into sacks and packs them for shipping to his customers.

A gallon of ladybeetles, say those who have counted them, contains 75,000 of the busy little insects. What's more, the

females will each lay about 500 eggs. The eggs hatch within a week, and the larvae are just as hungry for aphids as are their parents.

How do you catch 75,000 ladybeetles? It's easier than it sounds, but it is important to understand the strange habits of these little six-legged predators. California ladybeetles, over the centuries, have become migratory creatures. Their travels take them where their food supplies are best at various seasons.

In May and June the new crop of adult ladybeetles emerges in the grain and hay fields. Almost at once, they face starvation. The larvae have already consumed most of the aphids. The adults do not wander aimlessly about. Instead they fly straight upward into the sky for a mile or more. Here they find a tail wind that carries them off to the Sierra Nevada Mountains.

For nine months, the insects stay high in the mountains, where they feed on pollen. In February or March they mate, and then they fly upward again until they are picked up by the prevailing winds. This time they are borne on the easterly winds back to the valleys where they are welcomed by farmers if not by the aphids.

During their days in the mountains, the ladybeetles often gather in great swarms. These are what attract the commercial bug-dealers. Some dealers report having gathered up as many as 100 gallons of ladybeetles from a space the size of a 10-by-12-foot room.

A striped ladybeetle devouring one of the seven thousand aphids it consumes during its lifetime. This is what makes ladybeetles lovable!

There was even a period half a century ago when the California Department of Agriculture, impressed by the ladybeetles' good work on the cottony-cushion scale, supplied ladybeetles free to farmers. During the winters they collected the beetles by the ton. The following spring, landowners obtained 30,000 ladybeetles free for every 10 acres farmed. This program ground to a halt when specialists discovered, by marking them with paint, that the ladybeetles frequently flew out of the fields. However, the gains from transplanting ladybeetles were great enough that they are still bought and sold.

No one, to our knowledge, has ever figured out how ladybeetles learned to eat aphids in the first place; but it was a good thing they did. Without this skill, people might look upon the little beetle as just another bug. The ladybeetle is no ordinary insect, though. Treat one kindly. Let it live. It has work to do yet, perhaps 7,000 aphids to eat. It's good to have at least one insect around that everybody loves.

Author

George Laycock is an award-winning author of over thirty books on nature and conservation, and he is a contributor to a number of magazines, including *National Wildlife* and *Boys' Life*. He also serves as field editor for *Audubon Magazine*. Animals and the outdoors are subjects of lifelong interest to him.

The Wise Old Woman

from the book *The Sea of Gold and Other Tales from Japan*
by Yoshiko Uchida

Many long years ago, there lived an arrogant and cruel young lord who ruled over a small village in the western hills of Japan.

"I have no use for old people in my village," he said haughtily. "They are neither useful nor able to work for a living. I therefore decree that anyone over seventy-one must be banished from the village and left in the mountains to die."

"What a dreadful decree! What a cruel and unreasonable lord we have," the people of the village murmured. But the lord fearfully punished anyone who disobeyed him, and so villagers who turned seventy-one were tearfully carried into the mountains, never to return.

Gradually there were fewer and fewer old people in the village and soon they disappeared altogether. Then the young lord was pleased.

"What a fine village of young, healthy and hardworking people I have," he bragged. "Soon it will be the finest village in all of Japan."

Now there lived in this village a kind young farmer and his aged mother. They were poor, but the farmer was good to his mother, and the two of them lived happily together. However, as the years went by, the mother grew older, and before long she reached the terrible age of seventy-one.

"If only I could somehow deceive the cruel lord," the farmer thought. But there were records in the village books and every one knew that his mother had turned seventy-one.

Each day the son put off telling his mother that he must take her into the mountains to die, but the people of the village began to talk. The farmer knew that if he did not take his mother away soon, the lord would send his soldiers and throw them both into a dark dungeon to die a terrible death.

"Mother — " he would begin, as he tried to tell her what he must do, but he could not go on.

Then one day the mother herself spoke of the lord's dread decree. "Well, my son," she said, "the time has come for you to take me to the mountains. We must hurry before the lord sends his soldiers for you." And she did not seem worried at all that she must go to the mountains to die.

"Forgive me, dear mother, for what I must do," the farmer said sadly, and the next morning he lifted his mother to his shoulders and set off on the steep path toward the mountains.

Up and up he climbed, until the trees clustered close and the path was gone. There was no longer even the sound of birds, and they heard only the soft wail of the wind in the trees. The son walked slowly, for he could not bear to think of leaving his old mother in the mountains. On and on he climbed, not wanting to stop and leave her behind. Soon, he heard his mother breaking off small twigs from the trees that they passed.

"Mother, what are you doing?" he asked.

"Do not worry, my son," she answered gently. "I am just marking the way so you will not get lost returning to the village."

The son stopped. "Even now you are thinking of me?" he asked, wonderingly.

The mother nodded. "Of course, my son," she replied. "You will always be in my thoughts. How could it be otherwise?"

At that, the young farmer could bear it no longer. "Mother, I cannot leave you in the mountains to die all alone," he said. "We are going home and no matter what the lord does to punish me, I will never desert you again."

So they waited until the sun had set and a lone star crept into the silent sky. Then in the dark shadows of night, the farmer carried his mother down the hill and they returned quietly to their little house. The farmer dug a deep hole in the floor of his kitchen and made a small room where he could hide his mother. From that day, she spent all her time in the secret room and the farmer carried meals to her there. The rest of the time, he was careful to work in the fields and act as though he lived alone. In this way, for almost two years, he kept his mother safely hidden and no one in the village knew that she was there.

Then one day there was a terrible commotion among the villagers for Lord Higa of the town beyond the hills threatened to conquer their village and make it his own.

"Only one thing can spare you," Lord Higa announced. "Bring me a box containing one thousand ropes of ash and I will spare your village."

The cruel young lord quickly gathered together all the wise men of his village. "You are men of wisdom," he said. "Surely you can tell me how to meet Lord Higa's demands so our village can be spared."

But the wise men shook their heads. "It is impossible to make even one rope of ash, sire," they answered. "How can we ever make one thousand?"

"Fools!" the lord cried angrily. "What good is your wisdom if you cannot help me now?"

And he posted a notice in the village square offering a great reward of gold to any villager who could help him save their village.

But all the people in the village whispered, "Surely, it is an impossible thing, for ash crumbles at the touch of the finger. How could anyone ever make a rope of ash?" They shook their heads and sighed, "Alas, alas, we must be conquered by yet another cruel lord."

The young farmer, too, supposed that this must be, and he wondered what would happen to his mother if a new lord even more terrible than their own came to rule over them.

When his mother saw the troubled look on his face, she asked, "Why are you so worried, my son?"

So the farmer told her of the impossible demand made by Lord Higa if the village was to be spared, but his mother did not seem troubled at all. Instead she laughed softly and said, "Why, that is not such an impossible task. All one has to do is soak ordinary rope in salt water and dry it well. When it is burned, it will hold its shape and there is your rope of ash! Tell the villagers to hurry and find one thousand pieces of rope."

The farmer shook his head in amazement. "Mother, you are wonderfully wise," he said, and he rushed to tell the young lord what he must do.

"You are wiser than all the wise men of the village," the lord said when he heard the farmer's solution, and he rewarded him with many pieces of gold. The thousand ropes of ash were quickly made and the village was spared.

In a few days, however, there was another great commotion in the village as Lord Higa sent another threat. This time he sent a log with a small hole that curved and bent seven times through its length, and he demanded that a single piece of silk thread be threaded through the hole. "If you cannot perform this task," the lord threatened, "I shall come to conquer your village."

The young lord hurried once more to his wise men, but they all shook their heads in bewilderment. "A needle cannot bend its way through such curves," they moaned. "Again we are faced with an impossible demand."

"And again you are stupid fools!" the lord said, stamping his foot impatiently. He then posted a second notice in the village square asking the villagers for their help.

Once more the young farmer hurried with the problem to his mother in her secret room.

"Why, that is not so difficult," his mother said with a quick smile. "Put some sugar at one end of the hole. Then, tie a piece of silk thread to an ant and put it in at the other end. He will weave his way in and out of the curves to get to the sugar and he will take the silk thread with him."

"Mother, you are remarkable!" the son cried, and he hurried off to the lord with the solution to the second problem.

Once more the lord commended the young farmer and rewarded him with many pieces of gold. "You are a brilliant man and you have saved our village again," he said gratefully.

But the lord's troubles were not over even then, for a few days later Lord Higa sent still another demand. "This time you will undoubtedly fail and then I shall conquer your village," he threatened. "Bring me a drum that sounds without being beaten."

"But that is not possible," sighed the people of the village. "How can anyone make a drum sound without beating it?"

This time the wise men held their heads in their hands and moaned, "It is hopeless. It is hopeless. This time Lord Higa will conquer us all."

The young farmer hurried home breathlessly. "Mother, Mother, we must solve another terrible problem or Lord Higa

will conquer our village!" And he quickly told his mother about the impossible drum.

His mother, however, smiled and answered, "Why, this is the easiest of them all. Make a drum with sides of paper and put a bumblebee inside. As it tries to escape, it will buzz and beat itself against the paper and you will have a drum that sounds without being beaten."

The young farmer was amazed at his mother's wisdom. "You are far wiser than any of the wise men of the village," he said, and he hurried to tell the young lord how to meet Lord Higa's third demand.

When the lord heard the answer, he was greatly impressed. "Surely a young man like you cannot be wiser than all my wise men," he said. "Tell me honestly, who has helped you solve all these difficult problems?"

The young farmer could not lie. "My lord," he began slowly, "for the past two years I have broken the law of the land. I have kept my aged mother hidden beneath the floor of my house, and it is she who solved each of your problems and saved the village from Lord Higa."

He trembled as he spoke, for he feared the lord's displeasure and rage. Surely now the soldiers would be summoned to throw him into the dark dungeon. But when he glanced fearfully at the lord, he saw that the young ruler was not angry at all. Instead, he was silent and thoughtful, for at last he realized how much wisdom and knowledge old people possess.

"I have been very wrong," he said finally. "And I must ask the forgiveness of your mother and of all my people. Never again will I demand that the old people of our village be sent to the mountains to die. Rather, they will be treated with the respect and honor they deserve and share with us the wisdom of their years."

And so it was. From that day, the villagers were no longer forced to abandon their parents in the mountains, and the village became once more a happy, cheerful place in which to live. The terrible Lord Higa stopped sending his impossible demands and no longer threatened to conquer them, for he too was impressed. "Even in such a small village there is much wisdom," he declared, "and its people should be allowed to live in peace."

And that is exactly what the farmer, and his mother, and all the people of the village did for all the years thereafter.

Author

"Although I was born in California," says Yoshiko Uchida, "a good bit of Japan was inside me all along, for this was the country from which my parents came." Among the many award-winning books she has written are collections of Japanese folktales, such as *The Sea of Gold,* and stories of Japanese or Japanese-American children.

Midwest Town

by Ruth De Long Peterson

Farther east it wouldn't be on the map —
  Too small — but here it rates a dot and name.
In Europe it would wear a castle cap
  Or have a cathedral rising like a flame.

But here it stands where the section roadways meet,
  Its houses dignified with trees and lawn;
The stores hold tête-à-tête across Main Street;
  The red brick school, a church — the town is gone.

America is not all traffic lights
  And beehive homes and shops and factories;
No, there are wide green days and starry nights,
  And a great pulse beating strong in towns like these.

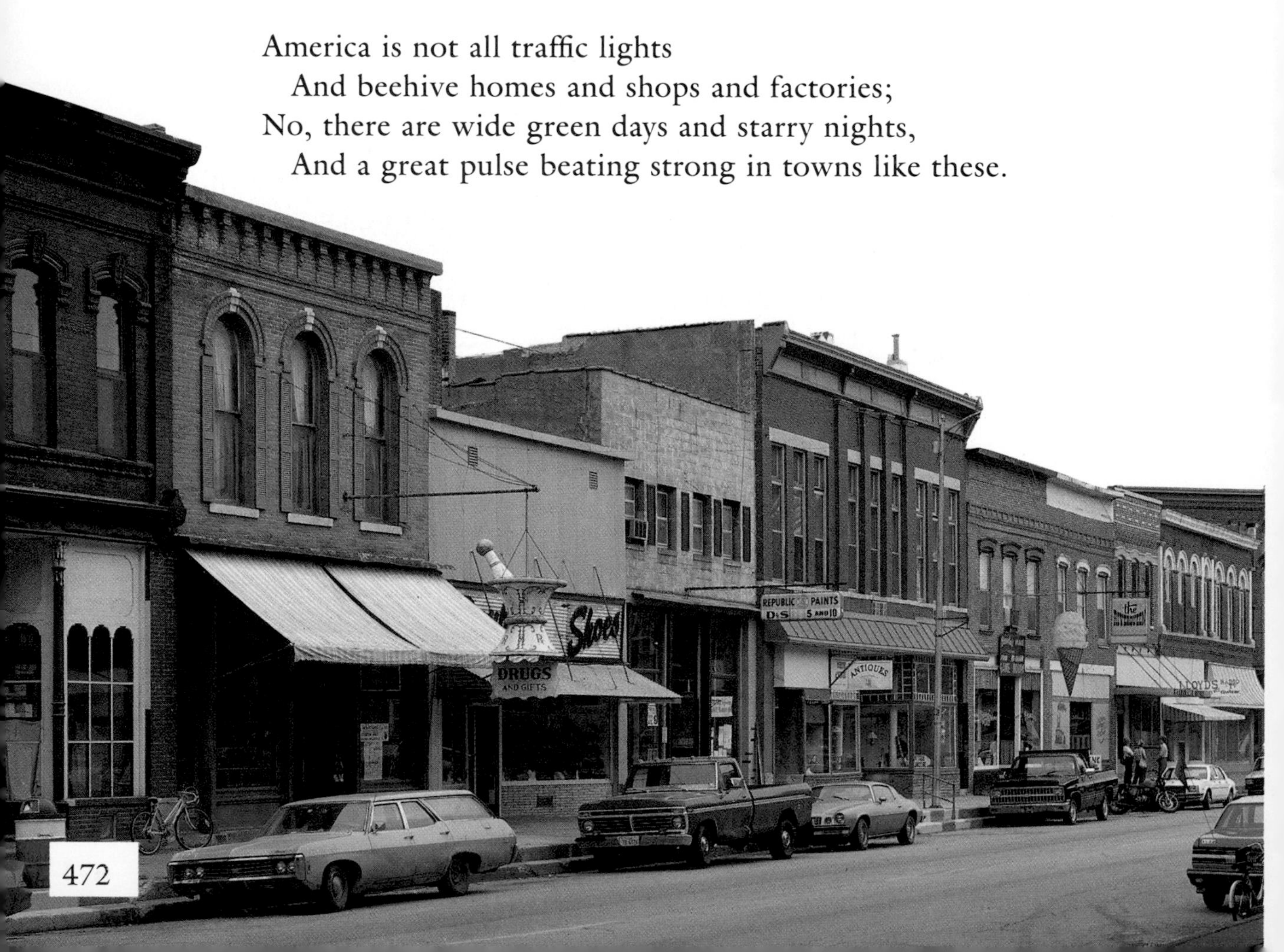

Houghton Mifflin Literature

In the selections you have just read from *Appearances Can Be Deceiving*, learning to see what is truly present was difficult or even impossible for some of the main characters.

Now you will read two stories that will ask you to think twice before you make a quick judgment about the main characters. In *The Ugly Duckling* by A. A. Milne, you will see a comical princess transformed. In Marianna Mayer's adaptation of *Beauty and the Beast*, you will be asked to look beyond ugliness.

Glossary

Some of the words in this book may have pronunciations or meanings you do not know. This glossary can help you by telling you how to pronounce those words and by telling you their meanings.

You can find out the correct pronunciation of any glossary word by using the special spelling after the word and the pronunciation key at the bottom of each left-hand page.

The full pronunciation key below shows how to pronounce each consonant and vowel in a special spelling. The pronunciation key at the bottom of each left-hand page is a shortened form of the full key.

Full Pronunciation Key

Consonant Sounds

b	**bib**
ch	**ch**ur**ch**
d	**d**ee**d**
f	**f**ast, **f**i**f**e, o**ff**, **ph**ase, rou**gh**
g	**g**a**g**
h	**h**at
hw	**wh**ich
j	**j**u**dg**e
k	**c**at, **k**i**ck**, pi**que**
l	**l**id, needl**e**
m	a**m**, **m**an, **m**u**m**
n	**n**o, sudde**n**
ng	thi**ng**
p	**p**o**p**
r	**r**oa**r**
s	mi**ss**, **s**au**c**e, **s**ee
sh	di**sh**, **sh**ip
t	**t**igh**t**
th	pa**th**, **th**in
th	ba**the**, **th**is
v	ca**v**e, **v**al**v**e, **v**ine
w	**w**ith
y	**y**es
z	ro**s**e, si**z**e, **x**ylophone, **z**ebra
zh	gara**g**e, plea**s**ure, vi**s**ion

Pronunciation Key © 1986 by Houghton Mifflin Company. Adapted and reprinted by permission from the *American Heritage Intermediate Dictionary*.

Vowel Sounds

- ă **pat**
- ā **ai**d, the**y**, pa**y**
- â **ai**r, c**a**re, w**ea**r
- ä f**a**ther
- ĕ p**e**t, pl**ea**sure
- ē b**e**, b**ee**, **ea**sy, s**ei**ze
- ĭ p**i**t
- ī b**y**, g**uy**, p**ie**
- î d**ea**r, d**ee**r, f**ie**rce, m**e**re
- ŏ p**o**t, h**o**rrible
- ō g**o**, r**ow**, t**oe**
- ô **a**lter, c**au**ght, f**o**r, p**aw**
- oi b**oy**, n**oi**se, **oi**l
- o͝o b**oo**k
- o͞o b**oo**t, fr**ui**t
- ou c**ow**, **ou**t
- ŭ c**u**t, r**ou**gh
- û f**i**rm, h**ea**rd, t**e**rm, t**u**rn, w**o**rd
- yo͞o ab**u**se, **u**se
- ə **a**bout, sil**e**nt, penc**i**l, lem**o**n, circ**u**s
- ər butt**er**

Stress Marks

Primary Stress **′**

bi•ol′o•gy (bī **ŏl′**ə jē)

Secondary Stress ′

bi′o•log′i•cal (bi′ə **lŏj′**i kəl)

a•ban•don (ə **băn′**dən) *v.* **1.** To leave and stop looking after (someone); desert: *abandon one's family.* **2.** To cease to use or occupy and leave behind: *abandon one's farm and move to the city.*

ab•scess (**ăb′**sĕs′) *n.* A mass of pus that forms and collects at one place in the body. An abscess usually comes from an infection and feels sore.

a•buse (ə **byo͞os′**) *n.* **1.** Improper use. **2.** Mistreatment.

a•dapt (ə **dăpt′**) *v.* To change so as to be suitable for a different condition or purpose.

af•fec•tion (ə **fĕk′**shən) *n.* A fond or loving feeling toward someone or something.

af•flict (ə **flĭkt′**) *v.* To cause to suffer, as from disease, pain, or trouble.

a•gil•i•ty (ə **jĭl′**ĭ tē)*n.* The quality or condition of being able to move quickly and easily.

ail (āl) *v.* To be ill: *My mother is ailing.*

a•li•as (**ā′**lē əs) *n.* An assumed name used by a person wishing to conceal his or her identity. —*adv.* Otherwise named: *William Blake alias James Flynn.*

al•ler•gy (**ăl′**ər jē) *n., pl.* **al•ler•gies.** A disorder in which exposure to a small amount of a substance, or to an environmental influence, such as heat or cold, often causes a violent reaction that may include difficult breathing, sneezing, watering of the eyes, and shock.

an•ces•tor (**ăn′**sĕs′tər) *n.* Any person from whom one is descended, especially if of a generation earlier than a grandparent.

an•guish (**ăng′** gwĭsh) *n.* Strong pain or suffering of body or mind.

an•i•ma•tion (ăn′ə **mā′**shən) *n.* The process or processes by which a cartoon appears to be alive.

an•i•ma•tor (**ăn′**ə mā′tər) *n.* An artist or technician who prepares or produces animated cartoons.

a•phid (**ā′**fĭd) *or* (**ăf′**ĭd) *n.* A tiny, soft-bodied insect that sucks sap from plants.

aphid

ap•pall (ə **pôl′**) *v.* To fill with horror and amazement; shock.

ap•pall•ing (ə **pô′**lĭng) *adj.* Causing amazement, confusion, dismay, or fright: *appalling work conditions.*

ap•pren•tice (ə **prĕn′**tĭs) *v.* **ap•pren•ticed, ap• pren•tic•ing.** To place in a position to learn a craft or trade.

ă pat / ā pay / â care / ä father / ĕ pet / ē be / ĭ pit / ī pie / î fierce / ŏ pot / ō go / ô paw, for / oi oil / o͝o book / o͞o boot / ou out / ŭ cut / û fur / *th* the / th thin / hw which / zh vision / ə ago, item, pencil, atom, circus

ar•ti•fi•cial (är′tə **fĭsh′**əl) *adj.* Made by man instead of occurring in nature: *an artificial sweetener; artificial flowers.*

as•sas•si•nate (ə **săs′**ə nāt′) *v.* **as•sas•si•nat•ed, as•sas•si•nat•ing.** To To murder (a public figure), usually for political reasons.

a•stir (ə **stûr′**) *adj.* Up and about; active: *Our family was astir early in the morning.*

as•ton•ish (ə **stŏn′**ĭsh) *v.* To fill with wonder; amaze; surprise.

a•stound (ə **stound′**) *v.* To strike with sudden wonder; astonish.

a•stray (ə **strā′**) *adv.* Away from the right path or direction.

at•tract (ə **trăkt′**) *v.* **1.** To draw or pull to oneself or itself by some special quality or action. **2.** To draw attention to.

au•di•tion (ô **dĭsh′**ən) *n.* A short performance to test the ability of a musician, singer, dancer, or actor. — *v.* To perform in an audition: *She auditioned for a part in the play.*

awe•struck (**ô′**strŭk′) *adj.* Full of a mixture of wonder, dread, and respect.

bail (bāl) *v.* To remove (water) from a boat by repeatedly filling a container and emptying it.

bank (băngk) *v.* **1.** To pile (earth, snow, etc.) in a ridge or sloping surface. **2.** To pile ashes or fresh fuel onto (a fire) to make it burn slowly.

bar•ren (**băr′**ən) *adj.* Not producing anything: *a barren field.*

bel•low (**bĕl′**ō) *v.* **bel•lowed, bel•low•ing. 1.** To roar as a bull does. **2.** To shout in a deep, loud voice.

berth (bûrth) *n.* A position of employment, especially on a ship.

bil•low (**bĭl′**ō) *v.* To rise in masses: *Flames and smoke billowed over the prairie.*

bleat (blēt) *v.* To make a crying sound, such as that made by a goat, sheep, or calf.

boast•ful (**bōst′**fəl) *adj.* Tending to brag.

bore (bôr) *v.* **1.** To make a hole or a hole in, as with a drill. **2.** To make a hole or tunnel, as by digging or drilling.

brace (brās) *v.* **braced, brac•ing. 1.** To prepare for a blow, shock, struggle. **2.** To prop or hold firmly in place: *She braced her feet against the floorboard.*

brash (brăsh) *adj.* **1.** Hasty and unthinking; rash. **2.** Shamelessly bold; saucy.

bril•liant (**brĭl′**yənt) *adj.* Extremely intelligent or inventive.

calm (käm) *v.* To become or make quiet and unexcited; to quiet down.

ca•pa•ble (**kā′**pə bəl) *adj.* **1.** Able; skilled; competent: *a capable teacher.* **2. — capable of.** Having the ability or capacity for.

cap•size (**kăp′**sīz′) *or* (kăp **sīz′**) *v.* **cap•sized, cap•siz•ing.** To overturn: *A huge wave capsized our boat.*

cap•tiv•i•ty (kăp **tĭv′**ĭ tē) *n., pl.* **cap•tiv•i•ties.** A period or the condition of being kept under control by another.

car•a•van (**kăr′**ə văn′) *n.* **1.** A large, covered vehicle; van. **2.** A home on wheels, as a trailer.

care•tak•er (**kâr′**tā′kər) *n.* A person employed to look after and take care of a house or a building.

car•pen•try (**kär′**pən trē) *n.* The work or trade of someone who builds or repairs wooden objects and structures.

cast (kăst) *v.* **cast, cast•ing.** To choose actors for a play or a movie.

cas•u•al (**kăzh′**o͞o əl) *adj.* **1.** Said or done quickly or without preparation; passing: *a casual question.* **2.** Not serious; superficial. **3.** Showing little interest.

cha•os (**kā′** os′) *n.* Great confusion or disorder.

char•ac•ter•is•tic (kăr′ĭk tə **rĭs′**tĭk) *adj.* Indicating a special feature of a person or thing: *the zebra's characteristic stripes.*

chasm (**kăz′**əm) *n.* A deep crack or opening in the surface of the earth.

cit•rus (**sĭt′**rəs) *adj.* One of a group of trees or fruits that includes the orange, lemon, and lime.

cleft (klĕft) *adj.* Split or partially split: *a cleft chin.*

cloak (klōk) *n.* A loose outer garment, usually having no sleeves.

coast•line (**cōst′**līn) *n.* The shape of the land next to the sea.

coax (kōks) *v.* **1.** To persuade or try to persuade by gentle urging or flattery. **2.** To get by coaxing: *I coaxed a smile from the baby.*

col•lapse (kə **lăps′**) *v.* **col•lapsed, col•laps•ing.** **1.** To fall down or inward suddenly; cave in: *Part of the roof collapsed under the weight of the snow.* **2.** To break down or fail suddenly and completely.

com•pan•ion•ship (kəm **păn′**yən shĭp′) *n.* The relationship of friends; friendly feeling.

con•ceit•ed (kən **sē′**tĭd) *adj.* Too proud of oneself or one's accomplishments; vain.

con•clu•sion (kən **klo͞o′**zhən) *n.* **1.** The close or end, as of a play or concert. **2.** A judgment or decision made after careful thought.

con•de•scend•ing (kŏn′ dĭ **sĕn′** dĭng) *adj.* Showing that one considers oneself superior to others: *He gave a condescending nod as his only greeting.*

con•di•tion (kən **dĭsh′**ən) *n. Idiom.* **on [the] condition that.** If; provided: *Connie will cook dinner on condition that she doesn't have to wash the dishes.*

ă **pat** / ā **pay** / â **care** / ä **father** / ĕ **pet** / ē **be** / ĭ **pit** / ī **pie** / î **fierce** / ŏ **pot** / ō **go** / ô **paw, for** / oi **oil** / o͝o **book** / o͞o **boot** / ou **out** / ŭ **cut** / û **fur** / *th* **the** / th **thin** / hw **which** / zh **vision** / ə **ago, item, pencil, atom, circus**

con•fi•dence (**kŏn′**fĭ dəns) *n.* **1.** A feeling of faith in one's abilities; self-assurance: *He doesn't have confidence in himself.* **2.** Trust or reliance: *She won my confidence.*

con•fu•sion (kən **fyoo͞′**zhən) *n.* **1.** The condition of being mixed up; bewilderment. **2.** Disorder or chaos: *The enemy retreated in confusion.*

con•quer (**kŏng′**kər) *v.* **1.** To defeat in war: *Has a smaller country ever conquered a larger one?* **2.** To get control over; overcome: *The girl tried to conquer her fear.*

con•stant•ly (**kŏn′**stənt lē) *adj.* Always; all the time; continually.

con•vict (kən **vĭkt′**) *v.* To find or prove guilty.

con•vince (kən **vĭns′**) *v.* **con•vinced, con•vinc•ing.** To cause (someone) to believe or feel certain; persuade.

cor•dial (**kôr′**jəl) *n.* A medicine; a stimulant.

cow•er (**kou′**ər) *v.* To crouch or draw back, as from fear or pain.

cred•it (**krĕd′**ĭt) *n.* A system of buying goods or services by charging the amount, with payment due at a later time: *buy on credit.*

cro•chet (krō **shā′**) *v.* To make (a piece of needlework) by looping thread or yarn into connected links with a hooked needle called a **crochet hook.**

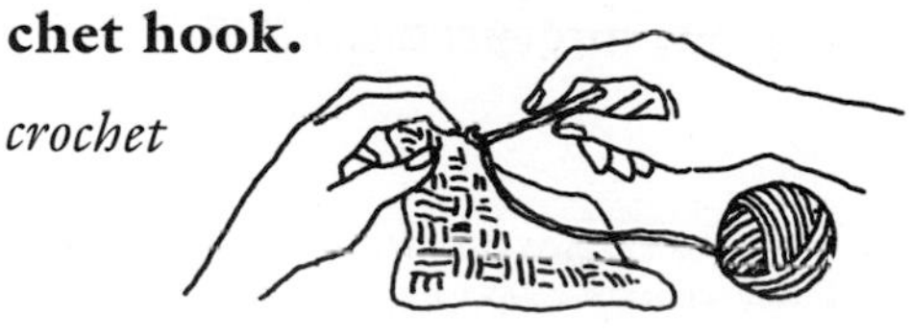
crochet

cus•tom (**kŭs′**təm) *n.* Something that the members of a group usually do.

de•ci•sive (dĭ **sī′**sĭv) *adj.* **1.** Deciding or having the power to decide an issue beyond doubt. **2.** Marked by decision; determined: *My reply was decisive.* — **de•ci•sive•ly** *adv.*

de•cree (dĭ **krē′**) *n.* An authoritative order; a law.

deft•ly (**dĕft′**lē) *adv.* Quickly and skillfully.

de•fy (dĭ **fī′**) *v.* **de•fied, de•fy•ing.** To oppose or challenge openly or boldly: *defy the law.*

de•lib•er•ate (dĭ **lĭb′**ər ĭt) *adj.* **1.** Done or said on purpose. **2.** Careful or cautious.

de•sert (dĭ **zûrt′**) *v.* To leave, especially when most needed; abandon.

des•o•late (**dĕs′**ə lĭt) *adj.* **1.** Having little or no vegetation. **2.** Having few or no inhabitants; deserted: *a desolate wilderness.*

de•spair•ing•ly (dĭ **spâr′**ĭng lē) *adv.* Feeling hopeless.

de•ter•mined (dĭ **tûr′**mĭnd) *adj.* Of firm mind; decisive: *a determined person.*

dis•as•ter (dĭ **zăs′**tər) *or* (**-zä′**stər) *n.* **1.** Great destruction, distress, or misfortune. **2.** A total failure.

dis•pleas•ure (dĭs **plĕzh′**ər) *n.* The condition of being annoyed, angry, or offended.

dis•pute (dĭ **spyo͞ot′**) *v.* **1.** To argue about; debate. **2.** To question the truth of; doubt. **3.** To quarrel.

dis•qui•et (dĭs **kwī′**ĭt) *v.* To make uneasy; to trouble. —**dis•qui•et•ing** *adj.* Causing unease or restlessness.

do•ry (**dôr′**ē) *n.* A flat-bottomed boat with high sides, often used in fishing.

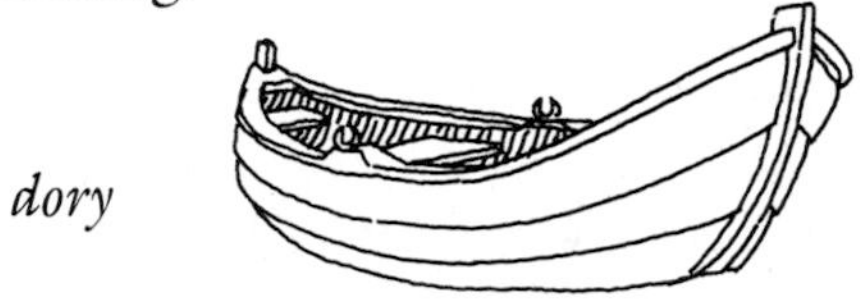
dory

down•heart•ed (**doun′här′**tĭd) *adj.* Low in spirits; sad; depressed.

dread (drĕd) *v.* To fear greatly: *I dreaded going to the dentist again.*

e•la•tion (ĭ **lā′** shən) *n.* An intense feeling of happiness or joy: *the elation that a musician or an athlete feels after a good performance.*

em•bark (ĕm **bärk′**) *v.* **1.** To go on board a ship or an airplane. **2.** To set out on a venture or task.

en•gi•neer (ĕn′jə **nîr′**) *n.* A person who uses scientific knowledge and rules for practical purposes, as designing and building bridges, roads, and tunnels.

en•vi•ron•ment (ĕn **vī′**rən mənt) *or* (**-vī′**ərn-) *n.* **1.** Surroundings and conditions that affect natural processes and the growth and development of living things.

ep•ic (**ĕp′**ĭk) *adj.* Like something described in an epic; tremendous: *an epic achievement.*

e•qua•tor (ĭ **kwā′**tər) *n.* An imaginary line around the middle of the earth at an equal distance from the North and South Poles.

e•ter•nal (ĭ **tûr′**nəl) *adj.* **1.** Having no beginning and no end; lasting forever. **2.** Going on and on; seeming never to stop.

e•vap•o•ra•tion (ĭ văp′ə **rā′**shən) *n.* The change by which any substance is converted from a liquid into a vapor.

ex•panse (ĭk **spăns′**) *n.* A wide and open extent, as of land, air, or water: *a vast expanse of desert.*

ex•pe•di•tion (ĕk′spĭ **dĭsh′**ən) *n.* **1.** A trip made by an organized group of people with a definite purpose: *an expedition to the South Pole.* **2.** A group making such a trip: *The expedition finally arrived.*

ex•pe•ri•enced (ĭk **spîr′**ē ənst) *adj.* Skilled or knowledgeable: *The experienced seaman was a veteran of thirty years at sea.*

ex•pla•na•tion (ĕk′splə **nā′**shən) *n.* **1.** The act or process of making something easier to understand. **2.** A statement, fact, etc., that serves to explain. **3.** A meaning; reason; interpretation.

ă **pat** / ā **pay** / â **care** / ä **father** / ĕ **pet** / ē **be** / ĭ **pit** / ī **pie** / î **fierce** / ŏ **pot** / ō **go** / ô **paw, for** / oi **oil** / o͝o **book** / o͞o **boot** / ou **out** / ŭ **cut** / û **fur** / *th* **the** / th **thin** / hw **which** / zh **vision** / ə **ago, item, pencil, atom, circus**

fac•to•ry (făk′tə rē) *n., pl.* **fac•to•ries.** A building or group of buildings in which goods are manufactured; a plant.

fail•ure (fāl′yər) *n.* Not achieving success.

faith (fāth) *n.* Confidence or trust in a person, idea, or thing: *You must have faith in yourself.*

fear•some (fîr′səm) *adj.* Causing or capable of causing fear; frightening; scary.

feat (fēt) *n.* An outstanding deed or accomplishment; an exploit.

fiend (fēnd) *n.* **1.** An evil spirit; demon. **2.** A wicked person.

for•mal (fôr′məl) *adj.* Stiff or cold: *a formal manner.*

for•mu•la (fôr′myə lə) *n., pl.* **for•mu•las** or **for•mu•lae** (fôr′myə lē′). **1.** A list of the ingredients and processes used in making something; a recipe: *the formula for a medicine.* **2.** A specially made, liquid food for an infant.

frame (frām) *n.* A single picture on a roll of movie film.

fret (frĕt) *v.* **fret•ted, fret•ting.** To be or cause to be uneasy or troubled; worry.

frus•tra•tion (frŭ strā′shən) *n.* A feeling of helplessness or discouragement.

fu•ri•ous (fyo͝or′ē əs) *adj.* Full of or marked by extreme anger.

gaunt (gônt) *adj.* **gaunt•er, gaunt•est.** Thin and bony; haggard; emaciated: *a gaunt face.*

gen•er•os•i•ty (jĕn′ə rŏs′ĭ tē) *n.* The quality of being willing to share or give.

go-be•tween (gō′bĭ twēn′) *n.* A person who helps to arrange an agreement between two sides.

good-tempered (go͝od′tĕm′pərd) *adj.* Having a nice manner; kind and easy to get along with.

gorge (gôrj) *n.* A deep, narrow passage with steep, rocky sides, as between mountains.

gourd (gôrd) *or* (gōrd) *or* (go͝ord) *n.* **1.** The fruit of a vine related to the pumpkin, squash, and cucumber. **2.** A dried, hollowed-out shell of such a fruit.

gov•ern•ess (gŭv′ər nĭs) *n.* A woman employed to educate and train the children of a private household.

grief-strick•en (grēf′strĭk′ən) *adj.* Suffering from sorrow or disappointment.

grove (grōv) *n.* A group of trees with open ground between them.

guar•an•tee (găr′ən tē′) *n.* Anything that makes certain a particular condition or outcome.

harp (härp) *v.* **harp on.** To write or talk about to an excessive or tedious degree.

head•quar•ters (hĕd′kwôr′tərz) *pl. n.* **1.** The offices of a commander, as of a military unit, from which official orders are issued. **2.** Any center of operations: *the headquarters of the company.*

helm (hĕlm) *n.* The steering gear of a ship, especially the tiller or wheel.

helm

helms•man (**hĕlmz′**mən) *n., pl.* **-men** (-mən). A person who steers a ship.

her•o•ine (**hĕr′**ō ĭn) *n.* **1.** The female counterpart of a hero. **2.** The main female character in a novel, movie, play, etc.

ho•ri•zon (hə **rī′**zən) *n.* The line along which the earth and sky appear to meet.

i•den•ti•ty (ī **dĕn′**tĭ tē) *n., pl.* **i•den•ti•ties.** Who a person is or what a thing is: *Some people try to hide their identities by wearing dark glasses.*

il•lu•sion (ĭ **lo͞o′**zhən) *n.* An appearance or impression that has no real basis: *The artist created the illusion of depth in the painting.*

im•pa•tient (ĭm **pā′**shənt) *adj.* **1.** Not able to wait calmly. **2.** Restlessly eager.

in•at•ten•tion (ĭn′ə **tĕn′**shən) *n.* Lack of attention, notice, or regard; heedlessness: *Inattention to the directions can cause you to make errors on the test.*

in•ci•dent (**ĭn′**sĭ dənt) *n.* A definite, distinct occurrence; an event.

in•con•sid•er•ate (ĭn′kən **sĭd′**ər ĭt) *adj.* Not taking into account other people's feelings; thoughtless.

in•dig•nant (ĭn **dĭg′**nənt) *adj.* Feeling or showing anger about something that is unfair, mean, or bad. — **in•dig′nant•ly** *adv.*

in•hab•it (ĭn **hăb′**ĭt) *v.* To live in or on.

in•land (**ĭn′**lənd) *adv.* In, toward, or into the interior of a country or region; away from the coast.

in•let (**ĭn′**lĕt′) *or* (-lĭt) *n.* A bay, cove, estuary, or other recess along a coast.

in•spire (ĭn **spīr′**) *v.* **in•spired, in•spir•ing.** To arouse to creativity or action: *a worker inspired by fear of poverty.*

in•stinct (**ĭn′**stĭngkt′) *n.* **1.** An inner feeling, that is not learned and that results in complex animal behavior such as building of nests, incubation of eggs, nursing of young, etc. **2.** A natural talent or ability.

in•su•late (**ĭn′**sə lāt′) *or* (**ĭns′**yə-) *v.* **in•su•lat•ed, in•su•lat•ing.** To prevent the passage of heat, electricity, or sound into or out of something.

in•su•la•tion (ĭn′sə **lā′**shən) *or* (ĭns′yə-) *n.* A material that stops or slows heat, electricity, or sound from passing through.

in·ten·tion (ĭn **tĕn′**shən) *n.* Something intended; a plan, purpose.

in·ter·vene (ĭn′tər **vēn′**) *v.* To be or come between things, points, or events: *A day of calm intervened between the two thunderstorms.*

ir·ri·gate (**ĭr′**ĭ gāt) *v.* **ir·ri·gat·ed, ir·ri·gat·ing.** To supply (farmland, crops, etc.) with water by means of streams, ditches, pipes, canals, etc. *We want to irrigate only our driest land.*

keen (kēn) *adj.* **keen·er, keen·est.** Very quick, sharp, or sensitive, especially in seeing, hearing, tasting, or smelling.

ken·nel (**kĕn′**əl) *n.* **1.** A small shelter for a dog or dogs. **2.** Often **kennels.** An establishment for the breeding, training, or boarding of dogs.

la·goon (lə **go͞on′**) *n.* A body of water, usually connecting with the ocean, especially one bounded by sandbars or coral reefs.

lar·va (**lär′**və) *n., pl.* **lar·vae** (**lär′**vē) or **lar·vas.** An insect in an early form, when it has just hatched from an egg. A larva has a soft body and looks like a worm.

laugh·ing·stock (**lăf′**ĭng stŏk′) *or* (**lä′**fĭng-) *n.* An object of mocking laughter, jokes, or ridicule.

list (lĭst) *v.* To tilt to one side, as a ship.

list·less (**lĭst′** lĭs) *adj.* Too tired or too weak to want to do anything. — **list·less·ly** *adv.*

loi·ter (**loi′**tər) *v.* To stand around doing nothing.

loy·al (**loi′**əl) *adj.* Faithful to a person, country, idea, custom, etc.

main·stay (**mān′**stā′) *n.* **1.** A strong rope or cable that holds in place the mainmast of a sailing vessel. **2.** The main support: *He is the mainstay of the team.*

make·shift (**māk′**shĭft′) *adj.* Something that serves as a temporary substitute: *They lived in a makeshift shelter until their house was finished.*

man·u·fac·ture (măn′yə **fak′**chər) *v.* **man·u·fac·tured, man·u·fac·tur·ing.** To make or produce.

me·sa (**mā′**sə) *n.* A flat-topped hill or small plateau with steep sides, common in the southwestern United States.

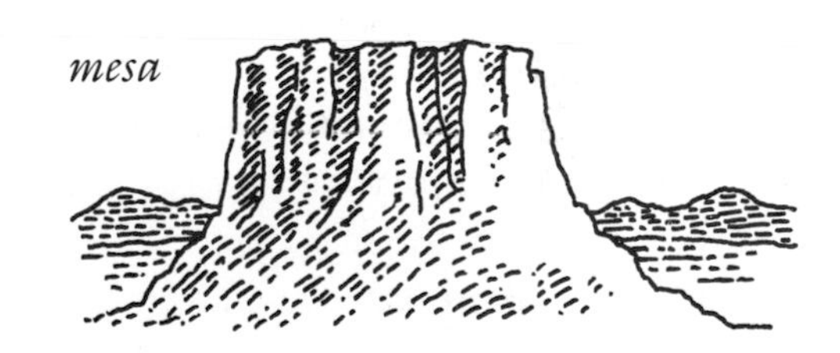
mesa

meth·od (**mĕth′**əd) *n.* A regular or deliberate way of doing something.

mi·gra·tion (mī **grā′**shən) *n.* The act of moving regularly to a different location, especially at a particular time of year.

mi·gra·to·ry (**mī′**grə tôr′ē) *or* (-tōr′ē) *adj.* Traveling from place to place; roving: *migratory birds.*

mim•ic•ry (**mim′**ĭ krē) *n.* The act of copying or imitating closely.

mis•for•tune (mĭs **fôr′**chən) *n.* **1.** Bad luck or fortune. **2.** An unfortunate occurrence.

mis•trust•ful (mĭs **trŭst′**fəl) *adj.* Feeling or showing suspicion or doubt: *mistrustful of everyone.*

mo•men•tous (mō **mĕn′**təs) *adj.* Very important or significant: *a momentous discovery.*

mow[1] (mō) *v.* **mowed, mowed** *or* **mown** (mōn), **mow•ing. 1.** To cut down (grass, grain, etc.): *Mow the grass before it gets too high.* **2.** To cut the grass, grain, etc., from: *mow the lawn.*

mow[2] (mou) *n.* **1.** A place for storing hay or grain. **2.** Feed that is stored, especially in a barn.

nar•ra•tion (nă **rā′**shən) *n.* The act of telling a story.

no•tice (**nō′**tĭs) *n.* A published or displayed announcement: *post a notice on the bulletin board.*

nui•sance (**no͞o′**səns) *or* (**nyo͞o**-) *n.* A source of inconvenience or annoyance; a bother.

o•blige (ə **blīj′**) *v.* **o•bliged, o•blig•ing.** To make grateful or thankful: *They were obliged to her for her help.*

ob•sti•nate (**ŏb′**stə nĭt) *adj.* **1.** Stubbornly holding to an attitude or opinion. **2.** Hard to manage, control, or cure.

ob•vi•ous (**ŏb′**vē əs) *adj.* Easily perceived or understood; evident: *an obvious reason.*

oc•ca•sion•al•ly (ə **kā′**zhə nə lē) *adv.* From time to time; now and then.

oc•cu•pa•tion (ŏk′yə **pā′**shən) *n.* **1.** A means of making a living; a profession or job. **2.** Any activity that keeps one busy.

o•men (**ō′**mən) *n.* A thing or event regarded as a sign of future good or bad luck.

or•deal (ôr **dēl′**) *n.* A very difficult or painful experience.

ounce (ouns) *n.* A measure of weight equal to one sixteenth of a pound. In the metric system, an ounce equals 28.350 grams.

out•lan•dish (out **lăn′**dĭsh) *adj.* Strange in appearance or manner: *outlandish clothes.*

o•ver•come (ō′vər **kŭm′**) *v.* **-came** (**-kām′**), **-com•ing.** To get the better of; conquer.

pace (pās) *v.* **paced, pac•ing.** To walk up and down or back and forth across.

pen•e•trate (**pĕn′**ĭ trāt′) *v.* **1.** To pass into or through; pierce. **2.** To come to an understanding of.

ă pat / ā **pay** / â **care** / ä **father** / ĕ **pet** / ē **be** / ĭ **pit** / ī **pie** / î **fierce** / ŏ **pot** / ō **go** / ô **paw, for** / oi **oil** / o͝o **book** / o͞o **boot** / ou **out** / ŭ **cut** / û **fur** / *th* **the** / th **thin** / hw **which** / zh **vision** / ə **ago, item, pencil, atom, circus**

pen•in•su•la (pə **nĭn′** syə lə) *or* (pə **nĭn′** sə lə) *n.* A piece of land that extends into water from a larger land mass.

per•sist•ent (pər **sis′**stənt) *adj.* Refusing to give up or let go: *A persistent salesperson finally sold them the car.*

phan•tom (**fan′**təm) *n.* A ghost.

phys•i•cal ther•a•pist (**fiz′**i kəl **thĕr′**ə pĭst) *n.* Someone who specializes in the treatment of injury or disease by such means as exercise, massage, and baths.

plot (plŏt) *n.* **1.** The series of actions or events in a novel, play, etc. **2.** A secret plan to accomplish an often illegal purpose: *a plot against the king.*

pop•u•lar•i•ty (pŏp′yə **lăr′**ĭ tē) *n.* The quality of being liked by many people.

prec•i•pice (**prĕs′**ə pĭs) *n.* A very steep mass of rock, as a cliff.

prem•ise (**prĕm′**ĭs) *n.* An idea that forms the basis for action.

pre•oc•cu•pied (prē **ŏk′**yə pīd′) *adj.* Deep in thought.

pre•tense (**prē′** tĕns′) *or* (prĭ **tĕns′**) *n.* **1.** The act of pretending; a false appearance or action intended to deceive. **2.** Something imagined or pretended; make-believe. **3.** A mere show without reality.

prog•ress (**prŏg′**rĕs′) *or* (-rĭs) *n.* **1.** Onward movement; advance: *made slow progress through traffic.* **2.** Steady improvement: *a baby making progress in learning to talk.* — *v.* **pro•gress** (prə **grĕs′**). **1.** To move along, advance, proceed. **2.** To make steady or regular improvements.

pros•per•i•ty (prŏ **spĕr′**ĭ tē) *n.* The condition of being successful, especially in matters of money.

pros•per•ous (**prŏs′**pər əs) *adj.* **1.** Vigorous and healthy; thriving: *a prosperous garden.* **2.** Economically successful; enjoying wealth or profit: *a prosperous business.*

pro•test (prə **tĕst′**) *or* (**prō′**tĕst) *v.* To express strong objections to something: *protest a law.*

rage (rāj) *v.* **1.** To feel or show violent anger. **2.** To move with great violence: *A blizzard raged across the northern states.*

re•as•sure (rē′ə **shoor′**) *v.* **re•as•sured, re•as•sur•ing.** To guarantee again; restore confidence to.

re•cov•er•y (rĭ **kŭv′**ə rē) *n., pl.* **re•cov•er•ies.** A return to a normal condition, as of health.

reef (rēf) *n.* A strip or ridge of rock, sand, or coral that rises to or close to the surface of a body of water.

reef

re•flect (rĭ **flĕkt′**) *v.* To give back an image, as does a mirror or clear water.

re•lapse (rĭ **lăps′**) *n.* The act or result of falling back into a previous condition, especially a return to illness after a change for the better.

rep•ri•mand (**rĕp′**rĭ mănd′) *n.* A severe scolding.

res•er•voir (**rĕz′**ər vwär′) *n.* **1.** A chamber or container used for storing a fluid: *the reservoir of a fountain pen.* **2.** A large supply of something built up over a long period of time: *a reservoir of good will.*

re•spect (rĭ **spĕkt′**) *n.* **1.** A feeling of honor or esteem. **2.** Regard or consideration.

re•sponse (rĭ **spŏns′**) *n.* **1.** An answer or reply. **2.** A reaction to another event.

re•trieve (rĭ **trēv′**) *v.* **re•trieved, re•triev•ing.** To find and bring back (birds or animals that have been shot), as a hunting dog does.

re•vive (rĭ **vīv′**) *v.* **re•vived, re•viv•ing.** **1.** To bring back or return to life or consciousness. **2.** To bring back or give vigor or strength to (something).

rheu•ma•tism (**ro͞o′**mə tĭz′əm) *n.* Any of several diseased conditions that affect the muscles, tendons, bones, joints, or nerves, causing pain and disability.

rig•ging (**rĭg′**ĭng) *n.* The system of ropes, chains, and tackle used to support and control masts, sails, and other equipment.

rouse (rouz) *v.* **roused, rous•ing.** **1.** To wake up; awaken. **2.** To cause to become active or excited: *a sight that roused her curiosity.*

sar•cas•ti•cal•ly (sär **kăs′**tĭk əl lē) *adv.* In a bitterly joking way, so as to make fun of someone or something.

scar•let (**skär′**lĭt) *adj.* Bright red or red-orange.

scheme (skēm) *v.* **schemed, schem•ing.** To plot or plan dishonestly, slyly, or secretly.

schol•ar (**skŏl′**ər) *n.* A person of great learning.

scorn•ful•ly (**skôrn′**fəl lē) *adv.* In a manner expressing a feeling that someone or something is inferior.

script (skrĭpt) *n.* The written text of a play, movie, or television or radio show. It contains the lines and speeches of all the actors and actresses.

scull (skŭl) *n.* **1.** An oar used for rowing a boat from the stern. **2.** A kind of short-handled oar. **3.** A small, light racing boat. — *v.* To move (a boat) with a scull or sculls.

scull

ă pat / ā pay / â care / ä father / ĕ pet / ē be / ĭ pit / ī pie / î fierce / ŏ pot / ō go / ô paw, for / oi oil / o͝o book / o͞o boot / ou out / ŭ cut / û fur / *th* the / th thin / hw which / zh vision / ə ago, item, pencil, atom, circus

set (sĕt) *n.* A structure on a stage, designed to represent the place where the action or scene of a play occurs.

sharp•en (**shär′**pən) *v.* To make sharp or sharper.

shed[1] (shĕd) *v.* **shed, shed•ding.** To lose, drop, or cast off by natural process.

shed[2] (shĕd) *n.* A small structure for storage or shelter: *a tool shed.*

site (sīt) *n.* The place where something was, is, or is to be located.

skein (skān) *n.* A length of yarn, thread, etc., wound in a long, loose coil.

skep•ti•cal (**skep′**tĭ kəl) *adj.* Doubting; questioning.

sledge (slĕj) *n.* A vehicle on runners, drawn by horses, dogs, or reindeer and used for transporting loads across snow and ice.

sleek (slēk) *adj.* **sleek•er, sleek•est.** **1.** Smooth and glossy.

slope (slōp) *n.* **1.** A slanting line, surface, or direction. **2.** A stretch of ground that is slanted upward or downward.

slur (slûr) *v.* **slurred, slur•ring.** To pass over or pronounce carelessly: *slur words.*

sol•emn•ly (**sŏl′**əm lē) *adj. Seriously; sincerely.*

so•lu•tion (sə **lōō′**shən) *n.* The answer to a problem.

sooth•ing (**sōō′***th*ĭng) *adj.* Bringing relief or comfort: *a soothing cream for sunburn.* —**sooth′ing•ly** *adv.*

spe•cial•ist (**spĕsh′**ə lĭst) *n.* A person, such as a doctor, who is involved in a particular activity or branch of study.

spe•cies (**spē′**shēz′) *or* (-sēz′) *n., pl.* **spe•cies.** **1.** A group of animals or plants that are similar and are considered to be of the same kind. **2.** A type, kind, or sort.

spite (spīt) *Idiom.* **in spite of.** Regardless of; despite.

spunk (spŭngk) *n. Informal.* Spirit; courage.

stalk (stôk) *v.* To move in a quiet, secretive manner, as if tracking prey or a victim.

star•va•tion (stär **vā′**shən) *n.* The act or process of suffering due to lack of food.

steth•o•scope (**stĕth′**ə skōp′) *n.* An instrument used to listen to sounds made within the body.

stilt (stĭlt) *n.* **1.** Either of a pair of long, slender poles, each with a foot support partway up, enabling the wearer to walk elevated above the ground. **2.** Any of various types of posts or pillars used as supports for a building, dock, etc. **3.** A long-legged wading bird with a long bill.

stilt

stock (stŏk) *n.* Domestic animals such as horses, cattle, sheep, pigs.

store (stôr) *or* (stōr) *n.* **1.** A place where merchandise is offered for sale; a shop. **2.a.** A stock or supply reserved for future use. **b. stores.** Supplies, as of food, clothing, or arms.

sus•pi•cious (sə **spĭsh′**əs) *adj.* Not trusting: *Mary was taught to be suspicious of anything out of the ordinary.*

swap (swŏp) *v.* **swapped, swap•ping.** To trade one thing for another; to exchange.

swin•dle (**swĭn′**dl) *v.* **swin•dled, swin•dling.** To cheat someone else of money or property.

tack (tăk) *n.* **1.** A small nail with a sharp point and a flat head. **2.** A course of action or an approach: *try a new tack.*

tan•trum (**tan′**trəm) *n.* An outburst of bad temper.

ten•ant (**tĕn′**ənt) *n.* A person who pays rent to use or occupy land, a building, or other property owned by another.

threat (thrĕt) *n.* **1.** An expression indicating that punishment or harm will follow. **2.** A warning of danger.

threat•en (**thrĕt′**n) *v.* **1.** To indicate that harm or punishment will follow. **2.** To serve as a warning of danger: *Dark skies threaten rain.*

tire•some (**tīr′**səm) *adj.* Causing a person to be tired, bored, or annoyed.

tol•er•ance (**tŏl′**ər əns) *n.* The willingness to let other people hold opinions or follow practices that are different from one's own.

tor•rent (**tôr′**ənt) *or* (**tŏr′**-) *n.* A heavy downpour; a great flood of water.

tra•di•tion (trə **dĭsh′**ən) *n.* **1.** The passing down of ideas, customs, and beliefs from generation to generation, especially orally. **2.** A custom or usage handed down in this way.

trans•fix (trăns **fiks′**) *v.* To make motionless, as with terror, amazement, or awe; *I was transfixed by the sight of the burning building.*

trans•plant (trăns **plănt′**) *v.* **1.** To remove (a living plant) from the place where it is growing and plant it in another placc. **2.** To transfer to and establish in a new place.

treach•er•ous (**trĕch′**ər əs) *adj.* **1.** Betraying trust; disloyal. **2.** Not to be trusted; dangerous: *The surf at this beach is treacherous.*

tre•men•dous (trĭ **mĕn′**dəs) *adj.* Extremely large.

tres•pass (**trĕs′**pəs) *or* (-păs) *v.* To go onto the property of another without the owner's permission.

trig•ger (**trĭg′**ər) *v.* To set off; to start; to set in motion.

ă **pat** / ā **pay** / â **care** / ä **father** / ĕ **pet** / ē **be** / ĭ **pit** / ī **pie** / î **fierce** / ŏ **pot** / ō **go** / ô **paw, for** / oi **oil** / ŏŏ **book** / ōō **boot** / ou **out** / ŭ **cut** / û **fur** / *th* **the** / th **thin** / hw **which** / zh **vision** / ə **ago, item, pencil, atom, circus**

tri•umph (**trī′**əmf) *n.* Joy from victory or success.

try (trī) *v.* **tried, try•ing, tries.** To put a person accused of a crime on trial in a court.

un•at•tain•able (ŭn′ ə **tān′**ə bəl) *adj.* Not able to be accomplished or achieved by effort.

un•checked (ŭn **chĕkt′**) *adj.* Not controlled or held back by anything.

un•con•scious (ŭn **kŏn′**shəs) *adj.* Temporarily lacking awareness, as in deep sleep or a coma.

un•der•tow (**ŭn′**dər tō′)*n.* The current beneath the surface of a body of water running in a direction opposite to that of the current at the surface.

urge (ûrj) *n.* A strong desire.

vast (văst) *or* (väst) *adj.* **vast•er, vast•est.** Very great in size, amount, and area; immense: *the vast Pacific Ocean.*

ven•ture (**vĕn′**chər) *n.* A task or activity that is risky or dangerous.

ves•sel (**vĕs′**əl) *n.* A ship or large boat.

vic•to•ri•ous (vĭk **tôr′**ē əs) *adj.* Having won a contest or struggle.

vine•yard (**vĭn′**yərd) *n.* A piece of ground on which grapevines are grown and tended.

vi•o•lent (**vī′**ə lənt) *adj.* **1.** Marked by or resulting from great physical force or rough action: *a violent attack.* **2.** Showing or having great emotional force: *a man with a violent temper.* **3.** Having great force or effect; severe; harsh: *a violent hurricane.*

vise (vīs) *n.* A device of metal, usually consisting of a pair of jaws that are opened and closed by means of a screw or lever, used in carpentry or metalworking to hold work in place.

vise

wake (wāk) *n.* **1.** The visible track of waves, ripples, or foam left behind something moving through water. **2.** The course or route over which anything has passed: *The hurricane left destruction in its wake.*

ware (wâr) *n.* **1.** Manufactured articles or goods of the same general kind, such as glassware or hardware. **2.** Pottery or ceramics, such as earthenware or stoneware. **3. wares.** Goods for sale.

war•ri•or (**wôr′**ē ər) *or* (**wŏr′**-) *n.* A fighter, especially an armed one, who fights in battle.

wheeze (hwēz) *v.* **wheezed, wheez•ing.** To breathe with difficulty, producing a hoarse whistling or hissing sound. —*n.* The sound made by wheezing.

whim•si•cal (**hwĭm′**sĭ kəl) *or* (**wĭm′**-) *adj.* Playful or fanciful.

whisk (hwĭsk) *or* (wĭsk) *v.* **1.** To brush or sweep with quick, light motions: *He whisked the crumbs off the table.* **2.** To move or carry or cause to move or carry quickly: *Dad whisked me to the dentist's office.*

winch (wĭnch) *n.* A machine for pulling or lifting, consisting of a drum around which a rope or cable attached to the load is wound or unwound as the load is moved.

wire (wīr) *v.* **wired, wir•ing.** To send (a message, information, etc.) by telegram: *wire congratulations.*

with•er (**wĭth′**ər) *v.* To dry up or cause to dry up from lack of moisture; shrivel.

wraith (rāth) *n.* The ghost of a dead person.

zil•lion (**zĭl′**yən) *n.* An extremely large, indefinite number: *There must be a zillion fish in the sea.*

ă pat / ā pay / â care / ä father / ĕ pet / ē be / ĭ pit / ī pie / î fierce / ŏ pot / ō go / ô paw, for / oi oil / o͝o book / o͞o boot / ou out / ŭ cut / û fur / *th* the / th thin / hw which / zh vision / ə ago, item, pencil, atom, circus

Continued from page 2.

"The Cat and the Golden Egg," from *The Town Cats and Other Tales* by Lloyd Alexander. Text copyright © 1977 by Lloyd Alexander. Reprinted by permission of the publisher, E.P. Dutton, a division of NAL Penguin, Inc.

"Catalogue," by Rosalie Moore, from the May 25, 1940 issue of *The New Yorker* magazine. Copyright 1940, © 1968. Reprinted by permission of the New Yorker Magazine, Inc.

"Courage," excerpted from *The Wizard of Oz.* Copyright 1939 Loew's Incorporated. Renewed 1966 Metro-Goldwyn-Mayer Inc.

"The Crow and the Pitcher," adapted from *The Fables of Aesop* retold by Joseph Jacobs. New York: Macmillan Publishing Company, 1950.

"Gramp," text abridged from Chapters 4 and 5 of *Gramp,* from *Luke's Garden and Gramp: Two Short Novels* by Joan Tate. Copyright © 1971; revised edition copyright © 1979 by Joan Tate. Reprinted by permission of Harper & Row, Publishers, Inc. and Pelham Books, Ltd.

"The Heroine of Kapiti," by Shirley Climo. Copyright © 1983. Originally appeared in the June 1983 issue of *Cricket* magazine. Reprinted by permission of the author.

"Home from the High Meadow," adapted from *The Macleod Place* by William Armstrong. Copyright © 1972 by William Armstrong. Reprinted by permission of the author.

"I never asked for no allergy," adapted from *Philip Hall likes me. I reckon maybe.* by Bette Greene. Text copyright © 1974 by Bette Greene. Reprinted by permission of the publisher, Dial Books for Young Readers.

"Lovable Ladybug," adapted from *Never Pet a Porcupine* by George Laycock. Copyright © 1965 by George Laycock. Reprinted by permission of the author.

"Marc Chagall," from *Marc Chagall* by Ernest Raboff. Copyright © 1982 by Bradley Smith. Reprinted by permission of Gemini Smith, Incorporated.

"Midwest Town," by Ruth De Long Peterson from *The Beauty of America.* Copyright 1954 by Ruth De Long Peterson. Reprinted by permission of the author.

"Mister Stormalong," adapted from *Mr. Stormalong* by Anne Malcolmson and Dell McCormick. Copyright 1952 by Mabel McCormick and Anne Burnett Malcolmson. Copyright renewed © 1980 by Anne Burnett Malcolmson Van Storch and Joshua Tolford. Reprinted by permission of Houghton Mifflin Company.

"One Day in the Desert," an excerpt adapted from *One Day in the Desert* by Jean Craighead George, illustrated by Fred Brenner. (Thomas Y. Crowell). Copyright © 1983 by Jean Craighead George. Illustrations copyright © 1983 by Fred Brenner. Reprinted by permission of Harper & Row, Publishers, Inc.

"Pearson: A Harbor Seal Pup," by Susan Meyers, photographs by Ilka Hartmann. Text copyright © 1980 by Susan Meyers. Photographs copyright © 1980 by Ilka Hartmann. Reprinted by permission of the publisher, E.P. Dutton, a division of NAL Penguin, Inc.

"Ride the Red Cycle," adapted from *Ride the Red Cycle* by Hariette Gillem Robinet. Copyright © 1980 by Hariette Gillem Robinet. Reprinted by permission of Houghton Mifflin Company and the author.

"Rustytoes," adapted from *Giant Kippernose and Other Storeis* by John Cunliffe. Copyright © 1977. Reprinted by permission of Andre Deutsch, Ltd.

"Saukin!" adapted from *Katzimo, Mysterious Mesa* by Bobette Gugliotta. Copyright © 1973 by Bobette Bibo Gugliotta. Reprinted by permission of the author.

"Sea-Fever," is reprinted by permission of Macmillan Publishing Company from *Poems* by John Masefield (New York: Macmillan, 1953).

"74th Street," from *The Malibu and Other Poems* by Myra Cohn Livingston. Copyright © 1972 by Myra Cohn Livingston. Reprinted by permission of Marian Reiner for the author.

"Shackleton's Epic Voyage," adapted from *Shackleton's Epic Voyage* by Michael Brown. Copyright © 1969 by Michael Brown. Reprinted by permission of Hamish Hamilton, Ltd.

"Something Told the Wild Geese," reprinted with permission of Macmillan Publishing Company from *Poems* by Rachel Field. Copyright 1934 by Macmillan Publishing Company, renewed © 1962 by Arthur S. Pederson.

"A Song of Greatness," from *The Children Sing in the Far West* by Mary Austin. Copyright 1928 by Mary Austin. Copyright renewed © 1956 by Kenneth M. Chapman and Mary C. Wheelwright. Reprinted by permission of Houghton Mifflin Company.

"The Spell of the Fog," an excerpt from *Fog Magic* by Julia L. Sauer. Copyright 1943, renewed © 1971 by Julia L. Sauer. Reprinted by permission of Viking Penguin, Inc.

"The Stormy Rescue," adapted from *The Midnight Fox* by Betsy Byars. Copyright © 1968 by Betsy Byars. All rights reserved. Reprinted by permission of Viking Penguin Inc.

"The Stranger Arrives," adapted from *Helen Keller's Teacher* by Margaret Davidson. Copyright © 1965 by Margaret Davidson. Reprinted by permission of Scholastic Inc.

"Thank You, Phoebe Fraunces," by Judith Berry Griffin adapted and reprinted by permission of Coward, McCann and Geoghegan from *Phoebe and The General* by Judith Berry Griffin. Text copyright © 1977 by Judith Berry Griffin.

"Tuck Everlasting," a selection from *Tuck Everlasting* by Natalie Babbitt. Copyright © 1975 by Natalie Babbitt. Reprinted by permission of Farrar, Straus and Giroux Inc.

"The Whimbrel," text abridged and adapted from Chapters I and II from *The Hammerhead Light* by Colin Thiele. Copyright © 1976 by Colin Thiele. Reprinted by permission of Harper & Row, Publishers, Inc. and Penguin Books Australia, Ltd.

"The Wise Old Woman," from *The Sea of Gold and Other Tales from Japan* by Yoshiko Uchida, Charles Scribners. Copyright © 1965 by Yoshiko Uchida. Reprinted by permission of the author.

"A Zillion Stars," by Yoshiko Uchida, copyright © 1983, by Yoshiko Uchida. Reprinted by permission of the author.

"Zlateh the Goat," from *Zlateh the Goat and Other Stories* by Isaac Bashevis Singer, pictures by Maurice Sendak. Translated from the Yiddish by the author and Elizabeth Shub. Text copyright © 1966 by Isaac Bashevis Singer. Pictures copyright © 1966 by Maurice Sendak. Reprinted by permission of Harper and Row, Publishers, Inc.

Grateful acknowledgment is made for permission to reprint for the Glossary, the pronunciation key and adapted definitions from *The Houghton Mifflin Intermediate Dictionary*. Copyright © 1986 by Houghton Mifflin Company. Adapted and reprinted by permission from *The Houghton Mifflin Intermediate Dictionary*.

Credits

Cover Design: James Stockton & Associates

Illustrators: 8–9 Robert Stein **10–27** Cherie Wyman **28–40** Ben F. Stahl **41** Tom Bobroski **42–61** John Shipperbottom **62–79** Larry Raymond **80** Jan Brett **81** E.L. Konigsburg **84–97** Alan Baker **98–99** Lynne Cherry **103–109** Chris Demarest **111–126** David Wenzel **127–135** Loretta Krupinski **139–140** Susanah Brown **144–164** Arvis Stewart **165** Paul Gobel **166–167** Alexander Farquharson **168–176** Mike Codd **177–186** Maurice Sendak **216–227** Nick Harris **228** Carol Schwartz **229** Lane Yerkes **230–231** Peggy Immel **232–251** Higgins Bond **252–269** Collette Slade **270–284** Michael Hague **285** Jan Wills **286–301** Donna Diamond **302–314** Ian Robertson **315** K. Christopher Schuh **316–336** Stella Ormai **337** William Steig **341–353** Mary Beth Schwark **376–387** Graham Humphreys **396–412** Jan Wills **413** Charles Robinson **414–415** John Marshall **428–453** Judy La Motte **460–471** Mou-Sien Tseng **473** Sal Murdocca, Mercer Mayer

Photographers: 82–83 Roy Morsch/Stock Market **100, 104** © Bill Melendez Productions, Inc. **101** © United Features Syndicate, Inc. **105** (left) "Ungloved Hand" film © Lisa Crafts, (right) "Opening New Frontiers" film/NASA **136** Dan Morrill/Reese Gibson **137** David C. Fritts/Animals, Animals **138** Ted Levin/Animals, Animals **140** © Ted Levin/Animals, Animals **141** Ron Austing/Bruce Coleman, Inc. **142** © Charles Palek/Animals, Animals **143** G. Ellis/Ellis Wildlife Collection/Manhattan Views **187–201** Courtesy of the Perkins School for the Blind **210, 215** The American Foundation for the Blind **338–339** C.D. Dietrich/FPG **340** © R. Hamilton Smith **374–375** TWO FIGURES BY THE SEA (detail) by Winslow Homer, 1821 Courtesy of the Denver Art Museum, Denver, Colorado **388** Stella Hardee/Bruce Coleman, Inc. **389** (top) James David Brandt/Earth Sciences, (bottom) Dr. E.R. Degginger **390** Dr. E.R. Degginger **391** (top) Francisco Erize/Bruce Coleman, Inc., (bottom left) Dr. E.R. Degginger, (bottom right) M.P. Kahl/Tom Stack Associates **392** (top) Dr. E.R. Degginger, (bottom) Stella Hardee/Bruce Coleman **392–393** Jen and Des

Bartlett/Bruce Coleman, Inc. **393** (top) Doug Allan/Animals, Animals, (bottom) Dr. E.R. Degginger **394–395** Russ Kline/National Science Foundation **414–415** John T. Marshall **416** THE MARKET PLACE by Marc Chagall, 1917 Courtesy of the Metropolitan Museum of Art, New York, bequest of Scofield Thayer, 1982 **419** I AND THE VILLAGE by Marc Chagall, 1911/Collection of The Museum of Modern Art, New York/Mrs. Simon Guggenheim Foundation **421** VITEBSK SEEN FROM MOUNT ZADUNOV, by Marc Chagall, 1917, photo by Bruce Jones **425** SELF PORTRAIT WITH SEVEN FINGERS by Marc Chagall, 1912, Stedelijk Museum, Amsterdam **426** PEASANT LIFE by Marc Chagall, Albright Knox Gallery, Room of Contemporary Art Foundation **427** GREEN VIOLINIST by Marc Chagall, Solomon R. Guggenheim Museum, New York **454** Ralymond A. Menden/Animals, Animals **456** Kim Taylor/Bruce Coleman, Inc. **456–457** C.W. Perkens/Animals, Animals **457** Keith Gunnar/Bruce Coleman, Inc. **458** Dr. E.R. Degginger **472** Shostal Association